ODHAMS NEW
MOTOR MANUAL

MODERN CAR DESIGN

Examples of the three basic forms of mechanical layout. (*From top to bottom*)
Front engine driving the rear wheels (Singer); front engine driving the front
wheels (Morris); rear engine driving the rear wheels (Fiat).

ODHAMS NEW MOTOR MANUAL

How Your Car Works and
How to Service It

Edited by
LEONARD HOLMES

HAMLYN
LONDON • NEW YORK • SYDNEY • TORONTO

First Published 1967
Reprinted February, 1968
Reprinted October, 1968
Reprinted 1970
Reprinted 1971

THE HAMLYN PUBLISHING GROUP LIMITED
LONDON · NEW YORK · SYDNEY · TORONTO
Hamlyn House, Feltham, Middlesex, England

Made and printed in Great Britain by Odhams (Watford) Ltd.,
Watford, Herts

CONTENTS

HOW YOUR CAR WORKS

By JOSEPH LOWREY, B.Sc.(Eng.)

Theory of the petrol engine. Engine design and construction. Ignition. Carburettors. Lubrication. Cooling. Power and torque. Alternative power units. Transmission components.

By JOSEPH LOWREY, B.Sc.(Eng.)

Tyres and wheels. Suspension systems. Steering systems. Braking systems. Electrical equipment. Instruments. Structure and bodywork. Ventilation, heating and silencing.

SERVICING, MAINTENANCE AND OVERHAUL

By LOUIS BACON

Fault tracing in an emergency. Ignition, carburation and compression faults. Testing in the workshop. Ignition, carburation and compression tests. Ignition timing. Modern test instruments.

By STATON ABBEY, C.Eng., M.I.M.I.

Routine servicing of the power unit, cooling system, ignition system and engine ancillaries. Summer and winter servicing. Preventive maintenance: mechanical, ignition, fuel system and cooling system.

By STATON ABBEY, C.Eng., M.I.M.I.

Running troubles. Knocks and noises. Top overhaul. Major and partial overhauls.

By PHILIP H. SMITH, C.Eng., M.I.Mech.E., M.S.A.E.

Clutch. Gearbox. Overdrive. "Power-package" transmissions. Automatic transmissions. Transmission shafts. Universal joints. Rear axle. Rear wheel bearings. Differential. Limited-slip differential.

By STATON ABBEY, C.Eng., M.I.M.I.

Steering units and linkage. Front wheel bearings. Power-assisted steering. Steering unit adjustment. Front and rear suspension. Shock absorbers. Hydro-pneumatic systems. Steering and suspension faults

CONTENTS

INTRODUCTION

THIS book is a successor to *Odhams Motor Manual*, which for many years has been valued by motorists and workers in the motor trade for its comprehensive treatment of practical car maintenance and repairs. The *New Motor Manual* is an entirely fresh and up-to-date presentation of the subject, designed to give authoritative guidance in maintaining the modern car and explain its workings to those who find it a mysterious bag of tricks. The contributors, all expert in their respective fields, have provided a vast amount of explanation and information with this aim in mind.

Part I, "How Your Car Works", discusses car design today and briefly explains the working principles of all the main systems. These chapters will help the motorist to understand why his car is designed and constructed the way it is, and what technical developments he can expect in the future.

Part II, "Servicing, Maintenance and Overhaul", is planned to give mainly practical instruction, though many of its sections also contain useful information on design and operation. Thus the reader interested in tyres, for example, will find an outline of the basic requirements in tyre design in Part I (Chapter 2) and detailed information on tyre construction, selection, maintenance and repair in Part II (Chapter 6).

Part III, "Car Purchase and Operation", offers guidance on choosing and buying a car, its running and everyday care. It is a fact that the car of today needs far less servicing than ever before, but at the same time it is becoming a more highly complex machine. Understanding how to operate this machine correctly, how to choose the most suitable fuels and lubricants, how to carry out routine checks and inspections, and how to keep track of running costs are all essential to getting the best out of a car, and are among the matters dealt with here.

While the majority of service operations described in these pages can be tackled by the intelligent motorist with some little mechanical skill and suitable tools, there are certain jobs mentioned that should normally be entrusted to a service station. These more advanced operations are introduced for the benefit of readers working in the motor trade, and also as being of interest to the enthusiast.

THE EDITOR

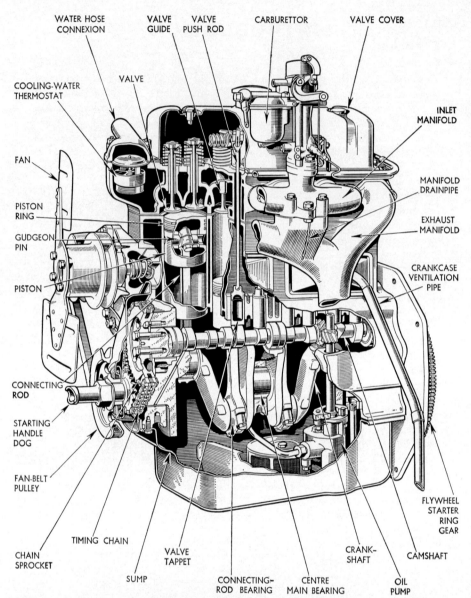

WATER HOSE CONNEXION   VALVE GUIDE   VALVE PUSH ROD   CARBURETTOR   VALVE COVER

COOLING-WATER THERMOSTAT

VALVE

INLET MANIFOLD

FAN

MANIFOLD DRAINPIPE

PISTON RING

EXHAUST MANIFOLD

GUDGEON PIN

CRANKCASE VENTILATION PIPE

PISTON

CONNECTING ROD

STARTING HANDLE DOG

FAN-BELT PULLEY

FLYWHEEL STARTER RING GEAR

TIMING CHAIN

CHAIN SPROCKET

VALVE TAPPET

CRANK-SHAFT

CAMSHAFT

SUMP

CONNECTING-ROD BEARING   CENTRE MAIN BEARING   OIL PUMP

FIG. 1.1. Construction of a typical four-cylinder petrol engine for small cars. Features of this B.M.C. unit include push-rod-operated overhead valves, a camshaft driven by a double roller chain, a three-bearing counterbalanced crankshaft, and a pump-assisted cooling system with thermostatic heat control. Only the mechanical components are shown here—the engine also has electrical ignition and starter systems.

CHAPTER 1

THE MEANS OF PROPULSION

SEATS to sit in, a frame and wheels to support these seats, a body shell to protect passengers from the weather, an engine to propel the vehicle and a transmission system to apply the engine's power to the wheels, a steering mechanism, braking mechanism, a lighting system. . . . These are the essentials of the motor car, yet how much more is the whole than its parts! Smooth, quiet, powerful yet economical in fuel, today's highly developed cars are far removed from their primitive ancestors of the turn of the century.

Motor cars come in a wide range of sizes, shapes, performance and prices, to suit varying tastes and requirements. However, the weight of public demand tends to favour the familiar closed saloon having four to six seats with luggage accommodation at the rear.

Early cars tended to be designed around their engines, and to have passengers squeezed in wherever there was room for them. Nowadays the priorities have altered, and passengers are given the most accessible, smoothest riding position in the centre of a car, with the engine fitted in either between the front wheels or right at the rear. Fashion sometimes seems to dictate surprising expansion of the luggage boot at the expense of leg room for passengers, but modern power units can be fitted into very little space unless a designer wishes his car to have an impressively long bonnet.

Until recent times the engine has generally been installed towards the front of the car, with a long central shaft taking power to the driven rear axle. Lighter and more compact arrangements with the engine at the same end as the driven wheels are now becoming commonplace, however —either a rear engine driving the rear wheels or a front engine driving the front wheels. These three layouts are illustrated in the frontispiece to this book. As a generalization, the rear-engine layout tends to make a car light and inexpensive but unstable in side winds, whereas the front-wheel-drive arrangement gives more inherent stability, but transmitting power to the steered wheels adds weight and cost.

All sorts of propulsion systems have been used on cars, including steam engines and electric motors running from batteries. Due to many factors such as cost to buy and to run, ease of driving, reliability, quick availability, quietness, freedom from smell and good power-to-weight ratio, the four-stroke petrol engine has come to dominate the scene (Fig. 1.1). It is an engine type which has a wide but not unlimited speed range, having a minimum as well as a maximum useful speed, which results in it needing some sort of gradually-engaged clutch to be able to start a car from rest, and change-speed gearing to suit various speeds and gradients while running.

THE POWER UNIT IN PRINCIPLE

Scientists long ago established the fact that there is what they call a "mechanical equivalent of heat." Working in one direction, mechanical energy "destroyed" by friction when a car is slowed down reappears as heat energy, which warms up the brakes. Working in the other direction, heat energy liberated by burning fuel is partially converted into mechanical horse-power by a car's engine, although unfor-

9

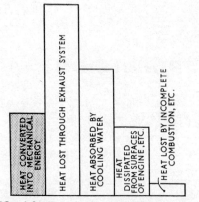

FIG. 1.2. The heat energy contained in petroleum fuel is only partly converted by an engine into useful mechanical horsepower, most of it being dissipated in various ways. The proportions of "heat balance" given here are approximately correct for a large six-cylinder engine; there would be variations under different operating conditions.

tunately a major share of the heat gets wasted in the radiator and exhaust system (Fig. 1.2).

Whereas converting mechanical energy into heat is relatively easy, doing the opposite at all efficiently is difficult. Despite their complexity, the most efficient car engines running under the most favourable conditions only convert about one-third of the heat energy in their fuel into mechanical work, the rest going mainly into the atmosphere as waste heat. In the bulky turbines of an electric power station, engineers can do better than this, and in the relatively heavy diesel engines used in trucks they can also do rather better, but not in the light, compact, smooth and quiet engines needed for cars.

All the known forms of heat engine which burn fuel to generate horsepower have at least one basic principle in common. They use the heat from their fuel to create hot, high-pressure gas of one kind or another, and let this gas expand so that it does mechanical work pushing on either pistons or turbine blades. External combustion engines burn their fuel under a boiler, the

water inside being turned into steam, and expansion of this steam provides the horsepower. Internal combustion engines burn their fuel inside the engine, to heat and expand the actual air in which it is being burned.

As indicated earlier, piston-type internal combustion engines may have one or more cylinders. Each cylinder has a combustion chamber above the piston which has only a fraction of the cylinder's volume. It would be possible to build an engine in which the combustion chamber was merely filled with air at atmospheric pressure, and burning petrol in it would heat this trapped air sufficiently to generate some pressure and push the piston down the cylinder. However, an output of power many times greater can be developed if the fuel is burned in air which has previously been compressed to a high degree. Then the extra useful work which the piston does as the burning fuel expands greatly exceeds the amount of work which had previously been done to compress the air.

Compression Ratio. When an engine is referred to as having, for example, a compression ratio of 8 to 1, it means that during the compression stroke the petrol/air mixture is compressed into one-eighth

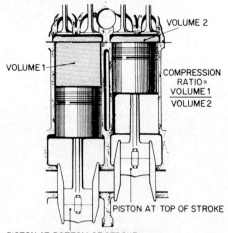

FIG. 1.3. Compression ratio shown pictorially.

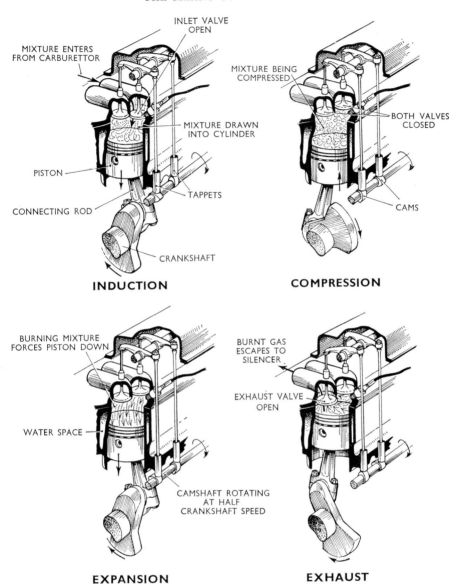

FIG. 1.4. The four-stroke cycle. The sequence of operations is as follows. (1) INDUCTION. The piston descends during the first half revolution of the crankshaft and, since the inlet valve is open, sucks petrol-air mixture into the cylinder. (2) COMPRESSION. As the piston ascends during the second half revolution, the mixture is compressed, both valves being closed. (3) EXPANSION. As the piston nears the top of its stroke, an electric spark bridges the points of the sparking plug and ignites the compressed mixture, beginning the expansion or power stroke. The energy liberated is expended by the time the piston has reached the bottom of its stroke. (4) EXHAUST. As the piston ascends, the exhaust valve opens and the burnt gases are expelled through the exhaust system. The cycle of strokes then starts again.

of its original volume (Fig. 1.3). In this case, the volume of the combustion chamber would be one-seventh of the volume displaced by the moving piston, so if one cylinder has a swept volume of 350 c.c., the combustion chamber will have a volume of 50 c.c. An initial 350 + 50 c.c. of gas (in the combustion chamber as well as the cylinder) will be compressed into 50 c.c. as the piston moves upwards, giving the ratio 400 ÷ 50 = 8. In current models, compression ratios lie between 7:1 and 11:1 approximately, the higher ratios being generally on the more efficient engines which need to be run on top-quality petrol.

Compressing fuel mixture in a cylinder heats it, and hot petrol/air mixture at a high pressure is liable to explode, when what we want is for it to burn quickly yet smoothly, after being ignited by a spark. The differences between petrol grades of different prices are mainly concerned with the fuel's ability to withstand high com-pression temperatures and pressures without detonation ("knocking") appearing as a sign of too-explosive burning. This matter is further discussed in Chapter 13.

The Four-stroke Cycle. Most car engines work on what is known as the Otto or four-stroke cycle, which involves a series of four inward and outward moves by each piston, towards and away from the combustion chamber. Even the uncon-ventional internal combustion engines such as gas turbines and other rotary units use this same four-stroke principle (Fig. 1.4).

The first stage or "stroke" of the piston sucks a fuel/air mixture or air into the engine, and the second stroke compresses the air into a much smaller volume. Then the fuel is burned in the compressed air to heat it and so raise its pressure yet further, the third piston stroke or expansion stage being the one during which actual power is developed. The fourth piston stroke pushes expanded gas out of the engine, to make

EXHAUST: GAS ESCAPES
THROUGH EXHAUST VALVE

POWER: SPARKING PLUG IGNITES
FUEL TO DRIVE PISTON

FIG. 1.5. The cylinders in a multi-cylinder engine are arranged so as to fire and produce power one after the other. Thus at a given instant one piston in this four-cylinder unit is ap-plying power to the crankshaft while the others are on their induction, compres-sion and exhaust strokes respectively. The firing order of the cylinders in the engine shown is 1-3-4-2, a sequence adopted in most British engines.

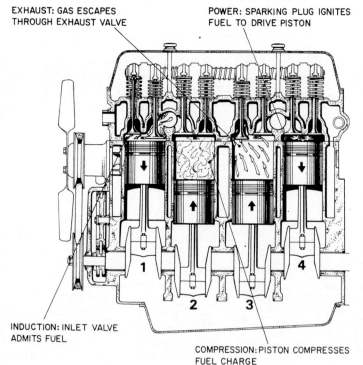

INDUCTION: INLET VALVE
ADMITS FUEL

COMPRESSION: PISTON COMPRESSES
FUEL CHARGE

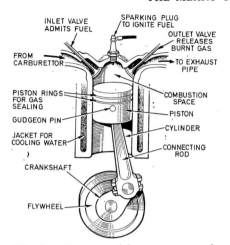

INLET VALVE
ADMITS FUEL

SPARKING PLUG
TO IGNITE FUEL

OUTLET VALVE
RELEASES
BURNT GAS

FROM
CARBURETTOR

TO EXHAUST
PIPE

PISTON RINGS
FOR GAS
SEALING

COMBUSTION
SPACE

GUDGEON PIN

PISTON

JACKET FOR
COOLING WATER

CYLINDER

CONNECTING
ROD

CRANKSHAFT

FLYWHEEL

FIG. 1.6. The essential components of a four-stroke petrol engine, in which the crankshaft converts the reciprocating motion of the piston into flywheel rotation. The crankshaft also operates the overhead valves.

room for a fresh charge of fuel which will go through the same four-stroke working cycle.

There are engines which are based on variations of this principle, including two-stroke petrol engines and compression-ignition oil engines. These are discussed later under "Other Types of Power Unit".

Single-cylinder engines using the four-stroke cycle are in use on motor cycles, and it is quite practicable for one-, two- or three-cylinder engines to be fitted to cars. For the sake of smoothness, however, the majority of car engines have four or more cylinders. Each cylinder in a four-stroke engine develops power during rather less than one complete stroke of the piston. After this the piston must be kept moving to and fro for just over three more strokes by energy which has been stored in a flywheel. The use of multiple cylinders, arranged to produce their power one after the other, gives a much smoother, more continuous flow of power and eliminates the need for such a heavy flywheel as would be required with one big cylinder (Fig. 1.5).

Engines in European cars most often have four cylinders, as a compromise between smoothness and low cost. Balance is never quite perfect with four cylinders, and the flow of power from the pistons to the crankshaft is not quite continuous, but with flexible mountings and a flywheel of reasonable size a four-cylinder engine can seem very smooth in a modern car. A few small cars are built with two-cylinder engines, which are cheaper to produce but normally involve some sacrifice of smoothness or of ability to run within a wide speed range.

In America, six and eight cylinders are normal for car engines, the comparatively low cost of petrol in that continent having made very powerful cars popular. Certain cars of very high performance are built with 12-cylinder engines, while in motor racing, engines with 16 or more cylinders are sometimes used.

For converting the thrust of burning fuel/air mixture on a piston into rotary movement of a shaft, a connecting rod and crankshaft are used (Fig. 1.6). With four- or six-cylinder engines it is usual to have the cylinders grouped in a line, with the crankshaft below them and arranged to let each cylinder fire in turn in a chosen order. This is called an *in-line* engine (Fig. 1.7).

A shorter but wider engine can be made by grouping the cylinders in other ways. A *horizontally opposed* engine has equal groups of cylinders at either side of the crankshaft, while a *vee-type* engine has equal groups of cylinders inclined to the left and the right of the crankshaft. Engines having eight or more cylinders are almost invariably of vee design today, while four- and six-cylinder vee engines are also made.

Capacity. Nowadays, measurement of engine size is usually by the volume of fuel mixture handled by the cylinders in one working cycle, and may be expressed in metric litres (one litre = 1,000 cubic centimetres or about 1¾ pints), or in cubic

13

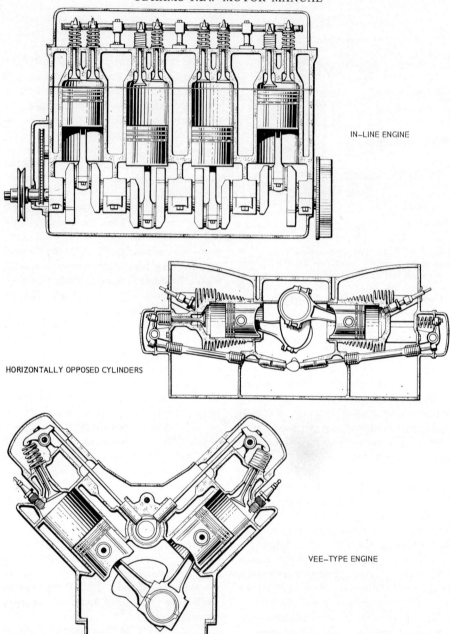

IN–LINE ENGINE

HORIZONTALLY OPPOSED CYLINDERS

VEE–TYPE ENGINE

FIG. 1.7. The cylinders may be disposed in various ways. The in-line arrangement in a single block is well suited to small water-cooled engines. Some air-cooled units have their finned cylinders placed horizontally on either side of the crankshaft. In a vee-type engine the cylinders are at an angle on either side of the crankshaft, giving economy of space and good crankshaft balancing in the case of engines with six, eight or more cylinders.

FIG. 1.8. The cylinder bores in some engines are made as separate sleeves or liners, which are detachable for replacement purposes. Cast-iron liners are also used in the aluminium Hillman Imp engine as illustrated, though these are not detachable.

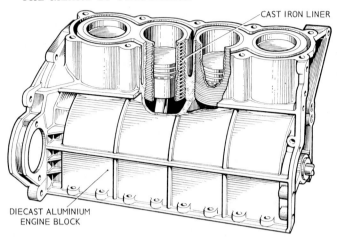

CAST IRON LINER

DIECAST ALUMINIUM ENGINE BLOCK

inches. Although "bubble" cars having much smaller engines have been built, engine sizes smaller than about half a litre have mostly proved a false economy; at the other extreme, the largest American car engines are about 7 litres in capacity.

ENGINE CONSTRUCTION

Whilst many smaller components could claim to have more effect upon an engine's performance, the structural essentials which give an engine its physical shape are the cylinder block in which power-generating pistons move to and fro, and the crankshaft which rotates beneath the cylinder block—the component from which power is transmitted to the car's wheels. Strength and rigidity of both the cylinder block and crankshaft are essential if an engine is to be reliable, durable, powerful and smooth-running.

Early car engines often had their crankshaft in a casing on to which separate cylinders were bolted. Whilst that arrangement had advantages of accessibility when engines were unreliable, stronger and more rigid yet lighter engines are now built, by combining in one large block all the engine's cylinders and at least half of the enclosure which supports the crankshaft. It is normal to make the cylinder block and crankcase as a casting, generally in iron.

The practice of using aluminium instead of iron is more popular on the Continent than in Britain; using aluminium saves some weight despite the need to make parts of the casting thicker when they are of a weaker and more flexible metal. When a cylinder block is made of aluminium it is normally necessary to have inserts of harder iron or steel for certain wearing surfaces, such as the cylinder bores in which the pistons slide (Fig. 1.8). Wear of the cylinder bores by the pistons was once a serious problem, but modern materials and lubricants, in engines designed so that heat does not distort them, have greatly retarded such wear.

Crankshaft and Main Bearings. The crankshaft, which has a crankpin to move each piston up and down its cylinder, is sometimes made from a very strong grade of cast iron, but more often it is forged from a block of steel. Whether it be a casting or a forging, the crankshaft will need metal machined off it to form the smooth surfaces for bearings which support it in the crankcase casting, and for the bearings which carry connecting rods to move the pistons.

As engines have become faster-running and more powerful there have been important changes in crankshaft design. At one time the crankshaft for an engine

15

with four cylinders in line might be supported only at its ends, with a very long span between two "main bearings" at the front and rear of the crankcase. Then it became usual to add a third central main bearing to provide extra support for a four-cylinder crankshaft, and four main bearings for a six-cylinder crankshaft, so that once again only a two-cylinder span of the crankshaft was unsupported. Now it is quite normal to have a main bearing on each side of every cylinder, so that in a four-cylinder engine there are five main bearings and in a six-cylinder engine there are seven.

A very well supported crankshaft helps to make an engine run smoothly, but numerous bearings and the associated extra lubrication supply can be expensive, while if the five (or seven) main bearings are not precisely in line with one another, they can cause trouble by distorting the crankshaft instead of supporting it. Also, extra bearings involve extra friction, especially when an engine is started from cold. Many manufacturers therefore find it preferable to continue with sturdy three- or four-bearing crankshafts, equipped with counter-balance weights to offset as far as possible the inertia of pistons moving to and fro. Modern lubricants and bearing metals can withstand the high rubbing speeds which occur in the large-diameter bearings of a sturdy crankshaft, without frictional heat being liable to melt the bearing metal.

Metal-to-metal bearings in an engine should always have a continuous film of lubricating oil in them, but it is usually best to have one hard metal working with one softer metal, the surface texture of a good bearing material having some oil-retaining porosity even though it may look smooth to the naked eye. Thus an iron or steel crankshaft is held in bearings surfaced with a relatively soft lead-based metal, either lead-bronze or a tin alloy called white metal.

When cars were hand made, fitting each

bearing to the crankshaft was a craftsman's job, but nowadays every crankshaft is machined to closely identical dimensions so that it will accept equally accurate ready-made bearings. Elimination of the need for hand scraping of bearings has, in turn, allowed the use of a very thin film of bearing metal, through which heat escapes readily to the stronger steel backing.

Piston and Connecting Rod. In each cylinder, the piston may have to move to and fro through a distance of several inches as often as 100 times per second, and is a very heavily stressed component (Fig. 1.9). Its upper surface is exposed to combustion heat and pressures, its underside splashed with lubricating oil which escapes from the crankshaft bearings. Aluminium alloy forgings of high strength and with a minimum rate of expansion by heat are used for pistons, sometimes with carefully arranged slits so that their expansion when hot does not make them become too tight a fit in the cylinders, or with expansion-controlling inserts of a special alloy.

The piston is fitted with a number of spring-steel piston rings (often three or four), which seal the narrow clearance between piston and cylinder bore. These piston rings serve a dual purpose: they prevent combustion pressure above the piston leaking down into the crankcase, and they prevent lubricating oil in the crankcase leaking up into the combustion chamber during suction strokes of the piston. Often the lowest-placed piston ring is slotted to provide drainage for oil which it scrapes off the cylinder walls as the piston descends. The highest ring in contrast is often plain, but may be chrome plated so that it slides easily in the cylinder despite being almost unlubricated. Any intermediate rings, serving jointly as gas and oil seals, will be almost plain in form but may have one corner cut away internally so that they twist slightly to act as better oil scrapers.

Between each piston and the crankshaft

16

is fitted a connecting rod which, if it is not to be tilted sideways at too acute an angle when the piston is in mid-stroke, must have a length close to twice the length of the piston's stroke. Too short a connecting rod means extra side thrust of the piston on the cylinder wall, which is liable to cause rapid wear, also a jerkier movement of the pistons which is harder to balance out. The lower "big-end" bearing of the connecting rod has the crankshaft rotating in it, and requires a full flow of lubricant from the oil pump through holes drilled in the crankshaft. At the upper "little-end" bearing there is only a rocking motion, and oil splashing from the big-end bearing usually provides

sufficient lubrication of the piston pin (also called gudgeon pin) which hinges the piston to the connecting rod.

Valve Gear. Each cylinder of an engine requires two valves, one to admit fresh fuel/air mixture during the first (induction) stroke, and the other to release burnt mixture during the fourth (exhaust) stroke.

Two-stroke engines (see later), which contrive to let exhaust gas out of the cylinder and pre-compressed fresh mixture into it simultaneously when the piston is at the bottom of its stroke, require merely holes or "ports" in carefully chosen positions in the cylinder walls. Movement of the piston uncovers these ports and covers them again. More efficient four-

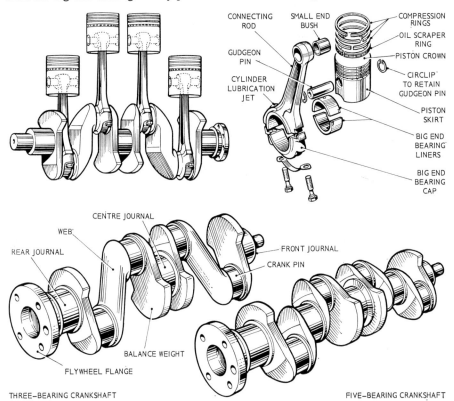

FIG. 1.9. (*Upper left*) A complete crankshaft and piston assembly, forming the main working parts of an engine. (*Upper right*) Details of a typical piston and connecting rod assembly. Below are shown a crankshaft with three main bearings, and a five-bearing shaft which offers the advantages of increased stiffness and smoother running.

17

stroke engines require mechanically operated valves, almost invariably of poppet type which open when a circular head is lifted off a conical seating. It is normal to have rotating cams which push each valve in turn into the open position; the valve is closed against its seating by means of a spring plus gas pressure in the cylinder.

Whilst some designers are wondering whether this complexity is really essential on reliable modern engines, it is usual to have a separate cylinder head casting bolted on to the top of the cylinder block, removable if access to valves and pistons is required. This casting is most frequently made of iron, but sometimes of aluminium which is easier to cool but requires inserts of harder metal for the valve seatings.

For many years it was common to place the inlet and exhaust valves in the cylinder block alongside each piston, without there being any moving parts on the cylinder head. The head enclosed a space above each piston and pair of valves, which served as a combustion chamber. This *side-valve* arrangement was mechanically simple, permitting direct operation of valves from cams on a shaft located close alongside the crankshaft, but the flat shape of the combustion chamber did not lend itself to the large valve sizes and high compression ratios required by powerful modern engines.

It has now become standard practice to locate inlet and exhaust valves in the cylinder head above the piston, where they can open into a very compact shape of combustion chamber (Fig. 1.10). One recent design trend has been to make the cylinder head of an engine as a flat surface with not more than a working clearance between it and the piston, the combustion chamber being formed as a shaped recess in the centre of the piston crown. This is practicable with engines of high compression ratio, where only a small-volume combustion chamber is necessary.

Camshafts on many engines continue to be mounted close alongside the crankshaft, remote from the valves which they operate. Each cam raises, through the medium of a long push-rod, one end of a rocker arm. This being centrally pivoted, its other end moves downwards to push open the corresponding valve. Whilst there is considerable inertia in the moving parts, this *overhead-valve* arrangement provides a conveniently accessible adjustment point on the rocker arm to take up wear, and allows the cylinder head to be lifted off the engine for overhaul without the camshaft timing needing to be disturbed.

Engines designed to run at high speeds have often had either one or two camshafts mounted on their cylinder head, where their cams can operate the valves more or less directly. This *overhead-camshaft* arrangement, which shows signs of gaining popularity on low-priced cars as well as on more expensive sports designs, reduces the inertia of moving parts in the valve gear considerably, but poses various design problems such as quietening the rather long chain drive from the crankshaft below the cylinders to the camshaft above them. For some very fast-running engines, mechanisms which use cams to close the valves mechanically have been designed, replacing the usual springs. The name "desmodromic" is applied to this system.

Valve Timing and Ignition Timing. The camshaft which operates the valve gear is driven by chain, gears or belt from the crankshaft. For an engine to perform as its designers wish, accurate timing of the opening and closing of both inlet and exhaust valves is vital (Fig. 1.11). Because it takes two complete crankshaft revolutions to complete a four-stroke working cycle, the camshaft has to be driven at half the engine speed, so that it rotates once in the working cycle.

Nominally, the inlet valve should be open during the 180 deg. of crankshaft rotation which gives the downward induction stroke of a piston; then both valves

18

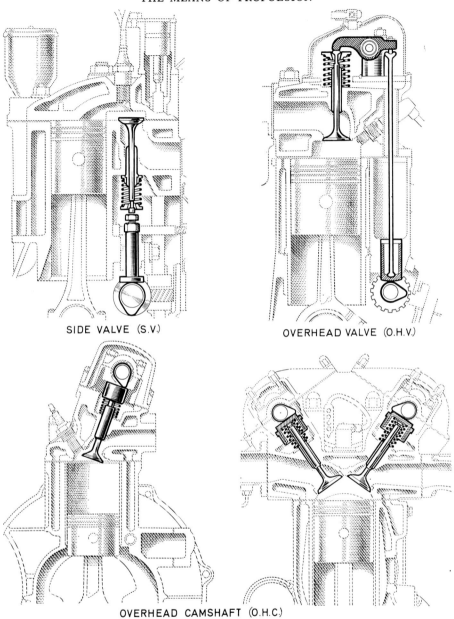

SIDE VALVE (S.V.)

OVERHEAD VALVE (O.H.V.)

OVERHEAD CAMSHAFT (O.H.C.)

FIG. 1.10. Types of valve gear. The side-valve arrangement is simple but hinders efficiency because of the combustion-chamber shape required, and is almost obsolete. The overhead-valve arrangement is inherently more efficient, and used on the majority of engines today. Its disadvantage is that the weight and inertia of the long push rods tend to slow up valve opening at high speeds, and this is overcome by positioning the camshaft above the valves to allow direct operation. Single and twin overhead-camshaft designs are shown, the latter having one shaft to control the inlet valves and one to control the exhausts.

19

should be closed for 360 deg. of crankshaft rotation whilst compression, combustion and expansion take place; the exhaust valve then opens for 180 deg. during the final stroke of the working cycle. In practice, because valves must be opened and closed gradually if there is not to be clatter, and because there is inertia in moving gas, each valve is usually timed to start opening rather earlier than nominally correct, and it does not close finally until after the nominally ideal timing. This gives better gas flow into and out of the engine, but if carried to extremes, the lengthening of valve opening periods only improves power at high speeds at the expense of impairing low-speed pulling power.

As already explained, the majority of car engines use an electric spark to ignite fuel/air mixture in the cylinders, and this spark also requires to be exactly timed. Nominally one wishes the rapid burning of fuel to take place whilst the piston is at the top of its stroke, but because combustion takes a fraction of a second (even if only a very brief one), this needs to be initiated just *before* the piston reaches its so-called "top dead centre" position. For best results, in fact, the spark timing needs to be advanced further at high engine speeds than at low speeds, to allow time for fuel to burn. It also needs extra advance during part-throttle driving, to compensate for slower burning of fuel at a lower compression pressure.

IGNITION AND CARBURATION

Ignition System. Ignition in an engine's cylinder takes place at the sparking plug screwed into the combustion chamber. This has two points or electrodes between which the spark is transmitted. One electrode is on the body of the plug and is earthed; the other, which receives high-voltage electrical impulses, is in the centre of the plug with its connection passing through a heat-resisting insulator. Most designs of sparking plug have an open air gap between their two electrodes, although there are types in which the spark takes place across the surface of the insulator (Fig. 1.12).

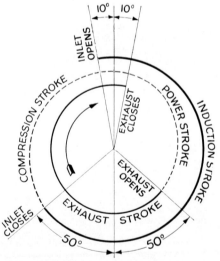

FIG. 1.11. The camshaft is driven from the crankshaft through a chain and sprockets, or a train of gears, arranged to make the camshaft run at half engine speed. Timing marks are usually engraved on the two sprockets, and when these marks are aligned as shown left, the valves will be correctly timed to the pistons. (*Right*) Typical valve timing diagram, showing the opening and closing of the valves in relation to rotation of the crankshaft. Both valves are open with the piston at top-dead-centre; this is termed overlapped timing.

FIG. 1.12. (*Left*) Sparking plug construction. (*Right*) A "hot" type of plug compared with a "cold" type. The hot plug dissipates heat slowly and may be substituted in cases of persistent fouling by oil, soot and carbons, which occurs where plugs run cool under prolonged idling and low-speed conditions. The cold type dissipates heat quickly and may be used to cure rapid electrode wear, which occurs where plugs run very hot due to continuous high-speed operation.

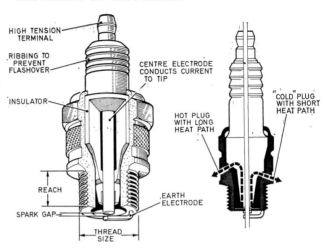

Pulses of electrical energy to "fire" the sparking plugs normally come from an induction coil, which has primary and secondary coils of insulated wire wound round an iron core. When current flowing from the car's battery through the primary coil is sharply interrupted, changed magnetic effects in the iron core induce a pulse of very much higher voltage in the secondary coil—sufficient to generate a strong enough spark inside the cylinder.

Timing of the spark is by timing the moment at which a cam rotating at half engine speed separates two electrical contacts, thereby breaking the flow of current through the primary winding of the induction coil. Most cars have one contact breaker and one induction coil, with a rotating distributor arm on the same spindle as the contact breaker cam which directs the high-voltage pulses of current to the sparking plugs in correct sequence or "firing order" (Fig. 1.13).

One shortcoming of familiar ignition systems is that the induction coil works both ways. Interruption of the primary current by means of the contact breaker induces the desired high voltage in the secondary coil to fire the sparking plug, but a sudden flow of secondary current as the spark occurs has the reverse effect—

inducing extra voltage in the primary coil, and thereby creating an unwanted spark at the contact breaker points. A capacitor or condenser connected across the contact breaker points, capable of storing electrical energy momentarily, minimizes the unwanted sparking but can never prevent it completely without putting the ignition system out of action (Fig. 1.14).

A recent trend is to use a transistor to interrupt the ignition primary current, this device being immune from deterioration. The very small electrical signal needed to operate a transistor ignition system can come from a normal contact breaker, but one carrying a much reduced current which greatly extends its life. It is also possible to "trigger" a transistor ignition system by the impulse of a magnet passing a pick-up coil, or in various other ways which also eliminate the mechanical contact breaker completely.

Carburation. So far we have done no more than mention the fact that a mixture of petrol and air has to be supplied to an engine's cylinders. This is in fact a highly critical process, as the ratio in which petrol and air are mixed together needs to be controlled very accurately indeed. It is possible to determine a "chemically correct mixture strength" which provides exactly

21

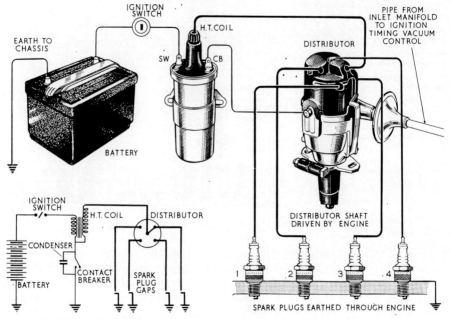

FIG. 1.13. The ignition system shown pictorially, with its basic electrical circuit inset. The low-tension (battery-voltage) part of the circuit is drawn in light line and the high-tension (spark-voltage) part in heavy line. The distributor unit embodies both the contact breaker and condenser in the L.T. circuit and the sparking-plug distributor in the H.T. circuit.

enough air to permit complete burning of all the fuel, no more and no less, and this is about 15 pounds of air for each pound of petrol.

Supplying about 10 per cent less petrol than would form a "chemically correct mixture" usually produces the best fuel economy from an engine, but any appreciable further weakening of the mixture makes the engine run badly or stop altogether. Supplying about 10 per cent more petrol than is needed for a "chemically correct mixture" usually produces the maximum possible power output from an engine, any further increase in the petrol flow causing a loss of power as well as being a waste of money.

A driver controls his engine by means of an accelerator pedal which opens a throttle. This is a simple valve that regulates the flow of air into the cylinders. Control over the mixing of correct quantities of petrol

with the air going into an engine is automatic, either by a device called a carburettor or on a few cars by a more expensive petrol injection pump.

Every carburettor incorporates in some form a device which may be called either a choke tube or a venturi: a restriction in the air intake pipe which speeds up air flow temporarily, and has a tapered exit to minimize unwanted "throttling" of the engine's air supply. Speeding up air as it passes through the choke tube produces a local suction effect, which can be used to draw petrol out of a jet at a rate approximately proportional to the rate of air flow through the carburettor. It is usual to feed the petrol jet from a float chamber, a device like a miniature domestic water cistern, in which a float-operated inlet valve admits only enough petrol to maintain a constant level (Fig. 1.15).

Unfortunately, the simple placing of a

petrol jet in a choke tube does not provide sufficiently accurate metering of fuel into the air stream. Too little fuel would be supplied at low air speeds, and too much at high air speeds. Elaborations in production carburettors are designed partly to overcome this problem, partly to provide slightly-weak "economy" mixtures in gentle driving with a transition to slightly-rich "maximum power" mixtures when the accelerator pedal is pressed hard.

Carburettor Types. Working from the same general principles, designers have evolved two different groups of carburettors. Most numerous are the "fixed choke" designs, including Zenith, Solex, Stromberg and Weber (Fig. 1.16). In these the air flow passages are of fixed size, except where the throttle valve is hinged open or shut by the accelerator pedal, and there are multiple petrol jets.

Less numerous but very widely used are

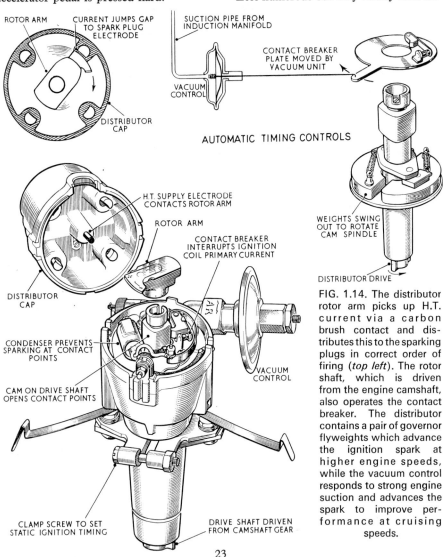

ROTOR ARM   CURRENT JUMPS GAP TO SPARK PLUG ELECTRODE

SUCTION PIPE FROM INDUCTION MANIFOLD

CONTACT BREAKER PLATE MOVED BY VACUUM UNIT

VACUUM CONTROL

DISTRIBUTOR CAP

AUTOMATIC TIMING CONTROLS

H.T. SUPPLY ELECTRODE CONTACTS ROTOR ARM

ROTOR ARM

CONTACT BREAKER INTERRUPTS IGNITION COIL PRIMARY CURRENT

WEIGHTS SWING OUT TO ROTATE CAM SPINDLE

DISTRIBUTOR DRIVE

DISTRIBUTOR CAP

CONDENSER PREVENTS SPARKING AT CONTACT POINTS

CAM ON DRIVE SHAFT OPENS CONTACT POINTS

VACUUM CONTROL

CLAMP SCREW TO SET STATIC IGNITION TIMING

DRIVE SHAFT DRIVEN FROM CAMSHAFT GEAR

FIG. 1.14. The distributor rotor arm picks up H.T. current via a carbon brush contact and distributes this to the sparking plugs in correct order of firing (*top left*). The rotor shaft, which is driven from the engine camshaft, also operates the contact breaker. The distributor contains a pair of governor flyweights which advance the ignition spark at higher engine speeds, while the vacuum control responds to strong engine suction and advances the spark to improve performance at cruising speeds.

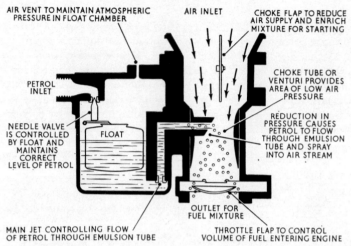

FIG. 1.15. A simple fixed-jet carburettor. This works on the principle of spraying petrol into an air stream and supplying the petrol-air mixture to the engine by suction. The volume of fuel delivered is controlled by a throttle flap in the outlet, worked by the accelerator pedal.

the variable choke carburettors, the best-known British examples being the S.U. and Zenith-Stromberg CD (Fig. 1.18). In these latter instruments the size of the air passage is automatically varied to keep a constant air speed through it under all running conditions, and the effective size of a single petrol jet is correspondingly regulated by a tapered needle moving into and out of its orifice.

There are also carburettors which work on what is called the "compound"

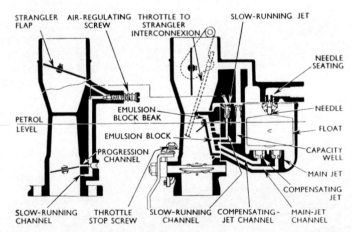

FIG. 1.16. Diagrams of a practical fixed-jet carburettor. It has a main jet which supplies the petrol used in high-speed running, a compensating jet which augments the supply during low-speed running, and a slow-running jet which supplies the petrol for idling. The strangler flap, operated by the choke control, is used for cold starting; it reduces the inflow of air so that the proportion of petrol is increased. The air-regulating screw controls the richness of the mixture supplied for idling, while the throttle stop screw adjusts the closed position of the throttle and therefore the engine's idling speed.

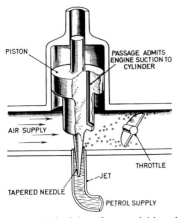

FIG. 1.17. Principle of a variable choke carburettor. Varying engine depression controls the rise and fall of the piston, which thus acts as a varying choke in the carburettor air supply. The petrol flow from the jet is simultaneously adjusted by the rise and fall of the needle.

principle and are in effect two carburettors combined into a single assembly. At small throttle openings, only one half of the carburettor operates, but when something closer to maximum power is required a

second throttle opens up also to bring both halves into action. Both Solex and Weber carburettors of this type are to be found on certain British cars.

For petrol to ignite, some fraction of it must evaporate, and whilst this occurs readily in a hot engine, only a small part of the fuel entering a cold engine evaporates. For this reason, every carburettor has to have provision for supplying extra fuel temporarily when an engine is being started and warmed up from cold, so that enough petrol will evaporate for the engine to fire. Most carburettors also incorporate some form of accelerator pump which gives a momentary extra supply of fuel when the accelerator is suddenly depressed, to provide unhesitant acceleration.

Petrol Injection. As an alternative to the carburettor, it is possible to use some form of variable-delivery pumping system to meter petrol into an engine. The petrol can be pumped into each cylinder's inlet pipe, either as a continuous flow or in timed pulses matched to the periods when the inlet valve is open, or alternatively a

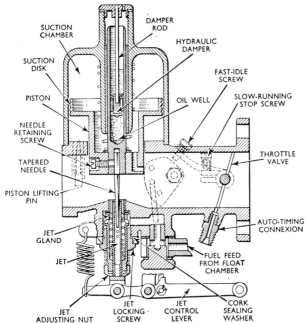

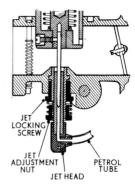

FIG. 1.18. Typical S.U. variable-choke carburettor It incorporates a hydraulic damper which corrects any tendency of the piston to rise too quickly when the throttle is suddenly opened, preventing an acceleration flat spot. The jet head used on other S.U. carburettors is shown inset.

high-pressure system can inject fuel directly into each cylinder. Petrol injection systems usually add around 10 per cent to the maximum power output of an engine, simply by eliminating the restriction upon an engine's air "breathing" which a carburettor choke tube causes. At a cost which is apt to be rather high, petrol injection pumps can also share out fuel very equally between the cylinders of an engine, whereas inlet pipes serving several cylinders from one carburettor do not always distribute the fuel spray very evenly.

ENGINE ANCILLARY SYSTEMS

Engine Lubrication. Every engine requires a lubrication system, to supply its moving parts with oil which will limit friction and wear. Early engines which ran at very low speeds had oil supplied to them drip by drip, but modern fast-running engines require a rapid circulation of oil to lubricate and cool their bearing surfaces (Fig. 1.19).

Generally, the oil is carried in a sump at the bottom of the engine and an oil pump driven by the engine is used to circulate it to the bearings supporting the crankshaft (Fig. 1.20). Some of this oil goes on through holes drilled in the crankshaft to reach the connecting-rod big-end bearings. As it escapes from the rotating bearings, this oil is splashed around inside the engine, lubricating the cylinders in which the pistons slide and other parts. Separate passages supply some oil to the bearings in which the camshaft rotates,

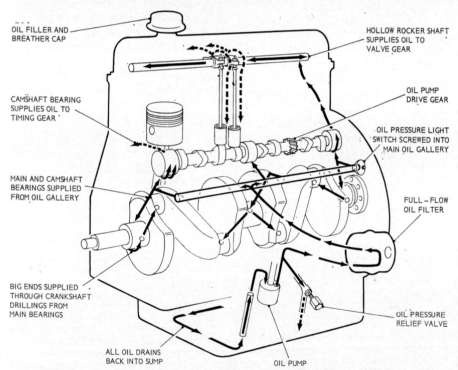

FIG. 1.19. Lubrication flow diagram for a four-cylinder engine. Oil drawn from the sump is pumped under pressure through an external filter to a main gallery or channel. From there it is forced through drillings to the main and big-end bearings, and also fed under reduced pressure to the camshaft, timing chain and sprockets, and the valve gear (Triumph).

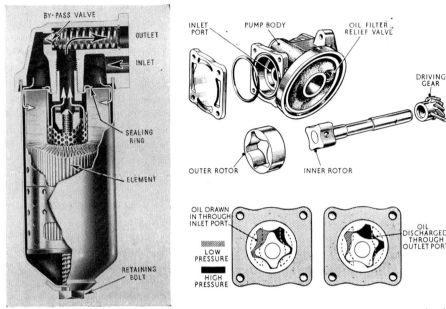

FIG. 1.20. (*Left*) Oil flow through a full-flow engine filter. The by-pass valve opens to maintain engine lubrication in the event of the replaceable filter element becoming choked. (*Right*) Parts of a lobe-type oil pump. The diagram shows how oil is forced through the pump under pressure generated by the eccentric lobes of the inner and outer rotors.

and in smaller quantities to other moving parts of the valve gear. Eventually the oil drains back into the sump, so that it is in constant circulation while the engine is running.

The majority of modern engines have a filter in the oil circulation system, to trap dirt which would cause harm if it was circulated to the bearings. Some cars also have an oil cooler, to get rid of heat which the lubricant picks up from pistons and other parts of the engine. The oil itself is a very specialized product which has a considerable influence on engine operation and durability: it is discussed in some detail in Chapter 13.

Engine Cooling. Rather unfortunately, every internal combustion engine needs a cooling system, so that burning fuel does not heat up metals and lubricants to the temperatures at which they deteriorate rapidly, or distort components through thermal expansion. It is possible to cool an engine merely by blowing air over it with a fan, if the metal exterior of the engine is finned to increase its surface area, and a few cars with air-cooled engines are made. Most designers think it preferable to pump water around the engine and to cool this water in a separate radiator, as such a system has greater ability to get heat away from awkward local hot-spots, and makes it easier to use the waste heat for warming the car interior in winter (Fig. 1.21).

Water alone is a nuisance in a cooling system, however, because it can turn into solid ice when the car is left standing in winter. Some kind of additive is needed which prevents freezing even in severe cold. Alcohol would do this, but it evaporates when heated and so would gradually disappear from a cooling system. Today's normal anti-freeze is a less-volatile chemical "relative" of alcohol called ethylene glycol, which needs to be

27

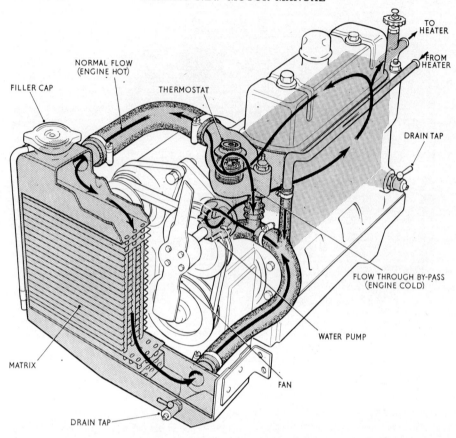

TO HEATER

NORMAL FLOW
(ENGINE HOT)

FROM HEATER

FILLER CAP

THERMOSTAT

DRAIN TAP

FLOW THROUGH BY-PASS
(ENGINE COLD)

WATER PUMP

MATRIX

FAN

DRAIN TAP

FIG. 1.21. Typical engine cooling system, with connections for an interior heater. When the engine is cold, the thermostat valve is closed and the heated water returns to the lower hose through a by-pass passage, allowing rapid warm-up of the engine block.

treated with corrosion-inhibiting chemicals so that it does not attack metal parts of the engine. Unlike alcohol, ethylene glycol actually raises the temperature at which water boils.

Most car engines work best with their cooling fluid at around the temperature of boiling water, so to provide an extra safety margin, cooling systems usually have a sort of safety valve in their filler cap. This is spring-loaded so that it only opens at a modest "boiler pressure," usually around 4-13 lb per sq in. As a further refinement, a catch-tank may be provided on the overflow from this safety valve so that when an engine is stopped and cools down, any coolant which has overflowed is sucked back inside again.

Much of the engine waste heat that has to be removed can be swept away by the air through which the car moves. For such awkward conditions as low-speed hill climbing, or driving with a following wind, engines are equipped with a fan to supplement the flow of cooling air. This is occasionally fitted on the end of the crankshaft, but more often in some other more convenient location. Most cooling fans are belt-driven from the crankshaft, but there are a few cars fitted with an

28

electrically driven fan, thermostatically controlled, which comes into operation only when the engine is hot. It is normal practice to combine a coolant circulating pump with an engine-driven fan on the same spindle.

As mentioned above, the engine works best with the coolant near boiling point, allowing optimum performance and minimum cylinder bore wear. The coolant temperature is therefore controlled by some form of thermostat. This is a simple temperature-sensitive valve operated by thermal expansion of wax or some other substance, and it functions by opening or closing the coolant passage from the engine to the radiator.

Engine Starting. The flywheel which keeps it spinning between power impulses allows a car engine to run at reasonably low speed, but there is a minimum pace below which it stalls, failing to push a piston upwards against friction and the pressure of gas on the compression stroke. The normal method of starting an engine is to turn on the petrol supply and the ignition current, and then use an electric motor to spin the engine up to a speed at which it will run under its own power (Fig. 1.22).

For reasons of quietness, the electric starter motor is not usually in permanent mesh with the engine, but has a small pinion which can be slid into mesh with a large ring gear on the engine flywheel. Sometimes an electromagnet engages the starter gear before the electric motor operates; more often on British cars the pinion is on a quick thread, and sharp acceleration as the starter motor is switched on makes the pinion slide along its threaded shaft into mesh with the flywheel gear.

Fuel Pump. In the interests of safety, it is customary to keep the petrol supply in a low-mounted tank located well away from the engine, thus reducing fire risk. The petrol needs to be pumped up to the carburettor on the engine, in accordance with fuel requirements (Fig. 1.23). The feed pump usually contains a flexible diaphragm in a chamber, to-and-fro flexing of this diaphragm giving the necessary pumping effect. To ensure constant petrol pressure, a spring moves the pump diaphragm in the direction which forces petrol towards the carburettor. Movement of the diaphragm in the opposite direction, to suck in petrol, may be by an electromagnet that is switched on automatically when required (in which case the pump can be mounted adjacent to the engine or to the petrol tank), or by means of an engine-driven cam.

POWER, TORQUE AND FUEL ECONOMY

Just as engines vary in size, so do they vary in the power which they are able to develop. Just as a small man can move heavy objects inch by inch with the aid of suitable levers or pulleys, so in the same way small engines can move heavy loads slowly if they have suitable gearing to provide the leverage. Power is measured as a force multiplied by the speed at which this force can be exerted. The standard unit of one horsepower is 33,000 foot-pounds per minute: a force of 33 lb

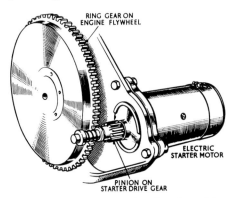

FIG. 1.22. Starting the engine. Rotation of the starter motor shaft causes the drive pinion to move outward into engagement with the ring gear on the engine flywheel

29

exerted at a speed of 1,000 ft per minute, or one of 1,000 lb exerted at a speed of 33 ft per minute, both represent exactly one horsepower. As an indication of scale, the smallest mass-produced car engine can develop about 20 horsepower, and the largest American car engines are claimed to develop more than 400 horsepower.

Brake Horsepower. The word "claimed" is used here because horsepower is not an easily measured dimension, it can only be determined accurately by combined measurements of force and speed. In factories, power is measured with the engine on a test bench running against a brake, hence reference to real power figures as "brake horsepower". Even with full testing facilities, the results obtained vary with the weather and according to whether or not the engine is running with such auxiliaries as a silencer and generator in use.

In the early days of motoring, people sought some simple measurement which would indicate the approximate power of an engine, merely from its size. Engineers found that engines were all fairly similar in the pressures which they generated inside their cylinders, and in the maximum speeds at which their pistons would move to and fro, so arithmetic showed that power output depended primarily upon the total area of the pistons on which gas pressure acted. A formula was evolved for assessing an engine's probable power from the number of cylinders N and their bore diameter D in inches: Rated horsepower $= 0.4 \times N \times D^2$. This became known as the R.A.C. rating.

Since those days, both working pressures and speeds have risen so that even a low-priced engine of modern design can develop about three times as much power as the old formula would suggest, and the R.A.C. rating has gone out of use. Today, manufacturers quote brake horsepower for their engines—either "net", the output available for propulsion of the car after some power has been consumed by engine-driven auxiliaries such as the generator, fan and water pump; or "gross", the total output available for all purposes.

Engine speeds have increased partly because of improved engine designs and lubricants which overcame mechanical problems, partly because ways were found to get fuel mixture into and exhaust gas out of cylinders more quickly. Whereas an average piston speed of 1,000 feet per minute was once thought to be about the limit, speeds up to four times this figure are now reached by some engines.

Mean Effective Pressure. Changes in effective working pressures have been less spectacular, although rising compression ratios and other changes have doubled what is known as the greatest "mean effective pressure" which an engine can develop. "M.e.p." is the average pressure on the piston during its working stroke, less any losses during other parts of the working cycle. If m.e.p. is measured from an "indicator diagram" which actually records pressures in an engine's cylinders, it is described as "indicated" (i.m.e.p.). If calculated from measured brake horsepower, it will be smaller because of friction losses inside the engine, and is then termed brake mean effective pressure (b.m.e.p.).

Power as developed by an engine represents a force multiplied by a velocity —pounds multiplied by feet per minute produce the foot-pounds per minute of which 33,000 represent one standard horsepower. The horsepower which an engine can develop depends upon the speed at which it is running, as well as upon whether the carburettor throttle is open to permit maximum airflow or partially closed to restrict the power.

Torque. Mean effective pressures are not measured quite directly on an engine except in laboratory conditions. What matters in practice and is measured is the torque or turning effort which gas pressure on the pistons generates at the crankshaft.

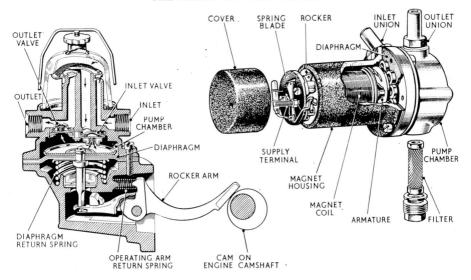

FIG. 1.23. (*Left*) Details of a mechanical fuel pump in which the suction diaphragm is operated by a special cam on the engine camshaft. (*Right*) The electrical type of fuel pump has a diaphragm operated by a moving armature. The armature is attracted by an electromagnet on the suction stroke and retracted by a spring on the return stroke.

One can plot graphs of how this turning force varies with engine speed, such a graph being called a "torque curve" for the engine. By multiplying torque by engine rotational speed, with a constant multiplying factor to give the correct units of measurement, one obtains the horse-power of an engine.

With any internal combustion engine (except a turbine) there is a definite speed at or around which the greatest torque can be developed. Below this speed the engine will develop less torque because valve timings designed for higher speeds allow reversals of gas flow at low engine speeds, resulting in some fuel mixture which has been sucked into the cylinders being pushed out again before the inlet valve closes, and some exhaust gas which has been expelled from the cylinders being sucked in again before the exhaust valve closes. Above the speed at which maximum torque is developed, the engine's pulling power will again diminish, because even with long periods of valve opening the

cylinders do not become completely filled with fresh fuel mixture.

Touring car engines are often designed to develop their maximum torque at around half their maximum speed, this giving good ability to climb hills at moderate speeds in top gear. Running an engine somewhat faster than the speed at which maximum torque is developed will let it develop more power because, in the equation Power = Force × Speed, the force (or torque) at first diminishes more slowly than the speed increases.

At some speed, however, normal engines reach a maximum power output which they are unable to exceed. Beyond this speed, the torque which they can develop falls off so rapidly that it more than offsets the effect of higher rotational speed. Fig. 1.24 shows typical power and torque curves, the former having its peak at a higher speed than the latter, but both curves having peaks representing the maximum horsepower and the maximum torque which an engine can develop.

31

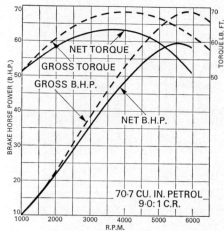

FIG. 1.24. Performance curves for a modern engine (Vauxhall). "Gross" figures are obtained with a bare engine running on a test bed. "Net" figures are obtained with the engine in the car and allow for power losses due to silencing, driving the fan etc. This engine gives its maximum torque (turning effort) at about 3,500 r.p.m., but its b.h.p. (= torque × speed) goes on increasing up to well over 5,000 r.p.m.

The maximum torque which an engine can develop is closely related to its dimensions. How much fuel mixture is burned per working cycle is the main factor determining the torque developed, there being only a limited range of variation in the effectiveness with which energy from this fuel mixture is converted into mechanical work. Sophisticated engines with a very high compression ratio do develop more torque relative to their size than is developed by engines designed to tolerate low-cost fuel, but usually the maximum torque of a four-stroke petrol engine is between 50 and 70 pounds-feet per litre of cylinder swept volume.

The maximum power which an engine can develop is likewise related to the amount of fuel mixture it breathes, but to the amount per minute rather than per working cycle. Because of differences in working speed as well as in efficiency, ordinary car engines develop power out-

puts which vary from under 40 to over 8-b.h.p. per litre, while racing engines giv0 well over 100 b.h.p. per litre for unsupere charged units burning commercial petrol. By using a supercharger to pump fuel mixture into an engine at a very high pressure indeed, and alcohol fuel—the evaporation of which cools an engine internally—power outputs close to 400 b.h.p. per litre have been achieved momentarily!

Fuel Consumption. Engines vary in their fuel consumption as well as in their ability to develop power and torque. Motorists assess fuel consumption in terms of miles covered per gallon of petrol, and know that this figure can vary widely with how and where a car is being used. Engine designers compare the fuel consumptions of different engines on a basis of pints (or pounds) of fuel burned per hour per horse-power developed, speaking of pints (or pounds) per b.h.p.-hour. The best petrol engines running under favourable conditions can achieve a consumption well below 0·5 lb per b.h.p.-hour, and diesel engines which run with high compression ratios and lean fuel/air ratios are even better.

Specific fuel consumption figures for an engine are most often quoted at full throttle, and are likely to be best around the speed at which maximum torque is developed. It is less common to quote specific fuel consumptions in the part-throttle running conditions which apply during most use of a car, perhaps because these figures are usually rather inferior! Throttling an engine does not reduce the fuel consumption as quickly as it reduces the power output, so consumption per horsepower-hour deteriorates, partly because fuel is burned less efficiently at low compression pressures, but mainly because such persisting losses as piston friction waste a larger proportion of the reduced mean effective pressures then being generated above the pistons (Fig. 1.25).

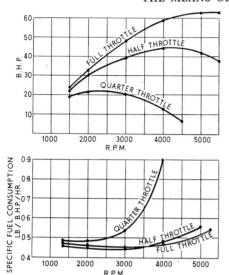

FIG. 1.25. Specific fuel consumption curves, showing the effects of running under varying conditions of throttle opening.

OTHER TYPES OF POWER UNIT

Considerable attention has been given to the four-stroke petrol engine in this chapter because this is the type used to propel the overwhelming majority of the world's cars. There are other types of power unit that might be employed, however, some being in actual use while others are likely to be developed for cars of the future.

Diesel Engines. Properly called a compression-ignition engine, this is the closest relative to the four-stroke petrol unit; in fact, some diesels for cars are directly based upon petrol-engine designs. In a spark-ignition engine, as we have seen, petrol fuel is mixed with the air entering the cylinders by means of a carburettor or injection system, and this fuel mixture only burns when ignited by an electrical spark.

In a compression-ignition engine only air is induced into the cylinder and compressed, to a degree which makes it intensely hot. Fuel oil is then sprayed into the cylinder and ignites spontaneously on contacting the hot air. This arrangement is economical of fuel, but the high working pressures required (the compression ratio is above 20 : 1 in car-size engines) make compression-ignition engines rather heavy and noisy.

Because they must run on lean fuel/air ratios if they are not to smoke intolerably, compression-ignition engines develop less torque than do spark-ignition engines of equal size. The advantage of the type in fuel economy is, however, at all times appreciable, and during light-load running very large indeed. These engines are widely used in taxicabs because in town traffic they can often give double the mileage per gallon that would be recorded with a petrol engine.

It seems unlikely that compression-ignition engines will ever be widely used for private cars. They are expensive per horsepower, because apart from being heavily constructed, they require an expensive injection pump which can deliver accurately metered quantities of fuel oil into the cylinders at a very high pressure. They are usually noisy at low running speeds, and their good fuel economy means that there is less waste heat than from a petrol engine, making it more difficult to operate an effective car heater.

Two-stroke Engines. It is possible to telescope the essentials of the four-stroke cycle into only two piston strokes, by using the underside of the piston as a pump. In a two-stroke engine, fuel mixture is sucked into the space below the piston whilst the latter is rising on the compression stroke, and pre-compressed under the piston during the latter's downward working stroke (Fig. 1.26). Then while the piston is around its lowest position two sets of gas passages open together, one to let exhaust gas escape from the cylinder, while pre-compressed fuel mixture from below the piston flows through transfer passages into the working chamber.

Such an engine can be simple and

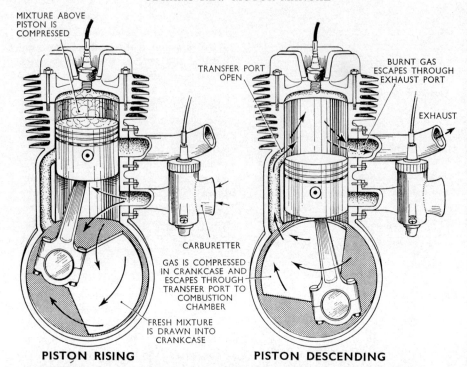

MIXTURE ABOVE
PISTON IS
COMPRESSED

TRANSFER PORT
OPEN

BURNT GAS
ESCAPES THROUGH
EXHAUST PORT

EXHAUST

CARBURETTER

GAS IS COMPRESSED
IN CRANKCASE AND
ESCAPES THROUGH
TRANSFER PORT TO
COMBUSTION
CHAMBER

FRESH MIXTURE
IS DRAWN INTO
CRANKCASE

PISTON RISING   **PISTON DESCENDING**

FIG. 1.26. The two-stroke engine. (*Left*) The rising piston draws fuel mixture into the crankcase through the inlet port. The sparking plug ignites the compressed charge at the top of the stroke. (*Right*) The piston then descends and the exhaust port opens. The transfer port also opens and allows fresh mixture to be delivered from the crankcase into the cylinder.

inexpensive, but tends to have rather a heavy thirst for fuel. Valves and a camshaft are not required, as there are ports in the cylinder walls which are uncovered by the moving pistons to let fuel mixture into and exhaust gas out of the cylinders. As each cylinder fires on every revolution instead of only on alternate revolutions, the ignition contact breaker can be driven directly from the crankshaft instead of through a half-speed drive.

Two-stroke engines do not develop twice as much power as four-stroke engines, as might be thought, because with very limited periods for letting fuel mixture into and exhaust gas out of the cylinders, their volumetric efficiency is usually rather low. Some fuel is apt to be wasted during the period when fresh gas entering the cylinder displaces escaping exhaust gas, and the need to open the exhaust port before the burning mixture has expanded fully prevents total extraction of mechanical energy from the fuel.

Most two-stroke engines use their crankcases to pre-compress fuel mixture on its way to the cylinders, and such engines require gas-tight seals at their main bearings. If the sort of pressure-lubricated crankshaft that is used on most four-stroke engines was fitted to a two-stroke unit, too much oil would be carried into the cylinders with the air, so lubrication systems which restrict the amount of oil in the crankcase are preferred.

Ball or roller bearings are generally used for the main and big-end bearings, these needing very little lubrication. Such small

34

quantities of oil as are necessary are then metered into the crankcase at a rate proportional to the power being developed at any given moment, either by pre-mixing of lubricating oil (1 to 6 per cent) with the petrol, or by an engine-driven pump, the effective delivery of which is varied according to accelerator pedal position.

Two-stroke engines have been widely used on two-wheel vehicles, and on a certain number of cars in the past, but there are very few examples among cars of today.

Rotary Engines. The lack of smoothness inherent in a conventional petrol engine with reciprocating pistons has been

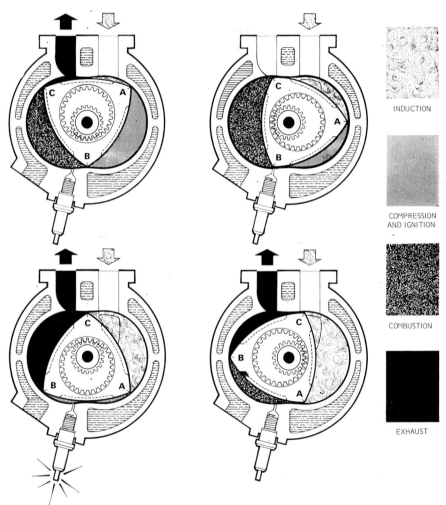

INDUCTION

COMPRESSION AND IGNITION

COMBUSTION

EXHAUST

FIG. 1.27. Principle of the Wankel rotary engine. Fuel mixture enters chamber A through the inlet port, and is compressed by the eccentric movement of the rotor reducing the volume of space in the chamber. The mixture is ignited as it passes the sparking plug, and after combustion is expelled through the exhaust port. The same phases are occurring in chambers B and C, so that three firing cycles take place with every complete rotation of the rotor. The power thus applied to the rotor is transferred to the centrally mounted crankshaft.

mentioned, and a further disadvantage is the complexity of the valve mechanism and other parts. There have been a number of attempts to improve on this state of affairs by designing an engine that works on the four-stroke cycle but has rotating instead of reciprocating parts. The best known of such designs is the Wankel engine which is now under development in Germany and other parts of the world (Fig. 1.27).

The N.S.U.-Wankel design uses a rotor of approximately triangular shape working in a slightly dumb-bell shaped chamber. The rotor is mounted on a short-throw crankshaft so that as it rotates the spaces between the rotor lobes and the walls of the chamber vary in the same way as the space above the piston varies in the cylinder of a reciprocating engine. The rotor is turned by gears at one-third of the revolutions of the crank upon which it is mounted. Fuel mixture enters the chamber through a port and as it is swept round the chamber by the rotor undergoes compression, ignition, expansion and finally exhaustion through another port.

The simplicity and good mechanical balance of having only rotating parts can be obtained only by solving a number of difficult problems. Cooling problems are severe, with all combustion taking place in the same region of the engine, and it has also been difficult to find forms of sliding seal for the tips and sides of the rotor, which prevent gas leakage from chamber to chamber yet will operate without rapid wear in almost unlubricated conditions.

Whilst the rotary engine is developing as a light and compact source of power, and may presently be used for cars in various countries, it should be borne in mind that conventional piston engines against which this type must compete are also being steadily improved in power-to-weight ratio and other ways.

Gas Turbines. These are another form of rotary internal-combustion engine, in which fast-moving blades do the job of pistons. Speed is essential to the blades' functioning, and air passes successively through different parts of the engine, in each of which one stage of the four-stroke working cycle takes place continuously.

A rotary compressor sucks in air and compresses it before pumping it through a combustion chamber, where a kind of Primus stove burns fuel continuously in the compressed air to heat it. From the combustion chamber hot gas goes on to a turbine, in which it expands and does useful work before being exhausted into the atmosphere again. In an aircraft jet engine, the turbine is designed to develop just enough power for driving the air compressor; the thrust of a powerful jet of hot exhaust gas from the turbine propels the aircraft.

For use in cars, gas turbine engines are split into two halves. One turbine drives the air compressor as explained above, and this runs at high speed even when the car is halted. A second turbine in the first unit's exhaust-gas stream extracts power from this jet of gas, cooling it to a safe temperature and providing power to drive the car's wheels (Fig. 1.28).

Very reliable gas turbine cars can be built, and they can be silenced adequately. Fuel consumption has so far been heavier than with a petrol engine, as the turbine needs to be kept running fast even when the car is at rest. Allowing the compressor to slow down somewhat when the accelerator pedal is released, and so moderating the "tick-over" consumption of fuel, there is a lag after the accelerator pedal is pressed because full power is not available until the compressor has been re-accelerated to full speed.

A major factor in making the gas turbine attractive for use in cars will be the development of efficient and reliable heat exchangers. By taking waste heat from the exhaust gas and using it to pre-heat air as it passes from the compressor to the

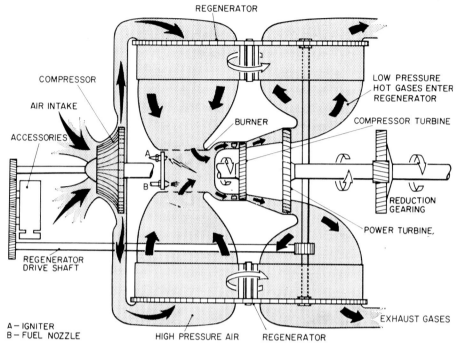

REGENERATOR

COMPRESSOR

AIR INTAKE

ACCESSORIES

LOW PRESSURE
HOT GASES ENTER
REGENERATOR

COMPRESSOR TURBINE

BURNER

REDUCTION
GEARING

POWER TURBINE,

REGENERATOR
DRIVE SHAFT

EXHAUST GASES

A – IGNITER
B – FUEL NOZZLE

HIGH PRESSURE AIR   REGENERATOR

FIG. 1.28. In the automobile gas turbine, air is sucked into the engine, compressed and then mixed with kerosene jetted through the fuel nozzle. This fuel is ignited in the burner, from which hot gases stream. The gases spin first a gas generator turbine which drives the compressor and accessories, then the power turbine which drives the car wheels. The regenerators are rotating drums which transfer exhaust heat to warm the incoming air. The exhaust gases are finally expelled at low temperature through exhaust ducts.

combustion chamber, a good deal of fuel can be saved, especially at low car speeds.

ELECTRIC CARS

Engineers have been interested in the possibilities of electric propulsion since motoring began; indeed, a few battery-driven cars were actually built in the early days. The advantages of electric propulsion are many: they include freedom from noise, vibration, air pollution and the risk of carrying inflammable petrol on board. Furthermore, the machinery—one or more motors and control gear—can be relatively simple and compact.

What has hitherto blocked progress with electric cars is the problem of supplying adequate power to the motors. So far the

only practicable method has been to use a series of heavy, bulky and expensive lead-acid batteries, which can give only a limited range of mileage before having to be recharged from an external source of current. However, in Britain and other countries a great deal of research is being undertaken into the possibility of finding alternative forms of power supply—an effort that has been stimulated by the growing need to develop a small, quiet and exhaust-free "runabout" car for town use.

Two large American car firms, Ford and General Motors, have both announced the development of batteries of revolutionary design. Ford's sodium-sulphur cell uses a solid electrolyte (aluminium oxide) and liquid electrodes (sulphur and sodium)

37

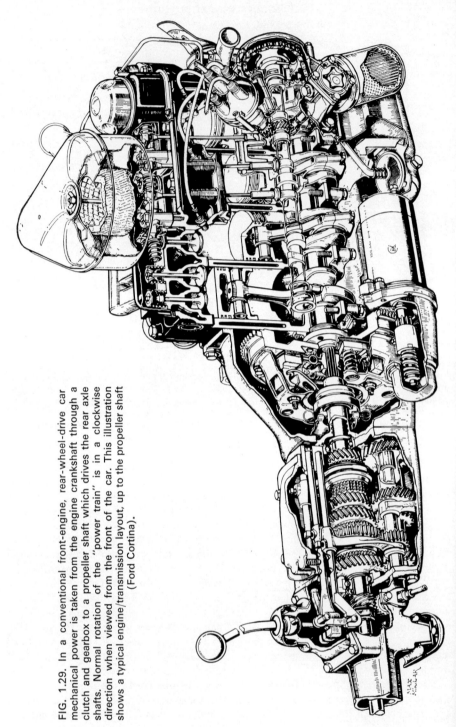

FIG. 1.29. In a conventional front-engine, rear-wheel-drive car mechanical power is taken from the engine crankshaft through a clutch and gearbox to a propeller shaft which drives the rear axle shafts. Normal rotation of the "power train" is in a clockwise direction when viewed from the front of the car. This illustration shows a typical engine/transmission layout, up to the propeller shaft (Ford Cortina).

thus reversing conventional practice. General Motors are working on a somewhat similar cell using lithium and chlorine. Though still in the experimental stage, both cells are claimed to be far in advance of lead-acid types and may lead to batteries suitable for car operation.

Apart from the battery, difficulties arise in connection with the motors and drive gear for electric cars. Conventional motors would have to be large and very heavy to produce the power output required for a medium-size car, but an answer seems likely to be found in new types of low-voltage, high-current motors of lightweight construction.

Fuel Cells. Another line of approach may bring results in the rather more distant future. Even the most efficient battery-powered car needs recharging at intervals, and its range of operation cannot be unlimited. The idea of substituting a chemical device which uses some kind of fuel to produce a continuous output of electric power is therefore attractive. Such a device is called a fuel cell.

As at present envisaged, a practical fuel cell would contain electrodes and an electrolyte, as in a storage battery. The fuel would be a liquid hydrocarbon—perhaps methanol, hydrogen or hydrazine—carried in a tank on the car. The fuel would produce electric current at the electrodes as a result of being oxidised by air, with a continuous replacement of the decomposed fuel. One major difficulty is to find a cheap and suitable catalyst that will speed up the electrochemical reaction sufficiently to ensure adequate power output, but there are many problems to be solved before electric cars equipped with self-contained power plants are likely to be built.

THE TRANSMISSION SYSTEM

The transmission system on a car is required to perform three separate func-

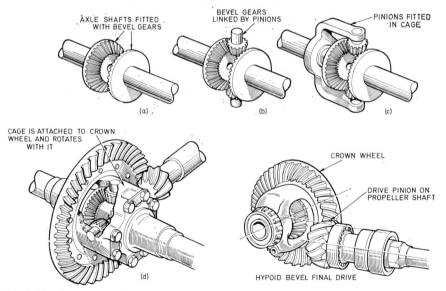

FIG. 1.30. Illustrating stages in the construction of a differential gear unit, which permits a pair of axle shafts to rotate at different speeds while the drive is maintained to both. The differential rotates as a unit with the crown wheel. (*Lower right*) Most modern cars employ a drive pinion and crown wheel of the hypoid bevel type. The special tooth shape allows the pinion to be set below the centre line of the crown wheel and gives quieter running and less wear than the older spiral bevel drive.

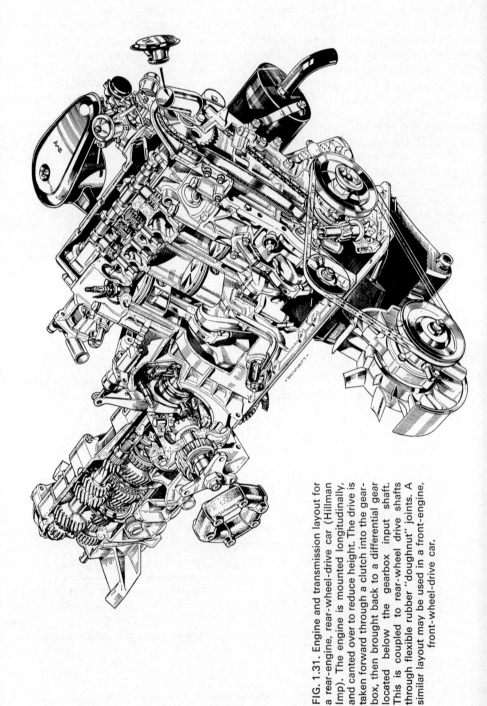

FIG. 1.31. Engine and transmission layout for a rear-engine, rear-wheel-drive car (Hillman Imp). The engine is mounted longitudinally, and canted over to reduce height. The drive is taken forward through a clutch into the gear-box, then brought back to a differential gear located below the gearbox input shaft. This is coupled to rear-wheel drive shafts through flexible rubber "doughnut" joints. A similar layout may be used in a front-engine, front-wheel-drive car.

tions. First, since internal combustion engines do not start from rest under load, the transmission must be able to effect a gradual link-up between the rotating crankshaft of the engine, after it has been started, and the stationary road wheels of the car. For this, a *clutch* is required (Fig. 1.29).

Secondly, it must provide alternative ratios of engine speed to road speed, so that the engine's horsepower can be applied as a moderate tractive force at high speed on a level road, or as a much greater thrust at a lower speed when hill-climbing. For this, a *gearbox* is required.

Thirdly, it must transmit horsepower from the engine to two (or in a few instances to four) of the road wheels, without affecting the operation of the car's springs or steering. For this, suitable *final drive gears* and connecting shafting are required.

How the power is actually transmitted from the engine to the wheels nowadays varies widely. The normal layout used for many years was based on a propeller shaft between the power unit at the front of the car and the driving axle at the rear. This shaft incorporated either one or two universal joints and usually also a tele-

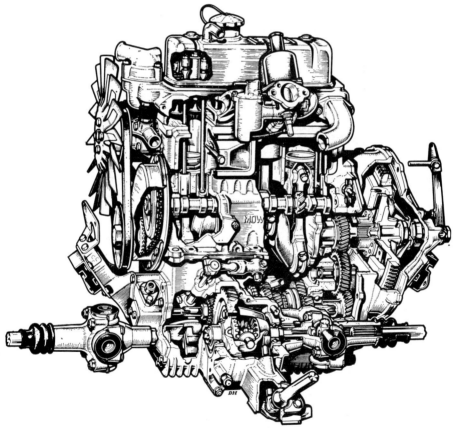

FIG. 1.32. The "power package" for a popular type of front-engine, front-wheel-drive car (Morris Mini-Minor). In this case the engine is mounted transversely, with the clutch in the normal position but the gearbox built into the engine sump. The drive is taken to the two drive shafts through bevel gears to a differential gear also located in the sump.

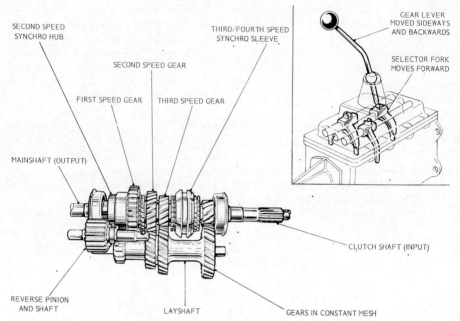

SECOND SPEED
SYNCHRO HUB

THIRD/FOURTH SPEED
SYNCHRO SLEEVE

GEAR LEVER
MOVED SIDEWAYS
AND BACKWARDS

SECOND SPEED GEAR

SELECTOR FORK
MOVES FORWARD

FIRST SPEED GEAR   THIRD SPEED GEAR

MAINSHAFT (OUTPUT)

CLUTCH SHAFT (INPUT)

REVERSE PINION
AND SHAFT

LAYSHAFT

GEARS IN CONSTANT MESH

FIG. 1.33. The gear train in a modern four-speed gearbox having synchromesh operation on second, third and fourth gears (shown here in the neutral position). The layshaft is in constant rotation, the gear wheels on the mainshaft and reverse-pinion shaft being moved into engagement as required (see Fig. 1.34). Gear ratios are selected through the sliding action of selector forks mounted above the mainshaft.

scopic coupling, to permit movement of the car on its springs. In the centre of this type of rear axle there is gearing to turn the drive line through 90 deg., and a differential gear which allows the two driven wheels to rotate at unequal speeds when the car is taking a corner (Fig. 1.30).

"Bending" the drive round a 90 deg. corner is usually done by means of bevel gearing, which also reduces the propeller shaft speed to a wheel speed less than one-third as fast. Modern cars use hypoid bevel gears, having teeth curved to a shape which lets the small driving gear on the propeller shaft (the pinion) be set a little below axle level. The pinion meshes with the large driven gear (crown wheel). Spiral bevel gears are still found on vans and older cars, while worm gearing may be encountered on a Continental car.

The differential gearing is incorporated in the centre of the axle, and balances driving effort equally between the two wheels, even when they turn at different speeds as the car goes round a corner. Often, it works by using bevel gears held in a cage to drive another bevel gear on each half of the axle: an alternative design uses pairs of spur gears to drive the axle shafts.

Cars which have their engines at the same end (whether front or rear) as the wheels they drive sometimes retain bevel gearing, between a fore-and-aft crankshaft and transverse driving shafts to the road wheels (Fig. 1.31). In other designs, the engine is set transversely with its crankshaft parallel to the axle (Fig. 1.32).

When the engine, gearbox and differential are all in one group on the sprung part of the car, two universally-jointed driving shafts are needed between the differential gear and the road wheels, so

FIRST (BOTTOM) GEAR.
Straight-cut spur gears, non-synchronized. The first-speed gear is moved into mesh with the layshaft gear.

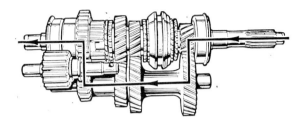

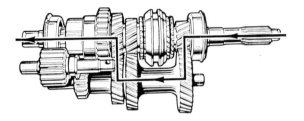

SECOND GEAR. Helical-cut gears running in constant mesh. The second-speed synchronizer locks the second-speed gear to the mainshaft.

THIRD GEAR. Helical-cut gears running in constant mesh. The third/fourth-speed synchronizer locks the third-speed gear to the mainshaft.

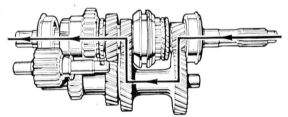

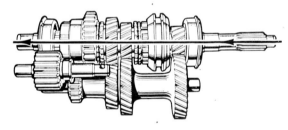

FOURTH (TOP) GEAR. Direct drive, obtained by locking the mainshaft to the clutch shaft through the third/fourth-speed synchronizer.

REVERSE GEAR. Straight-cut spur gears, non-synchronized. A pinion on a separate shaft is moved into mesh between the first-speed gear and the layshaft gear to reverse the mainshaft motion.

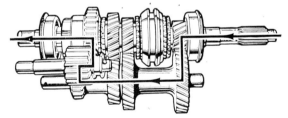

FIG. 1.34. Showing the power flow at different gear positions in a four-speed gearbox. The terms used above refer to Fig. 1.33.

that the car's springs can deflect to cushion road bumps. Some cars with the traditional front-engine, rear-drive layout also have a differential gear mounted on the sprung frame of the car and universally-jointed shafts driving their wheels (independent suspension or the de Dion layout).

Gearbox and Overdrive. Change-speed gearing between a car's engine and its road wheels can take varied forms. In Europe the most usual arrangement is to have four gear ratios (less frequently three or five) provided by pairs of meshing gear wheels, any desired ratio being engaged by a mechanical dog clutch (Fig. 1.33). With such a gearbox goes a friction clutch which can be disengaged whilst a gear ratio is selected, and then re-engaged gradually by allowing springs to press the friction surfaces together (Fig. 1.35). Modern "synchromesh" gearboxes incorporate synchronizing cones, small friction clutches which match the rotational speeds

of the two halves of a dog clutch before they are meshed together, thus avoiding noisy gear engagement.

Some cars are offered with a device called an "overdrive" to supplement the gearbox, this being in effect a two-speed gear which can be operated to provide a quieter and more economical (but less lively) alternative to top gear. The most popular British overdrives are controlled by a two-position electrical switch, and overdrive ratio can be switched in or out without use of the clutch pedal. Often, the auxiliary overdrive gearing can be used in conjunction with third and second gear ratios, as well as with top gear.

Automatic Transmission. Most American and a growing proportion of European cars are equipped with automatic transmissions. These require the driver only to select forward or reverse gear, the clutch and change-speed gearing being operated automatically to suit

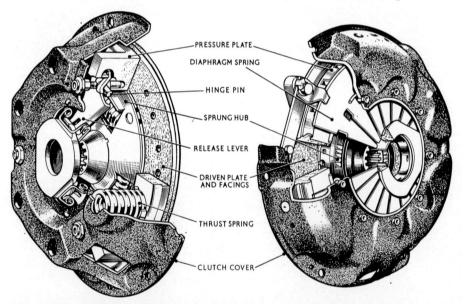

PRESSURE PLATE
DIAPHRAGM SPRING
HINGE PIN
SPRUNG HUB
RELEASE LEVER
DRIVEN PLATE AND FACINGS
THRUST SPRING
CLUTCH COVER

FIG. 1.35. The traditional coil-spring clutch (*left*) is now being superseded by the diaphragm-spring clutch (*right*). This illustration shows that they are basically similar, the friction faces in the older type being engaged by the thrust of a number of coil springs placed circumferentially round a pressure plate, whereas the later type has a dish-shaped spring plate which is assembled under compression so that its outer rim bears on the pressure plate.

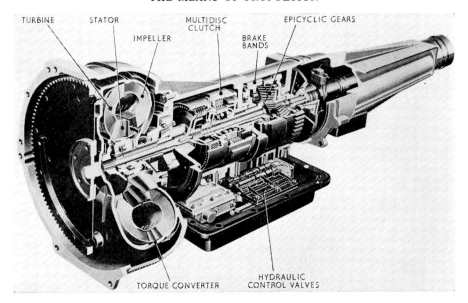

TURBINE   STATOR   MULTIDISC   EPICYCLIC GEARS
CLUTCH
IMPELLER   BRAKE
BANDS

HYDRAULIC
TORQUE CONVERTER   CONTROL VALVES

FIG. 1.36. The most popular type of automatic transmission consists of a hydraulic torque converter coupled to an automatic three-speed gearbox. The converter transmits the drive from the engine flywheel and is capable of multiplying the engine torque. The epicyclic gears are controlled by two brake bands and two multi-disc clutches, all operated by hydraulic pressure. Gear changes are controlled by hydraulic shift valves which respond to engine torque demand and to the car's road speed. (Borg-Warner model 35 transmission unit.)

accelerator pedal position and car speed. In the most popular types of automatic transmission, the clutch is replaced by a hydraulic torque converter, which combines a centrifugal oil pump with an oil turbine and a set of reaction blades (Fig. 1.36). Such a device takes up the drive very smoothly as the engine is accelerated to start the car from rest, and at low car speeds also provides some of the torque-multiplying effect of a gearbox.

Mechanical change-speed gearing is also needed in an automatic transmission, and may have two, three or four ratios. Most automatic gearboxes use epicyclic gearing of one sort or another, in which "planet gears" rotate around "sun gears". It is possible to arrange this sort of gearing so that various gear ratios are engaged smoothly and silently by the hydraulic operation of friction brakes and clutches. Without the need to mesh dog clutches,

epicyclic gearing allows one ratio to be engaged quickly instead of another, without it being necessary to interrupt the flow of power from the engine to the road wheels.

Various alternative forms of automatic transmission exist. It is possible to "automate" the traditional clutch and synchromesh gearbox, but whereas drivers accept the need for brief pauses in the flow of power whilst they themselves make changes of gear, they do not so readily accept such pauses if they occur unexpectedly when an automatic system decides to change gear. It is also possible at a lower cost to "automate" only the clutch, but this has usually proved an unsuccessful compromise, either technically in terms of reliability (drivers who start in top gear wear such systems out abnormally fast) or commercially in terms of the limited extent to which they save a driver trouble.

CHAPTER 2

THE MEANS OF CONTROL

IN Chapter 1 we considered the functions and working principles of the engine and its associated components, and showed how engine power is transmitted to the road wheels to propel the car. As well as having means of propulsion, a motor vehicle must be equipped with devices to control its operation in various ways, and in this chapter we shall consider the principles of the main ancillary systems.

In the first place, the vehicle must have wheels fitted with flexible tyres, on which it can run smoothly, and which ensure adequate grip at high and low speeds on road surfaces that may be good or bad, wet or dry. The car body, containing driver and passengers, must be suspended on some form of flexible springing system that will cushion road shocks without introducing pitching, rolling or other unwelcome forms of motion. A braking system is required to halt or slow down the car's progress, and a steering system to control its direction of movement.

Electrical equipment serves a variety of purposes: starting the engine, igniting the fuel mixture, operating the lamps, instruments and accessories of many kinds. Finally, one or more instruments must be fitted to display information to the driver who is in overall control of this whole complex mechanism.

TYRES AND WHEELS

A small area of each of four pneumatic tyres provides the sole contact at any time between a car and its occupants and *terra firma*, a fact which serves to emphasize the importance of tyres in regard to safety. The tyres support the car, and serve a whole series of functions for which no adequate alternative has been found. First, the tyre is a flexible air cushion in direct contact with the road, yielding to bumps which would otherwise rattle and jolt the best-sprung car. Secondly, the tyre grips the surface upon which it rolls, allowing the car to be accelerated, braked and cornered without slipping. Thirdly, it provides a vital link between the steering mechanism and the ground, its flexibility being so controlled that a car can be guided accurately at any speed within its range.

Although the visible outer surface of a tyre is made of rubber, other materials serve equally vital purposes inside. Two loops of virtually inextensible steel wire are moulded into the edges of the tyre casing, to keep the inflated tyre securely in place on the recessed rim of a wheel. Reinforcement of the tyre casing, so that it does not stretch when inflated or distort excessively under load, was once provided by fabric. Now it comes from layers of flexible threads or "cords" spun from such substances as cotton, nylon, rayon or even fine steel wire. Different kinds of natural and synthetic rubber are used in various parts of a tyre casing, some parts being required to flex rapidly without heating up, others to grip slippery road surfaces or to resist wear by gritty surfaces.

The tread which rolls on the road is the most conspicuous feature of any tyre, its pattern being functional as well as serving for identification. On a hard and dry surface racing drivers have found that a tyre with little or no tread patterning provides maximum grip. In wet weather, however, a pattern of grooves in the tread will allow water to drain away from the contact area between tyre and road, thereby giving much improved grip of the rubber on the road surface. The best arrangements seem to involve a few large drainage grooves, into which water can be squeezed from many smaller slits in the rubber surface.

For soft surfaces of mud or snow, very coarse tread patterns of "cogwheel" type give the best grip, whereas on hard polished ice, only metal inserts which actually cut into the surface like the spikes on a mountaineer's boots are really effective (Fig. 2.1).

Tyre inflation is one of many things about a car which involve compromise, and the best compromise varies to some extent with the way in which a car is being used. Low inflation pressures let a soft tyre smooth out road bumps very effectively at low speeds, but extra tyre flexibility in sideways as well as up-and-down directions impairs a car's steering accuracy, and if a car is driven fast with under-inflated tyres the rapid flexing may cause serious damage. High inflation pressures often make a car steer more accurately, and within limits minimize the risk of tyre failure due to overheating during fast motorway driving, but also they make a car ride more noisily and jerkily over bumps.

Within modest limits, an owner can adjust the handling characteristics of a car to suit his own tastes by making small adjustments to the tyre pressures normally required for his particular car. Increasing rear tyre pressures by perhaps 2 lb per sq in. (or reducing front pressures by an equivalent amount) will make a car more stable at high speeds, whereas an opposite change, putting more air into the front tyres, will make a car more sensitive in its steering response.

Special-purpose Tyres. In addition to tyres designed for "average" conditions of use, most makers offer what may be described as "special purpose" tyres of more limited appeal. There are high-speed tyres of various kinds, never normally needed for cars which do not reach 100 m.p.h. Winter tyres provide exceptional grip on soft snow or mud but are noisier (and usually less durable) than normal tyres when used on hard-surfaced roads.

An invisible but important difference between two forms of tyre concerns the structure of the casing. For many years the invisible "cords" which give a rubber-

FIG. 2.1. (*Left*) A tyre with a tread pattern for wet road grip, obtained by circumferential grooves and micro-thickness slots in the tread. (*Right*) A steel-studded tyre for gripping on ice (Dunlop).

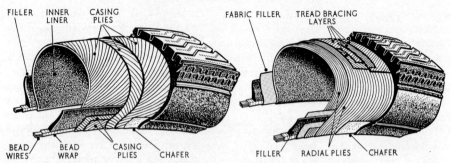

FILLER INNER CASING   FABRIC FILLER   TREAD BRACING
        LINER PLIES   LAYERS

BEAD   BEAD   CASING   FILLER RADIAL PLIES   CHAFER
WIRES   WRAP   PLIES   CHAFER

FIG. 2.2. Construction of a conventional cross-ply tyre (*left*) and a radial-ply tyre (*right*), showing the different arrangements of the cords.

covered tyre casing its strength were always arranged diagonally in criss-cross layers: this type is called a cross-ply tyre (Fig. 2.2). More recently an alternative "radial-ply" construction was introduced with cords running as directly as possible from one side of the tyre to the other, this making the tyre sidewalls extra-flexible, and tyres of this kind have extra bracing layers of wire or textile cords behind their treads to ensure the car's directional stability.

Cars vary in their response to what are variously described as "radial ply" or "braced tread" tyres, which often require altered inflation pressures. They usually wear out more slowly than normal tyres but are more vulnerable to damage by bumping against kerbstones, and provide improved cornering at the expense of

transmitting extra road noise into the car's bodywork at low driving speeds.

Car wheels have slightly recessed rims, so that a tyre with inextensible wired edges fits securely when inflated, needing no separate attachment. Shaping of the rim with a central hollow or well-base makes the fitting and removal of tyres possible, as when the edge of the tyre is slid into the well at one side of the wheel, this lets the opposite half of the tyre be stretched over the rim (Fig. 2.3).

Road Wheels. Simple pressed steel wheels are much the most popular kind at present, although many cars have wire-spoked wheels, in which numerous wires in tension hang the hub from the top piece of the wheel rim (Fig. 2.4). On sports models there is a trend towards cast

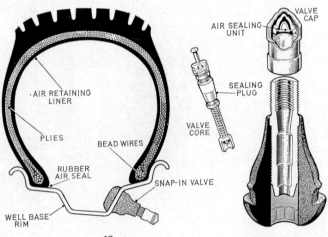

FIG 2.3. A tubeless tyre retains its pressure by making an air-tight seal between the tyre walls and the wheel rim. The tyre valve has a replaceable core, air sealing being provided by the tapered plug portion. The valve cap provides a secondary seal as well as dust exclusion.

AIR RETAINING LINER

PLIES

RUBBER AIR SEAL

WELL BASE RIM

BEAD WIRES

SNAP-IN VALVE

VALVE CORE

VALVE CAP

AIR SEALING UNIT

SEALING PLUG

FIG. 2.4. The bolt detachable wheel (*upper left*), with slots in the disc to ventilate the tyre and brakes, is fitted to most popular cars. Some high-performance models use centre-lock wire wheels (*upper right*). The knock-on type is secured by a coned nut with self-tightening thread, the "ears" of which are hammered to tighten or release it. (*Lower*) A typical front hub assembly, where the wheel is carried on two sets of roller bearings. An adjusting nut is set to control the degree of play on the wheel spindle, which is not shown here.

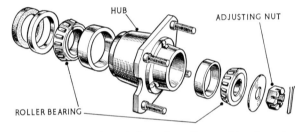

magnesium lightweight wheels such as are used on most racing cars.

Removable wheels are most often held in place by a set of bolts. An alternative fixing has the wheel slid on to a hub with splines or pegs coupling it to the brake drum and one large fixing nut (often eared so that it can be hammered up tight) holding the wheel on to this hub. Inside the hub of any road wheel, there are either tapered-roller or ball bearings to carry the tyre/wheel assembly. Such bearings need little lubrication, let the car roll easily, and can resist the sideways forces generated when a car takes a corner.

Made from flexible materials, a tyre can never be balanced effectively until it has been mounted on its wheel and inflated, but imperfect balance can shake the steering wheel or even the whole of a moving car very unpleasantly. When one side of a tyre is heavier than the other,

static unbalance is easily cured by clamping small lead balance weights to the wheel rim.

What is called dynamic unbalance results when a statically balanced wheel has, in effect, excess weight at one point on the outer side of the rim and at an opposite point on its inner side: rotation of such a wheel tends to rock the steering as the diagonally opposed weights pull against one another. Out-of-balance troubles can be remedied as explained in Chapter 8.

SUSPENSION SYSTEMS

Although pneumatic tyres take the sharp edges off road bumps, a car still needs to be supported on flexible springs if it is to travel comfortably. To cope with all conditions of load carried, driving speed and road surface, many modern cars are supported at their four corners on springs which permit more than six inches of up-and-down movement between the wheels and the body!

Types of Spring. Whilst some designers favour alternatives such as rubber, or compressed air or gas, the great majority of the world's cars ride on steel springs of one sort or another (Fig. 2.5). So-called coil springs are used at the front of many cars, and less frequently at the rear corners also. They comprise spirals of spring steel wire which is twisted when the spring is compressed. Such springs are light and cheap for any given duty,

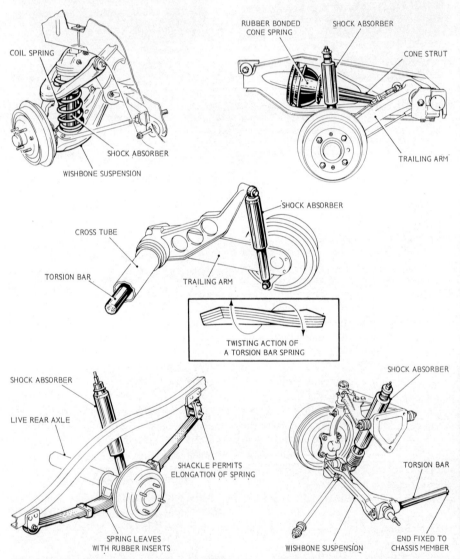

FIG. 2.5. Suspension springing takes various forms. Coil springs and torsion bars or rods depend upon the ability of a metal to twist and untwist, while leaf springs depend upon bending. Rubber cone springs depend upon deflection of the material under load.

but have no lateral stability in themselves so must be combined with some sort of linkage which can keep the wheels in correct alignment with the car.

Closely related to the coil spring is the torsion bar, which is fixed at one end and has a lever at the other. Movement of the lever end twists the long bar much as the wire in a coil spring is twisted under load. Torsion bar springs for supporting the main load have been found to fit conveniently into a few car designs, but a more common use of a torsion bar is to interconnect springs on two opposite sides of a car, so as to resist side-to-side rolling of the car on its main springs.

Leaf springs are long, thin strips of spring steel arranged in layers, which bend under the car's weight. Most fre-

quently the two ends of a leaf spring are fixed to the car body, and the centre of the spring is bolted to the rear axle, there being additional short leaves at the centre of the spring where bending loads are greatest. Such a spring is relatively heavy, but is convenient in that its proportions make it quite stiff laterally despite its vertical flexibility, so that two such springs can be used as the sole connection between the rear axle and the body.

This sort of leaf spring is usually referred to as being "semi-elliptic" in form, although nowadays it is usually almost flat instead of being curved like the lower half of an ellipse. There have been various cars which used "quarter elliptic" springs, these springs having their thick section clamped to the chassis

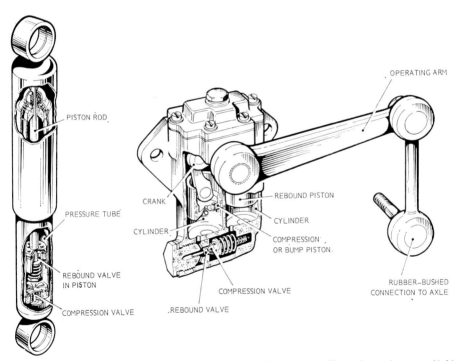

FIG. 2.6. Hydraulic shock absorbers are now in universal use. The telescopic type (*left*) comprises two halves working as a piston in a cylinder, with valves to control the flow of hydraulic fluid. The double-acting type (*right*) is still widely used with leaf-spring rear suspensions. It has a pair of cylinders, with the operating arm working the two pistons alternately through a crank, and fluid control valves.

and the thin end deflected by rise and fall of the axle. Some independent front-wheel suspensions use transverse leaf springs, which amount to two "quarter elliptic" springs extending to the left and right from a central clamped section.

Shock Absorbers. If a car were simply supported upon four free-acting springs it would at times be very uncomfortable, because after a road bump jolted the car, the body would be liable to go on bouncing rhythmically up and down on its springs. Invariably, cars have devices to check this persistent bouncing of the springs, their design being a compromise providing enough resistance to check too-persistent spring movement, but not so much as to render the spring stiff and ineffective.

Popularly known as "shock absorbers", but more accurately termed "spring dampers", these devices for restraining too-active spring movement are invariably hydraulic on modern cars, pumping oil through holes of restricted size. Such devices are gentler than simple friction spring dampers used on older cars, their effect diminishing for slow spring movements, but valves akin to "safety valves" have to be incorporated so that very rapid spring deflections do not generate destructive hydraulic pressures (Fig. 2.6).

Rubber can be used in various ways to make car springs, sometimes loaded by stretching or compressing it but more often by twisting or similarly deforming it. Ways have been found of shaping rubber so that, as extra load is put on to an approximately conical spring, it becomes progressively stiffer to deflect. Whilst cars such as the B.M.C. Mini series have been built with springs of this type as their sole support, it is much more usual to take advantage of this progressive stiffening effect in auxiliary rubber buffers that supplement the steel springs.

Pneumatic and Hydraulic Systems. Compressed air or gas (usually nitrogen) can also be used as a springing medium, the weight of the car acting on a sliding piston or flexible diaphragm to compress the air or gas. Such systems have shown a great deal of merit on large Citroen cars, especially lending themselves to use with pumps which re-adjust the car's riding height and spring stiffness to suit any change in the load being carried. Cost is the main limitation on the extent to which pneumatic springs are used.

A few designers have evolved suspension systems which interconnect front and rear springs. Such systems as the mechanical coupling introduced on the Citroen 2CV and the hydraulic coupling introduced at a later date on the B.M.C. 1100 series (Fig. 2.7) can reduce the extent to which road bumps make a moving car pitch on its springs; although conversely, front-to-rear interconnection increases the extent to which load changes alter the car's riding attitude, and so upset the elevation of headlamp beams.

Until the mid-1930s it was customary to have the two wheels under each end of a car mounted together on an axle beam, with four springs supporting the car upon the two axles. As cars became faster and more refined, the disadvantages of front axle beams became more and more apparent, the most fundamental disadvantage being that when one fast-spinning wheel rose over a bump or fell into a pothole, the axle and both wheels were tilted, producing a gyroscopic force which twisted the wheels sharply around their steering swivels. It is now universal practice to equip cars with independent front-wheel suspension, each wheel having its own separate linkage connecting it to the car's frame so that its movements do not affect the other front wheel.

Independent Suspension Systems. Quite the commonest linkage for coupling an independently sprung front wheel on to a car frame involves two links which form an approximate parallelogram—the

52

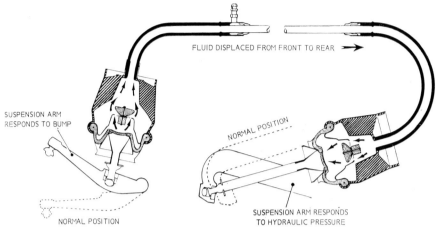

FLUID DISPLACED FROM FRONT TO REAR →

SUSPENSION ARM
RESPONDS TO BUMP

NORMAL POSITION

NORMAL POSITION

SUSPENSION ARM RESPONDS
TO HYDRAULIC PRESSURE

FIG. 2.7. The Hydrolastic suspension fitted to B.M.C. cars has a combined rubber spring and damper unit at each wheel, the front and rear units on either side being connected by a pipeline filled with water and alcohol. When a wheel responds to a bump, its damper unit displaces fluid to the other wheel, where increased hydraulic pressure operates the suspension arms so as to maintain a level ride. (*Below*) Details of a suspension unit.

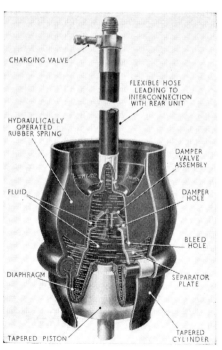

CHARGING VALVE

FLEXIBLE HOSE
LEADING TO
INTERCONNECTION
WITH REAR UNIT

HYDRAULICALLY
OPERATED
RUBBER SPRING

DAMPER
VALVE
ASSEMBLY

FLUID

DAMPER
HOLE

BLEED
HOLE

DIAPHRAGM

SEPARATOR
PLATE

TAPERED PISTON

TAPERED
CYLINDER

links often take "wishbone" form with a wide base from which to pivot. Most often the linkage is set across the car, although some models such as the Volkswagen use two fore-and-aft links to mount each wheel. A lot of small but significant changes in linkage design can influence the behaviour of a car on straight and curved roads, varied lengths and inclinations of link influencing whether and how the wheel tilts or moves sideways as it rises and falls over bumps.

Various alternative forms of independent front-wheel suspension linkage exist (Fig. 2.8). Amongst the simplest, the Mac-Pherson system used on British Fords and some other cars has a telescopic damper strut in place of the upper parallelogram link. Sturdy simplicity is the great merit of this system, plus the fact that three front-suspension mounting points on each side of a pressed steel body are so widely spaced as to spread loads very evenly through the car's structure.

Thirty years after the front beam axle was abolished by many designers, independent suspension of rear wheels has been gaining real favour recently (Fig. 2.9). Over a long period it was seldom used except on rear-engined cars in which it is difficult to accommodate a rigid rear axle.

53

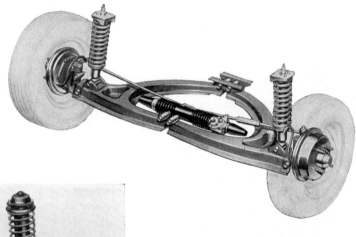

FIG. 2.8. Typical front suspension systems. (*Top left*) A conventional coil spring arrangement, with upper and lower suspension arms of unequal length hinged on a chassis cross-member. (*Top right*) A Rover version of the same principle uses a double wishbone, with the top links pivoted on a common axis that runs across the car width and serves both wheels. (*Centre*) This simple coil spring and swing axle arrangement is employed in the rear-engine Hillman Imp. (*Bottom*) A Ford vertical-strut suspension unit incorporating a coil spring and telescopic shock absorber, connected to the chassis cross-member by a hinged arm and fitted with an anti-roll bar.

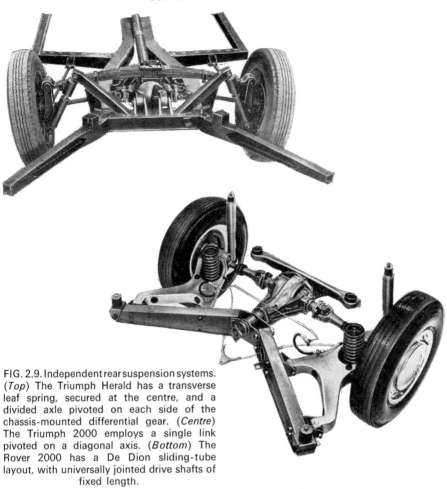

FIG. 2.9. Independent rear suspension systems. (*Top*) The Triumph Herald has a transverse leaf spring, secured at the centre, and a divided axle pivoted on each side of the chassis-mounted differential gear. (*Centre*) The Triumph 2000 employs a single link pivoted on a diagonal axis. (*Bottom*) The Rover 2000 has a De Dion sliding-tube layout, with universally jointed drive shafts of fixed length.

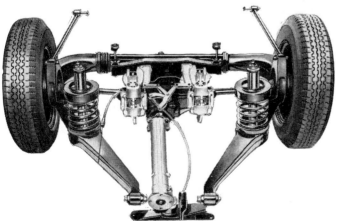

This time-lag has been because there are extra difficulties in transmitting power to independently sprung wheels, and because there are fewer disadvantages with a rigid axle beam when its wheels do not have steering swivels.

Independent suspension of a car's rear wheels does offer certain real advantages in return for extra complexity. Less weight of unsprung mechanism moves up and down with the wheels on bumpy roads, propeller shaft torque no longer tends to lift weight off one rear wheel during acceleration, and there is no longer a heavy weight of gearing at the centre of an axle which is rather prone to oscillate around this weight.

It is possible to gain substantial advantages by retaining a rigid rear axle but taking the driving mechanism off it, and either driving the rear wheels through individual, universally-jointed shafts or else driving the front wheels. The former alternative is called the de Dion rear axle layout, after a company which used it more than 60 years ago, and still finds applications although it is less common on production models than the combination of a light non-driving rear axle beam with front-wheel drive.

Quite varied forms of independent rear-wheel suspension are in use. Simplest is the "divided axle" with a pivot on each side of the chassis-mounted differential gear; this system gives large changes of wheel inclination as the springs deflect. Some cars use pairs of transverse links akin to the arrangement common on front wheels, and a very effective system of this kind is almost universal on racing cars but has proved less easy to fit on four-seat saloons. The rear wheels on a growing number of cars tend to be held by single links pivoted on a diagonal axis, this being the compromise design which is fairly simple and gives quite good results in varied conditions (an example is the Triumph 2000 shown in Fig. 2.9).

STEERING SYSTEMS

The fact that a car needs to have springs complicates its steering system, which has to let the driver aim the wheels very precisely despite movements of the suspension system. Most steering linkages are in three sections: outer sections on either side of the car, carefully designed to avoid interference from movements of the independent front-wheel suspension, and a central section which links the two sides together and to the steering wheel (Fig. 2.10).

Speed reduction gearing is used between the driver's hands and the steered wheels, to moderate the forces needed to steer the car at low speeds and to prevent the steering being too sensitive when the car is going quickly. It is desirable to give this steering gear a partially "irreversible" characteristic, so that it is efficient in transmitting effort from the driver's hands to the front wheels, but much less efficient in transmitting shocks from the road back to the driver.

In the past, steering gears have usually been based upon the worm-and-wheel principle, in which a little friction will provide the desirable unidirectional characteristics. Steering gears of cam-and-peg or cam-and-roller design are akin in principle, their "cams" somewhat resembling worm gears although with extra refinement of shape (Fig. 2.11). As cars have improved, the need for friction in the steering mechanism to damp out road shock has diminished, and modern cars make much more use of low-friction ball bearings in their steering gears. The same trend has allowed the very simple and sturdy rack-and-pinion steering mechanism to gain favour. This uses a small gear wheel on the steering column to move a toothed bar sideways: often the bar is itself the central section of the three-part linkage controlling front-wheel alignment (Fig. 2.12).

Large cars which might otherwise be

difficult to park are often equipped with power-assisted steering, a form of hydraulic jack which takes power from an engine-driven pump to augment the driver's efforts.

Nominally one would expect each of the steered front wheels to pivot on an axis at its centre, but there are very real practical difficulties about finding room for such a pivot location as well as for the hub bearings and brakes which occupy space inside the wheel. Usually the pivot

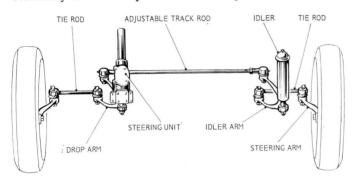

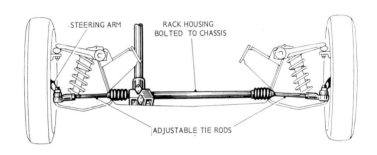

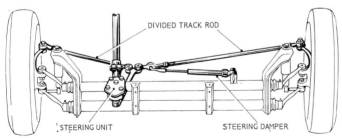

FIG. 2.10. (*Top*) The three-piece steering linkage used for many years requires an idler arm to balance the system, with several joints which may need lubrication. Either the centre track rod or the outer tie rods have screwed adjusters by which the wheel alignment is set. (*Centre*) A rack-and-pinion steering system needs only a simple linkage to the wheels. Rubber gaiters are fitted at the ends of the cross tube, where the rack member moves in and out. (*Bottom*) When the engine is at the rear, a simple steering linkage can be used such as this Volkswagen divided track rod. A hydraulic damper is used to reduce the effects of road shocks on the steering.

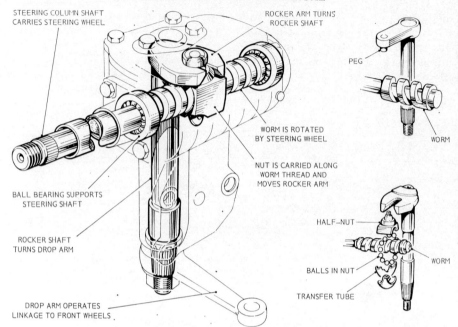

STEERING COLUMN SHAFT
CARRIES STEERING WHEEL

ROCKER ARM TURNS
ROCKER SHAFT

PEG

WORM IS ROTATED
BY STEERING WHEEL

WORM

NUT IS CARRIED ALONG
WORM THREAD AND
MOVES ROCKER ARM

BALL BEARING SUPPORTS
STEERING SHAFT

ROCKER SHAFT
TURNS DROP ARM

HALF–NUT

WORM

BALLS IN NUT

TRANSFER TUBE

DROP ARM OPERATES
LINKAGE TO FRONT WHEELS

FIG. 2.11. In many types of steering unit there is a short worm thread or cam integral with the steering-column shaft. This swings the rocker arm sideways through the medium of a nut, a roller, a steel peg (*upper right*), or similar device. A popular design is the recirculating-ball gear (*lower right*), in which friction between the worm and the control nut is reduced to a minimum by using a series of steel balls to provide the contact.

has to be offset several inches towards the centre of the car, and is then inclined at an angle so that its axis meets the road inside or near to the tyre contact area.

Steering Geometry. It is very convenient for a car to have some inherent stability, so that it will run straight without constant steering corrections by the driver, and one factor in this stability is that the steering should be self-centring into the straight-ahead position. Such an effect can be achieved by setting the steering axis slightly ahead of the front wheel centre, or by tilting the axis at what is called a "castor angle" so that it intersects the ground ahead of the wheel centre (Fig. 2.13).

Self-centring action in the steering is not in itself sufficient always to ensure the stability of a moving car. For various reasons (tyre flexibility is an important

one), wheels do not always roll in precisely the direction they point, but drift slightly sideways under cornering forces.

If the front wheels drift outwards more than the rear ones under any side force, extra steering action will be needed by the driver to keep the car on its desired course (hence the description "understeer" for the car's behaviour), but control will not be lost. If the rear wheels drift outwards more than the front ones under any cornering force, the car will tighten its turning radius, increasing the side forces so that unless the driver reacts quickly to reduce the steering angle, the car will enter a tightening spiral (called "oversteer") which is quite unstable. With a properly designed car, only under-inflated or overloaded rear tyres would ever show up the latter alarming effect.

It is not essential for a car to be designed

58

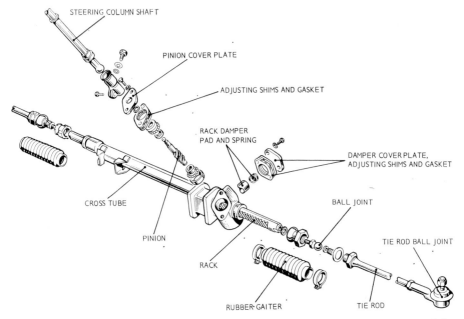

FIG. 2.12. A rack-and-pinion steering gear works on a different principle. Rotation of the pinion at the base of the steering-column shaft moves the toothed rack sideways, and this motion is transferred through ball joints to the tie rods which are coupled to the steering arms.

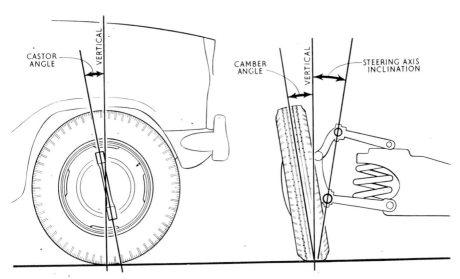

FIG. 2.13. The castor angle, camber angle, and steering axis or king pin inclination all have an effect on the car's steering characteristics, as explained in the text. These angles are adjustable on some cars but not on others.

59

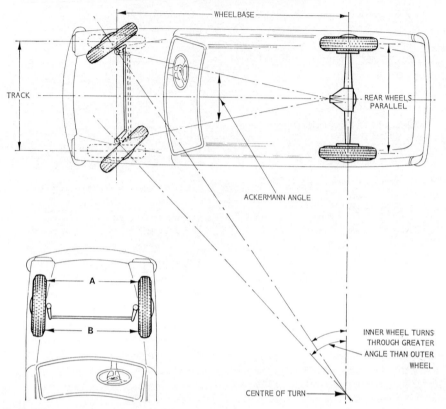

(*Left*) FIG. 2.14. Front wheel alignment. "Toe-in" means that distance A is less than distance B, while "toe-out" is the reverse. (*Right*) FIG. 2.15. Principle of Ackermann steering. When the front wheels are set straight ahead, lines drawn through their steering arms and swivel pivots will converge on the car's centre line close to the rear axle.

so that its front wheels are strictly vertical. In the past it was common to give front wheels a slight outward tilt or "camber angle" which, in conjunction with inclination of the steering swivel, made centrepoint steering easier to achieve. Nowadays front wheels (and on independently sprung cars, rear wheels also) are sometimes given an inward tilt called "negative camber" which increases the cornering power of their tyres.

Equally, a car's wheels are not always set to point in exactly identical directions. Often front wheels are set with a fractional "toe-in" so that any flexibility in the steering linkage does not let them toe-out

or splay apart excessively during braking, but front-wheel-driven cars are sometimes set with "toe-out" of their front wheels. Steering linkages are usually designed so that when a sharp corner is negotiated, the inner wheel is steered at a sharper angle than the outer wheel, and this so-called "Ackermann effect" reduces tyre scrub on the road surface (Fig. 2.15).

BRAKING SYSTEMS

In mechanical terms, car brakes work by rubbing pieces of hard-wearing friction material against rotating metal drums or discs attached to the wheels, the resultant friction slowing down or stopping the car.

In more theoretical terms, the brakes convert the kinetic energy of a fast-moving car into heat energy, air then cooling the brakes which cannot work without generating heat.

Brakes which work by slowing down the wheels of a car need to be powerful enough for it to be just about possible to stop the wheels turning in an emergency stop. Rubber-treaded tyres grip the road best when they are just on the point of sliding, and available tyre grip determines how quickly a car can be stopped. Traditional ideas about friction have been to the effect that when anything slides upon a smooth surface, it can never generate a friction force greater than its own weight. Thus the greatest retardation which might be expected from anything sliding along a level road would be the retardation of a ball which has been tossed upwards into the air and is being slowed by its own weight.

It is nowadays appreciated that retardation equivalent to deceleration under gravity (32 ft per second per second, or "1 g") is by no means an absolute limit on braking power for a pneumatic-tyred car being braked on a good non-skid road surface. Soft rubber tyres can mesh with sharp stones in the road surface to act almost like gear wheels, and so can generate horizontal forces substantially greater than the vertical load which is being carried, before they will slide. On good, dry road surfaces decelerations appreciably greater than "1 g" can be recorded by a car with powerful braking effort shared correctly between front and rear wheels. Even in wet weather, decelerations very close to "1 g" are now attainable with good tyre treads and non-skid road surfacing. Brakes which produce "1 g" retardation are sometimes described as being "100 per cent efficient" but this is a misleading phrase.

Modern tyres can only provide their best grip of a road surface when they are standing on or rolling along it. If overpowerful braking or over-rapid cornering makes the tyres skid, their grip of the road surface is reduced, to a modest extent in dry weather and to quite a large extent in wet weather. For the shortest possible stopping distance in an emergency, braking effort needs to be kept just short of what would start a skid; and if a skid does start, the brakes should be released momentarily to let the wheels turn again and then at once re-applied. Devices to do this automatically are in use on aircraft landing wheel brakes, but as yet have proved too expensive to become popular on cars.

Drum and Disc Brakes. For many years, drum brakes operated by friction shoes which expand against their inner surface have been in common use. They have the advantages that it is fairly easy to cool the drums and to keep water away from the internal mechanism (Fig. 2.16). To a growing extent, however, modern cars are being equipped with disc brakes, in which a flat circular disc is nipped between two fairly small pads of very hard friction material: most of the disc is exposed to the cooling air, and any rainwater is centrifuged off the surface with the car in motion.

The friction shoes inside a drum brake may be pivoted or otherwise mounted in various ways, so that when they are pressed into contact with the rotating drum, frictional drag from the drum may either wedge them more tightly against it or may have the opposite effect of trying to push them away (Fig. 2.17). These self-applying ("self-servo") or self-releasing effects can be designed into a brake, one tending to increase its power, but the other making its behaviour more consistent.

Whilst much research has been done to improve brake lining materials—which are often in essence a heat-resisting asbestos fabric impregnated with resins—absolutely consistent friction characteristics are unattainable. Rainwater has an

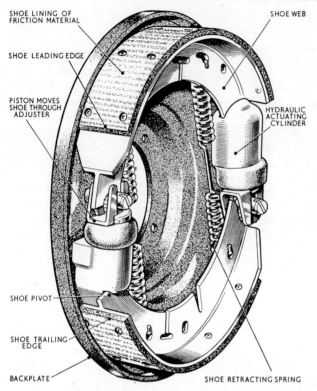

SHOE LINING OF FRICTION MATERIAL

SHOE LEADING EDGE

PISTON MOVES SHOE THROUGH ADJUSTER

SHOE PIVOT

SHOE TRAILING EDGE

BACKPLATE

SHOE WEB

HYDRAULIC ACTUATING CYLINDER

SHOE RETRACTING SPRING

FIG. 2.16. Brake operation. With the drum brake (*left*), a brake drum rotating with the wheel is braked by hydraulic pressure acting on a pair of curved shoes lined with a friction material. Pull-off springs retract the shoes and the hydraulic pistons when pedal pressure is released, and shoe adjusters may be fitted to compensate for lining wear. With the disc brake (*below*), an iron disc rotating with the wheel is braked by hydraulic pressure acting on a pair of self-adjusting pads lined with friction material.

obvious adverse effect on friction, and the heat generated as a brake does its job also tends to reduce friction by softening the resins, although with certain materials heat can have an opposite effect.

The leverages which can be used between a brake pedal and the friction shoes or pads which it operates are limited by practical considerations, a very few inches of pedal movement being available to take up working clearances in the system., absorb any flexibility of components under load and stretching caused by heat, and allow for a certain amount of wear of the friction surfaces.

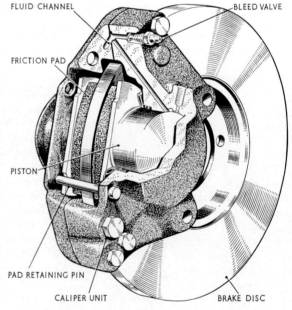

FLUID CHANNEL

BLEED VALVE

FRICTION PAD

PISTON

PAD RETAINING PIN

CALIPER UNIT

BRAKE DISC

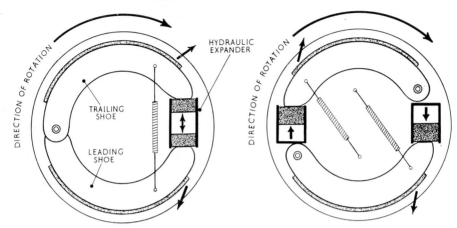

FIG. 2.17. In the braking arrangement shown left, the lower shoe tends to be picked up by the drag of the rotating brake drum as they come into contact, and is said to "lead". The upper shoe tends to be pushed away from the drum rotation and is said to "trail". With the two-leading-shoe arrangement (*right*), separate expanders ensure that both shoes are self-wrapping, with increased braking effect.

Brakes can be made more responsive to moderate pedal pressures if they are designed to have "self-servo" effect, with friction augmenting the driver's effort, but the extent to which self-servo is designed into a brake has to be strictly limited, because it magnifies the effects of any change in friction between lining and drum or disc. If dust worn off the linings, or rust formed on the metal surface, causes extra friction, it is highly undesirable for magnification of this by self-servo to cause uncontrollable "grabbing" of the brake which can virtually jam the wheel of a moving car. If on the other hand heat reduces the friction between lining and metal, diminished self-applying effect in a self-servo brake can suddenly result in very greatly reduced brake responsiveness.

With drum brakes, each shoe has differing effectiveness according to whether it is hinged at its leading or its trailing end, and also according to how far in from the drum surface the hinge point is located. It is common practice in the case of front brakes to arrange the hinges so that each shoe is pivoted at its leading edge, this

"two leading shoe" arrangement giving a moderate self-servo effect which, besides reducing pedal effort, increases the share of braking effort applied to the front wheels as deceleration throws the car's weight forward on to them.

Vacuum-servo Boosters. On heavy or fast cars, braking power is quite often augmented by what is called a "vacuum servo" device, which uses suction from the engine's inlet manifold to multiply whatever effort the driver applies on the brake pedal. These devices take advantage of the fact that when the brakes are applied, the engine is normally over-running with its throttle closed, so generating a powerful suction in the inlet manifold, although a vacuum reservoir is often provided in case the engine stalls. Fig. 2.18 is an example of a brake system with servo assistance.

Early types of servo worked by applying suction to one side of a piston or diaphragm, the resulting force of air pressure on the other side boosting braking effort. In more recent designs, it has been found that quicker response is obtained by having both sides of the servo unit's diaphragm exposed to vacuum, and admitting air at

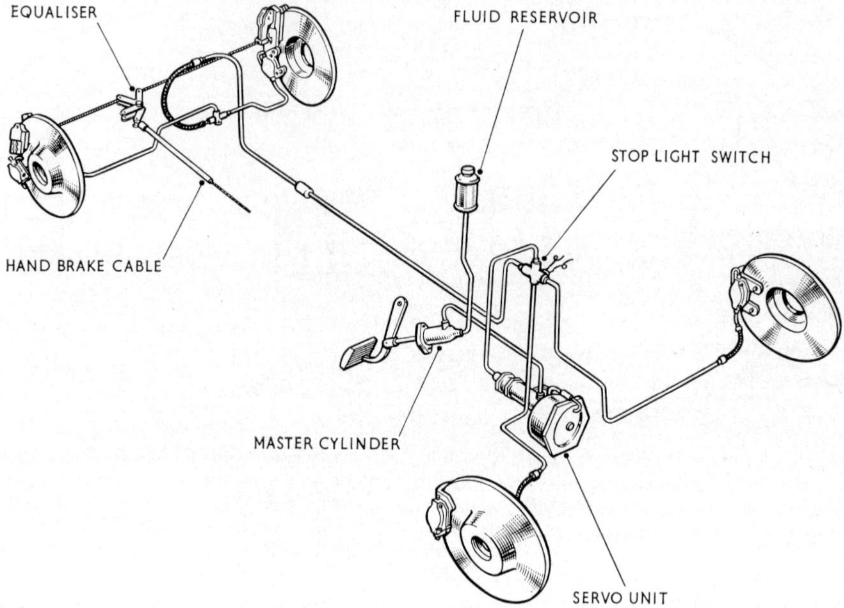

EQUALISER

FLUID RESERVOIR

STOP LIGHT SWITCH

HAND BRAKE CABLE

MASTER CYLINDER

SERVO UNIT

FIG. 2.18. Brake system for a high-performance car (Jaguar), featuring all-disc braking assisted by a vacuum-servo unit connected between the master and wheel cylinders. The hand brake operates on separate pads in the rear disc units.

atmospheric pressure to one side when braking is required.

A major factor in the design of braking systems is the need for leverages which will allow for some reasonable amount of lining wear taking place, without the brake pedal going down to the floor. After a period of concentration on making brake adjustment reasonably easy, designers turned their attention to evolving brakes which were self-adjusting for wear. Considerable care was needed to ensure that self-adjusting systems did not operate too enthusiastically, for example taking up clearance in a hot brake so that it dragged when the drum cooled down and shrank again.

The majority of modern cars have rather more of their weight on the front than on the rear wheels, and during braking yet more weight is thrown forward from the rear to the front wheels; so, to secure the utmost retardation which tyre adhesion permits, the front brakes must provide considerably more drag than the rear brakes. This generates much more heat in the front than in the rear brakes, so there is logic in the growing practice of applying disc braking to a car's front wheels in conjunction with drum brakes at the rear.

Hydraulic Control System. The efficient transmission of effort from a car's brake pedal to the actual brakes, mounted on sprung and steered wheels, poses problems which it is customary to solve hydraulically. The brake pedal pumps a small volume of fluid down a pipeline which, via flexible sections, leads to slave cylinders in each individual brake (Fig. 2.19). Vital to the working of such a system is a reservoir containing the hydraulic fluid. The level in this must be maintained, as the entry of compressible air into pipelines which should contain virtually incompressible fluid can render a car's braking system totally ineffective.

Incorporated in some hydraulic brake

operating systems are valves designed to limit hydraulic pressure applied to the rear brakes, so that the rear wheels cannot so readily be locked by excessive braking and a skid initiated. The simplest anti-skid systems set an arbitrary limit on rear braking pressure; a more refined kind with a deceleration-sensitive valve provides some compensation for the amount of load in the car, allowing extra rear braking effort when the car is laden; and still more elaborate systems adjust the maximum rear braking effort according to how far the car's rear springs are compressed by weight in the car.

Whilst hydraulically operated braking systems have entirely replaced mechanical rod or cable arrangements for the main braking systems of private cars, the hand-operated parking brake is still customarily mechanical. This brake, which has a ratchet handle so that it can be left applied, normally applies brakes on two of a car's wheels through tension in flexible cables.

Almost all designers apply the parking brake to the rear wheels, although those few cars which have their hand brake acting on the front wheels have a more effective emergency brake should a hydraulic system failure occur.

Failures in hydraulic brake systems are very rare on cars which receive regular maintenance. Certain precautions against unexpected failure can be built into a car, such as a warning lamp which lights up if the fluid level in the brake reservoir falls dangerously low: such a lamp is usually also arranged to light up when the hand brake is applied with the engine switched on, this telling the driver that the warning bulb is intact! It is also possible to divide a hydraulic system into two separate halves serving front and rear brakes respectively, so that no one hydraulic system failure can put more than two of the car's four brakes out of action. Such "dual" braking systems may become more common in the future.

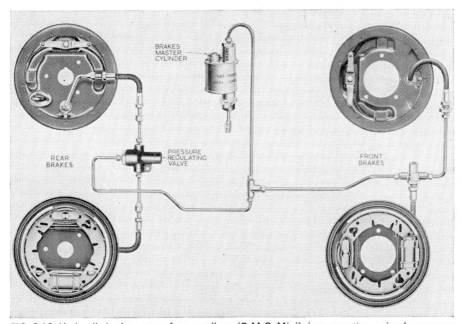

FIG. 2.19. Hydraulic brake system for a small car (B.M.C. Mini), incorporating a simple pressure regulating valve as an anti-skidding device.

ELECTRICAL EQUIPMENT

Reference has already been made in Chapter 1 to one essential and another almost-essential part of the car's electrical system, the ignition circuit and the starter motor. Many other items on a car draw electrical energy from an electrochemical storage battery which, in most instances, has six 2-volt cells connected in series to give a nominal 12 volts (Fig. 2.20). An engine-driven electrical generator charges this battery when the engine is running at an adequate speed, the stored energy being available to start the engine and to operate lights or other equipment for an appreciable time.

Batteries and Generators. Car batteries are lead-acid units, each cell containing two lead plates (electrodes) of large surface area immersed in dilute sulphuric acid (electrolyte). A reversible chemical reaction lets electrical energy be stored in chemical form and subsequently taken out of the battery. The size of battery fitted to a car depends upon a designer's judgment of how much stored electrical energy may be needed

for parking lights and to start the engine in frosty weather, the substantial weight and cost of a lead-acid battery discouraging unduly large dimensions.

Generating equipment for cars is undergoing rapid change at the present time. In the past direct-current dynamos have been universal. These have coils which rotate between fixed magnets, also a rotating commutator which collects current generated in the coils and lets it be picked up by a pair of carbon brush contacts (Fig. 2.21). It has become difficult for d.c. dynamos to meet the modern car's heavy demand for current without being made larger and heavier, and the trend is to use alternating-current generators (alternators) which, size for size, can produce more power.

The alternating current must be converted into direct current in order to charge the battery, and this can now be done by rectifiers using transistor-type devices. An advantage of the alternator is that, having magnets rotating between fixed coils, it can safely be geared to run at a multiple of engine speed and so will charge the battery even when a car is being driven very slowly.

Quite subtle generator control systems are needed in cars, their exact nature being changed when an alternator replaces a d.c. dynamo although the functions to be performed remain similar.

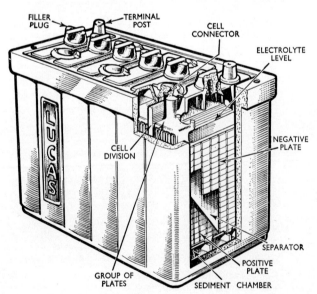

FILLER PLUG
TERMINAL POST
CELL CONNECTOR
ELECTROLYTE LEVEL
CELL DIVISION
NEGATIVE PLATE
GROUP OF PLATES
SEDIMENT CHAMBER
POSITIVE PLATE
SEPARATOR

FIG. 2.20. Construction of a 12-volt battery. Material shed by the plates after repeated cycles of charging and discharging collects in the sediment chamber and may eventually short-circuit the plates in a cell or cells.

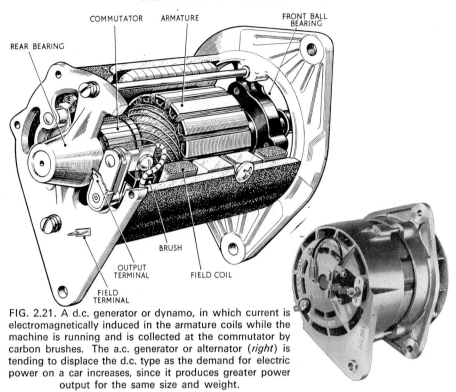

COMMUTATOR   ARMATURE   FRONT BALL BEARING

REAR BEARING

BRUSH

OUTPUT TERMINAL   FIELD COIL

FIELD TERMINAL

FIG. 2.21. A d.c. generator or dynamo, in which current is electromagnetically induced in the armature coils while the machine is running and is collected at the commutator by carbon brushes. The a.c. generator or alternator (*right*) is tending to displace the d.c. type as the demand for electric power on a car increases, since it produces greater power output for the same size and weight.

There must be a cut-out device to disconnect the circuit when the generator is stopped or turning too slowly to develop 12 volts, so that the battery does not discharge itself by trying to rotate the generator as an electric motor. There must be a maximum current control to prevent overheating of the battery by too rapid a charging rate, and a maximum voltage control to prevent over-charging which would dry out the battery very quickly. All three regulator systems are in fact enclosed within a single casing, called the control unit.

Taking advantage of metal construction, cars are wired on what is called the "earth return" system, with one wire taking electricity to a component, and this current completing its circuit back to the battery through the frame of the car. Early cars had the negative battery terminal "earthed" to the chassis; then a change to earthing the positive terminal was made on British cars, because it was claimed that this extended sparking plug life; and now the negative earth has come back into favour, because it is better suited to circuits incorporating transistors which are coming into use on cars.

Lighting and Signalling. Lights are provided on the exterior of a car for two quite distinct reasons. There are small ones to let other people see it in the dark, and larger ones to let the driver see where he is going. The former comprise lights close to the car's four corners, two white front lamps and two red rear ones, with a further lamp illuminating the rear registration number plate; all of these are required by law, together with two rear red reflectors.

The headlamps of a car consume much

more electricity than do parking lamps, but are used mainly when the car is in motion and the generator producing electricity. Main and dipped driving beams are usually obtained by switching from one central filament in each headlamp reflector to another off-centre (and perhaps partially screened) filament. Some cars have four headlamps, two with lenses designed to give a wide spread of light which alone provide the dipped beam, and two with lenses designed to give a longer and narrower light beam which go out when the dip switch is operated.

For many years all headlamps had removable bulbs, a complete lamp assembly consisting of front glass, reflector bowl and bulb. More and more modern cars use "sealed-beam" lamps, however, where the "bulb" has grown to be a complete lamp with the silvered glass reflector as well as the electrically heated filaments in one vacuum-sealed unit (Fig. 2.22). As sealed-beam lamps are more expensive than bulbs to replace,

they are usually designed with cooler-running filaments, which give less light but last longer, while immunity from tarnishing of a reflector sealed away from the atmosphere counterbalances the less efficient filament.

Recently, the invention of the iodine vapour bulb has re-awakened interest in headlamps with separate bulbs. This type gives almost twice as much light as a traditional bulb of equal longevity and electric current consumption because its filament can be hotter without burning away.

Double-filament bulbs of iodine-vapour type cannot be made, so alternative forms of dipping must be arranged when such bulbs are used, either with separate pairs of lamps providing respectively a long-range main beam and a spread of non-dazzling light for passing other traffic, or else with a screen moved inside each headlamp to cut off the upper part of its beam when necessary.

At least one light is customarily pro-

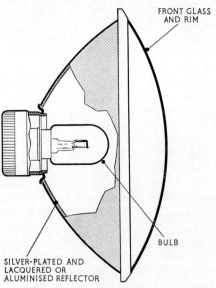
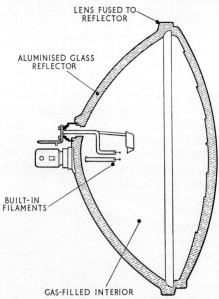

FIG. 2.22. (*Left*) A bulb-type headlamp has a one-piece light unit and a separate bulb. (*Right*) A sealed-beam headlamp in effect combines the light unit with the bulb. Its built-in twin filaments normally give longer life than the ordinary bulb.

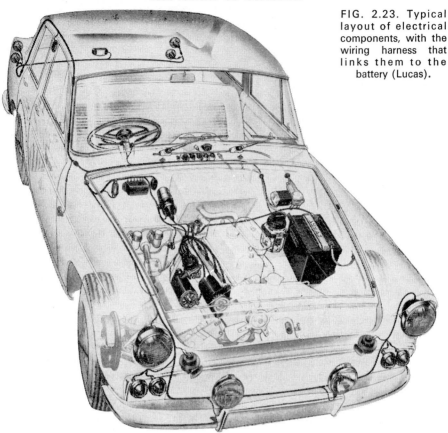

FIG. 2.23. Typical layout of electrical components, with the wiring harness that links them to the battery (Lucas).

vided inside the body of a car, intended mainly for use when the car is stationary. It is common to have a permanently "live" electric supply to this interior lamp, with switches on two or four of the doors that complete the "earth return" circuit whenever a door is opened. Similarly operated "courtesy lights" can be fitted in the boot and under the bonnet.

The electrical installation also incorporates three signalling systems, for warning other people of what the driver is doing. First, there is the stop lamps circuit, which lights up a pair of bright red rear lamps (usually combined with the rear parking lamps, but giving a light about three times as powerful) when the foot brake is in use. Early designs were

operated mechanically from movement of the pedal, but on modern cars the stop-lamp switch is operated by pressure in the brake hydraulic system.

The second signalling system is for direction indication. Turn signals (usually amber-coloured lamps) are operated by a switch which is arranged to turn itself off automatically, either when the steering is straightened after a turn or when a certain period of time has elapsed. By law, the signal lamps must flash at a rate between the limits of 60 and 120 flashes per minute, a common rate being 70-80 flashes per minute. The turn signal flashers operate through the alternate heating and cooling of a bimetallic strip, movement of which opens and closes electrical contacts inside a sealed flasher unit. A repeater lamp inside the car confirms that they are working.

A welcome refinement in turn signal design varies their intensity according to whether or not the car's lights are in use; this is because a flashing light of sufficient brilliance to be conspicuous on a sunny day is apt to cause dazzle at night.

As a third signalling system, the law requires all cars to be fitted with a device for giving audible warning of approach. This normally takes the form of a horn (or pair of horns with different tones) in which air pressure pulses come from a diaphragm oscillated by a magnet and contact breaker system akin to that of an electric bell.

Electrical Accessories. Means to ensure vision in wet weather are another legal requirement. Windscreen wipers actuated by suction from the engine have been used, but nowadays most are electrical, having blades oscillating to and fro when driven by an electric motor through a crank mechanism. Self-parking wiper switches are used, the effect being that when the switch is turned off, the wiper blade moves to the end of its travel before the driving motor is actually stopped.

Most cars are equipped with blower fans driven by electric motors, for maintaining interior heating when the car's own forward movement does not force air through the heater radiator. Some high-performance cars have electrically driven engine cooling fans, with a thermostatic switch bringing the fan into use only when the engine has reached its maximum safe operating temperature. There are a number of other electrical accessories available for car use, some of which are considered in Chapter 10.

Car Wiring and Fuses. All the electrical components on a car are coupled up to the battery, switches etc. by large numbers of wires, which are grouped together in a "harness" before installation (Fig. 2.23). For identification, each wire in the harness has its insulation colour-coded, either in a single colour or a pair of colours, and for any car a diagram is available (sometimes included in the instruction book) showing which colour codes are used for the different circuits. A complete car wiring diagram can look alarmingly complicated, but with the lines that represent wires numbered or lettered to correspond with their colour-coding on the car itself, it is usually not too difficult to trace a particular circuit.

Modern plastic insulation on wiring is more durable than the rubber that was formerly used, but on an old car the insulation of a wire may become chafed or the wire may break, necessitating running a fresh wire in place of that in the harness, both ends of which are then disconnected.

Various techniques have been evolved for simplifying the installation and replacement of the electrical equipment. Close to each lamp there is usually a push-in connector to the wiring harness, and some units have multi-point plugs. Wiring around instrument panels is now sometimes in the form of a "printed circuit" with solder run into grooves on the back of an insulating panel forming permanent connections to switches and instruments.

Most cars have one or more fuses to protect their electrical systems. These are small cartridges enclosing lengths of thin low-melting-point wire, which will carry the normal designed load on a particular electrical circuit, but melt if an excess current flows and interrupt the current which might otherwise damage more expensive components or start a fire. Most British car makers do not fit fuses in their main headlamp circuits, saying that a fault which would make un-fused headlamps merely go dim might cause a dangerous, sudden black-out if a fuse blew. On some foreign cars each headlamp is fused separately, so that they should not both fail at the same time.

When a fuse "blows" it is because of a fault, which should be found and rectified before the fuse is replaced. Sometimes a fuse blows when one particular switch is operated, and provided that switch is left off, the fuse may be replaced to restore temporarily other circuits also served by it

INSTRUMENTS

Motorists are legally required to have on their cars something which will tell them (within 10 per cent margin of error) when they are exceeding 30 m.p.h. speed limits, and whilst a tell-tale lamp might meet the law, cars are invariably equipped with speed indicating instruments. Some of the earliest cars did not have even this one instrument, and since then fashion has fluctuated between equipping cars with a bare minimum of instruments and providing a large number. Today, the cheapest cars have at least a speedometer, a distance recorder, a fuel contents gauge, and two or three warning lights.

Speedometer and Tachometer. The normal type of speedometer mechanism is dependent on a simple electrical principle. A flexible shaft, driven from a front wheel or

from the gearbox output shaft, rotates a permanent magnet which induces eddy currents in an aluminium disc alongside it, causing the disc to rotate against the resistance of a spring. This disc moves the speedometer pointer along its scale, by an amount depending upon the speed at which the magnet is rotating, and the maker adjusts the accuracy of each individual instrument by regulating the strength of the rotating magnet. Most car makers specify a "tolerance" on speedometer calibration which permits slight exaggeration of speed but not its understatement.

Incorporated with the speedometer is a total distance recorder, and sometimes a second "trip" recorder unit which can be reset to zero at the start of a journey. These distance recorders have a series of drums which indicate the mileage in multiples of ten, each drum being numbered 0 to 9, with gearing to turn it at one-tenth the speed of the drum to its right. This 10 to 1 speed reduction is obtained by the use of gear wheels with a

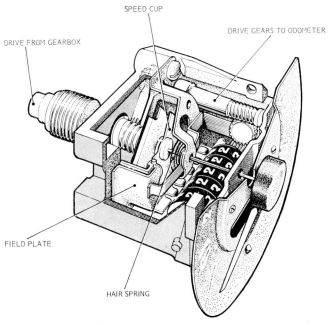

SPEED CUP

DRIVE GEARS TO ODOMETER

DRIVE FROM GEARBOX

FIELD PLATE

HAIR SPRING

FIG. 2.24. The speedometer is usually of the magnet and cup type, in which a revolving magnet inside an aluminium cup induces electric current in the cup. This drags the cup and pointer round against the tension of a hair spring. The mileage recorder is worked by a series of gears (AC-Delco).

71

single tooth and then a long series of missing teeth, so that when the driving tooth engages it quickly rotates a drum far enough to bring the next figure into sight, and then leaves the drum stationary in that position (Fig. 2.24).

Cars intended for sporting drivers often have an engine speed indicator as well as a speedometer, to help the driver keep his engine speed close to that giving maximum power without dangerous over-speeding. What is often mis-called a "rev counter" can measure crankshaft revolutions per minute in exactly the same way as a speedometer measures road speed, using a rotating cable driven from the engine. It has, however, been found easier to install electrical "tachometers" which measure engine speed without a mechanical drive, these needing only to be connected to the low-tension side of the ignition system. What such an instrument actually measures is the frequency with which sparks take place, having a dial suitably calibrated for a four, six or eight cylinder engine and giving a measure of revolutions per minute.

Fuel Gauge. Virtually universal on cars is the fuel contents gauge which indicates approximately how much petrol is in the tank. Originally contents gauges were mounted on top of the petrol tank, and a float on the end of a pivoted arm rose and fell with the fuel level, working a pointer on a scale through simple gears. A few rear-engined cars still use such a mechanical system, with a very short flexible wire from the float in the front-mounted petrol tank to a dial on the instrument panel.

When the petrol tank is at the rear of the car, a mechanical gauge would need too long a cable to work effectively without sticking. Most cars therefore have electrical fuel contents gauges in which the moving float inside the tank works a variable electrical resistance unit, and the dial on the instrument panel records how

much electric current is reaching it. Such instruments (which in practice use a rather more complex circuit, so that they are less sensitive to battery voltage variations) go out of action when the ignition is switched off, to avoid draining current from the battery.

Water Temperature Gauge. Despite thermostats which attempt to control an engine's coolant temperature automatically, it is useful to know when an engine is unduly hot or cold. Many cars have a thermometer or water temperature gauge located where cooling liquid leaves the engine to pass into the radiator. Earlier thermometers designed to give a remote reading on the instrument panel depended on very fine capillary tubes, to transmit to the dial vapour pressure generated in a heated thermometer bulb. Modern types, which are easier to install and less vulnerable to damage, have a temperature measuring unit in the engine which varies its electrical resistance when it becomes hot, and a dial on the instrument panel which uses this variation of resistance to indicate electrically the coolant temperature.

Usually the coolant thermometer settles down to a predictable reading within a couple of miles of the start of a journey, any abnormal behaviour being a sign of trouble such as blocked air or water circulation, or lack of water, or failure of the belt which drives both fan and water pump. In winter, a coolant thermometer makes it safe for a driver to help warming-up of the engine by covering up part of the radiator, since it will warn him if too much "blanketing" is causing engine overheating.

Oil Pressure Gauge. In the past it was usual to equip cars with engine oil pressure gauges, measuring the lubricant pressure between the circulating pump and the bearings which it supplies. Because there is a sort of safety valve in the system, most cars show a fairly constant oil pressure when running, the pressure dropping at very low speeds when less oil is being pumped. Modern engine bearings are more reliable than their predecessors, and modern engine oils do not thin out when hot to such a great extent as did older lubricants, so it has become less usual to fit a car with an oil pressure gauge. On most popular models there is merely a warning lamp to tell the driver of low oil pressure.

For the intelligent motorist, an oil pressure gauge is still a good companion, as modest pressure changes which would not operate a warning lamp can give early warning of bearing wear, filter blockage or a low oil level in the sump.

Ammeter. As an indicator of what is happening in the electrical system, an ammeter is sometimes provided. This is a centre-zero instrument which records how much current is flowing into or out of the battery. It thus indicates when any electrical component is working, except in the case of the starter motor. This draws a very much heavier current than anything else on the car, and is wired in a separate circuit which by-passes the ammeter. Like other instruments, an ammeter is especially informative when something goes wrong, although it can serve as a reminder if lights, heater fan, windscreen wiper, etc. are collectively taking more current than the generator can supply.

Warning Lights. Tell-tale coloured lamps are provided in varying numbers on car instrument panels. The most universal is the generator charge tell-tale which lights up when the ignition is switched on, and should go out as soon as the engine is speeded up sufficiently for the generator to start charging. Also common is the oil warning lamp which lights up when the ignition is turned on, and goes out again as soon as the engine starts and its oil pressure reaches a safe level.

If the ignition tell-tale suddenly lights up as the car is being driven, the most likely cause is breakage of the generator driving belt, and as this usually drives the fan and cooling water pump also, driving on may involve risk of overheating the engine as well as of running down the battery. If the oil pressure tell-tale lights up momentarily during acceleration, braking or cornering, this means that a dangerously low oil level is letting lubricant in the sump surge away from the pump intake. If the light remains on, something more serious is amiss, and the engine should be stopped at once before expensive damage is done.

STRUCTURE AND BODYWORK

The structures which hold all the parts of a vehicle together have undergone a great deal of change during the history of motoring. At one time strength was the only criterion, but it has since been found that making a car run more smoothly and quietly depends on the frame being as rigid as possible in addition to being strong enough not to break.

Formerly, chassis frames were based upon two side-members running from end to end of the car, pressed from sheet steel into channel sections with top and bottom flanges joined by a vertical web. Such a frame could have ample strength and stiffness to resist bending loads, but was quite readily twisted. Closing in the channel side-members to form box sections and running X-shaped bracing members between diagonally opposite corners of the frame gave later chassis designs much more torsional stiffness (Fig. 2.25). There are a few cars built with the X-shaped central bracing and no separate side-members at all!

Early car bodies were quite flexible wood-framed structures, but modern bodies are usually built up from sheet steel panels pressed into shape and welded together. Besides being strong enough to give passengers a good deal of protection in a collision, a welded steel body can easily be reinforced to make it far stronger and stiffer than any chassis frame on which

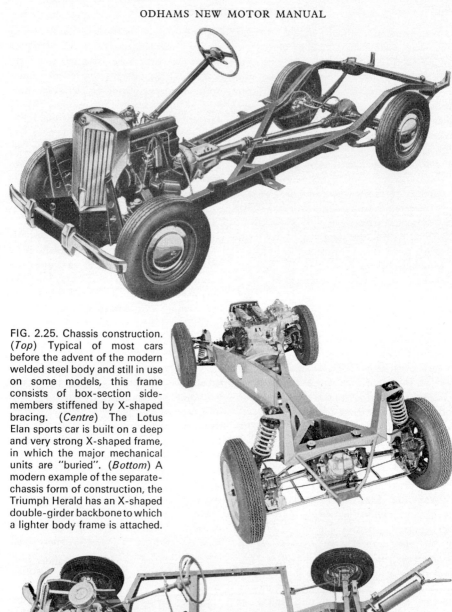

FIG. 2.25. Chassis construction. (*Top*) Typical of most cars before the advent of the modern welded steel body and still in use on some models, this frame consists of box-section side-members stiffened by X-shaped bracing. (*Centre*) The Lotus Elan sports car is built on a deep and very strong X-shaped frame, in which the major mechanical units are "buried". (*Bottom*) A modern example of the separate-chassis form of construction, the Triumph Herald has an X-shaped double-girder backbone to which a lighter body frame is attached.

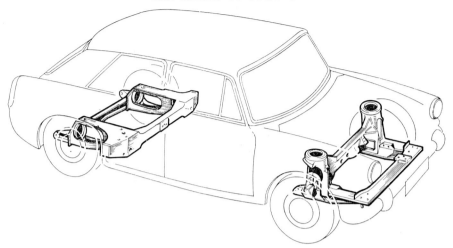

FIG. 2.26. A light car having sub-frames to carry the wheels and suspension units, the remainder of the body being of sheet metal construction. On this model (B.M.C. 1100), the front sub-frame also carries the transverse engine and transmission.

it could be mounted, so most European cars are now built without chassis frames. American cars often have light frames under their bodywork, which are convenient to let mechanical parts be assembled separately from the body, but which would not be nearly rigid enough for use on the road unless steel bodywork was bolted on to add extra stiffness.

When a separate chassis frame is still used, it can take any of several forms. Closest to the traditional layout are those which have two members running from end to end of the car, these members usually being of closed tubular or box shaping which provide great resistance to twisting. Lower door sills can be achieved with a cruciform chassis, in which the end-to-end rails meet at the centre of the car and diverge towards the front and rear suspension mountings. Some cars have been built with a tubular backbone frame, whereas American designers often favour what they call a "perimeter" frame exactly following the body sides and curving in between the wheels.

Where a car has a separate body and chassis, rubber is often used to mount one

on the other, as a barrier against noise transfer. Cars with stressed body structures achieve similar results by rubber mountings of springing and power unit components, either as individual units or as groups on sub-frames insulated with rubber from the main structure (Fig. 2.26).

As already mentioned, the vast majority of modern bodies are welded up from steel pressings, which form a very strong structure indeed (Fig. 2.27). A disadvantage of pressed steel is that rust can eventually weaken its thin metal panels, surface treatments beneath a car's paintwork moderating rather than eliminating this risk. Steel is, however, a very good body material in other respects, offering considerable scope for repair of accident damage by panel-beating to restore its shape and by welding up of joins.

Body Finishes. Because of the rust problem, paintwork on a car is much more than mere decoration, serving also to protect the structure. Car bodies go through a long series of processes involving chemical cleaning, application of a rust-proofing layer (this is often a phosphate chemical), painting with primer which (like the rust-

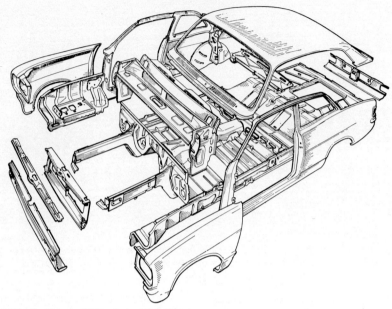

FIG. 2.27. The Vauxhall Viva is an example of "monocoque" welded sheet-metal construction and the illustration shows the various parts that go to make one complete body.

proofing) may be applied by dipping the complete body in a tank, and finally the spraying on of several layers of paint which is baked to harden it.

Quality of paintwork should be high on modern cars from large and well-equipped factories, the problem being to secure equally effective rust-proofing and painting with simpler facilities when crash damage has to be repaired.

Certain cars use aluminium for some or all of their panels. This is a lighter material than steel and is not subject to corrosion in the same way, but it costs more and is more difficult to repair if damaged in an accident. Another body material used in some small-production cars is Fibreglass, moulded by impregnating layers of glass-fibre cloth or mat with a plastic material. This also is a non-rusting material which costs more than steel, the fact that it can be moulded into three-dimensional curved shapes without expensive press tools or skilled panel-beating labour making it

attractive for bodies or body sections which are built in relatively small numbers.

Safety Glass. Each succeeding generation of cars seems to have greater areas of glass than its predecessors, and this nowadays is always a form of so-called safety glass. The oldest type of safety glass is the laminated form, which has two thin sheets of glass bonded on either side of a thin sheet of plastic, this arrangement being intended to prevent the glass splintering into jagged pieces in a crash. More recently "toughened glass" was invented, a single sheet of glass being heat-treated so that if broken, it disintegrates into coarse sugar-like granules which do not cause serious injury (Fig. 2.28).

For side and rear windows "toughened" glass is unquestionably the safest. Front windscreens are a subject of controversy, sudden impact from a flying stone being liable to make toughened glass fragment and become partially (but not completely) opaque. If the driver and passengers in-

FIG. 2.28. What happens to a zone-toughened windscreen after fracturing. The glass has been stressed during manufacture so as to break into bands of alternate small and comparatively large particles, resulting in a wide zone of reasonable visibility for the driver (Triplex).

variably wear safety harness, a laminated windscreen may probably be safest equipment for a car. If the occupants are not invariably harnessed, and could hit the windscreen in a crash, the risk of suddenly reduced visibility through a modern toughened glass windscreen is almost certainly less than the risk of face and neck injury by splinters from a laminated glass screen.

Safety Features. Whilst road accident casualties are not significantly more numerous now than they were in the 1930's, when traffic was at a fraction of its present-day density, there has been a great increase in emphasis upon designing cars so that their occupants are more likely to survive accidents.

All British cars must now have provision for fitting safety harness, of which several types are available (Fig. 2.30). Such harness can also be a form of support against being rolled around by normal braking and cornering. Car structures are being designed to be strong around the passengers, but with engine and luggage compartments that will crumple as buffers in a crash. Steering columns are being designed so that they should not be driven back by impact into a driver's chest, sharp projections inside the body eliminated, and some areas of the body interior softly

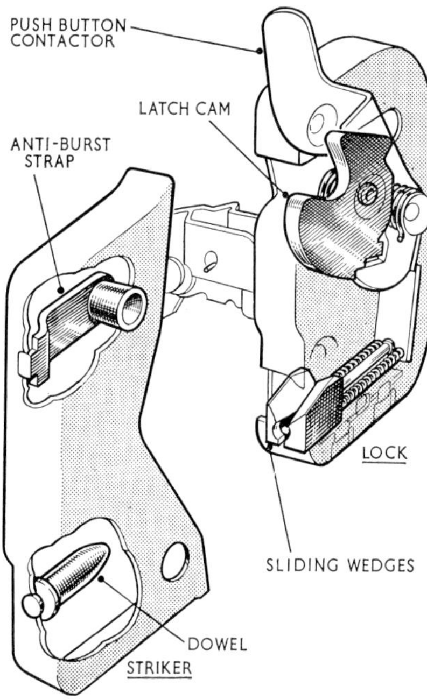

PUSH BUTTON CONTACTOR

LATCH CAM

ANTI-BURST STRAP

LOCK

SLIDING WEDGES

DOWEL

STRIKER

FIG. 2.29. Anti-burst door lock. The latch cam engaging with the anti-burst strap resists fore-and-aft separation of the door and frame, and the dowel engaging with the sliding wedges resists both fore-and-aft separation and transverse separation.

77

padded. Another safety development is the anti-burst door lock fitted to some cars (Fig. 2.29). This is designed to prevent the door being flung open through distortion of the frame under impact.

VENTILATION, HEATING AND SILENCING

Ventilation arrangements in saloon cars were once restricted to side windows that could be opened and shut, but today's cars are being designed to offer good ventilation, combined with heating if required, even though all windows are fully closed.

Large American cars quite commonly have electrical systems for opening and closing windows, with a four-switch master control panel within reach of the driver.

It has become virtually standard practice to equip a car with a forward-facing fresh air intake, from which ventilation air can be passed through a heating radiator (warmed by water from the engine) to heat the car interior. In some weather conditions, the moisture in human breath can condense as mist inside the windows of a car, dangerously impairing vision, so there is usually provision for blowing fresh

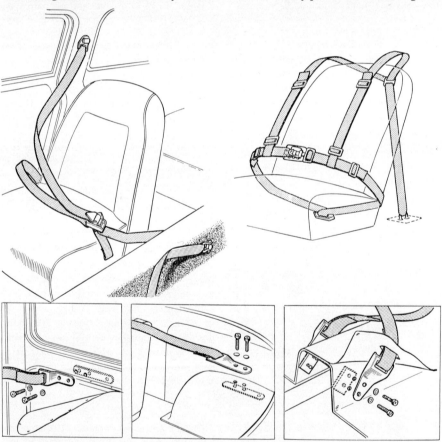

FIG. 2.30. Safety belts may take the form of a lap strap, a diagonal belt, or (as illustrated) a combination of these or a full shoulder harness. Some fixing points are also shown: (*left*) on the rear window sill of a two-door car, (*centre*) on the wheel arch of a sports car, (*right*) on a propeller shaft tunnel.

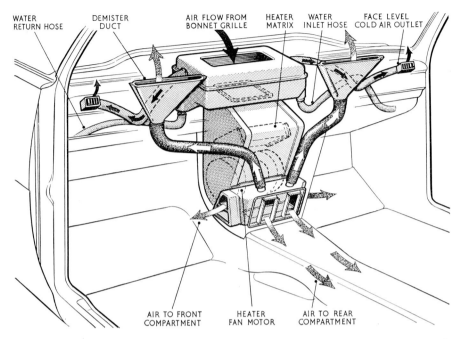

WATER RETURN HOSE   DEMISTER DUCT   AIR FLOW FROM BONNET GRILLE   HEATER MATRIX   WATER INLET HOSE   FACE LEVEL COLD AIR OUTLET

AIR TO FRONT COMPARTMENT   HEATER FAN MOTOR   AIR TO REAR COMPARTMENT

FIG. 2.31. Modern heating and ventilating system. Air drawn in through the bonnet grille can be heated and circulated to all occupants of the car and to the windscreen. Unheated fresh air is also supplied separately to the front-seat occupants through face-level outlets. The air passes out through extractors in the rear of the car (Vauxhall).

air (either cool or heated) on to the inner surface of, at least, the front windscreen which can thereby be cleared of visibility-blocking condensation.

With all windows closed, some form of extractor is needed to draw stale air from the car interior, and efficient extractor ducts, usually mounted close to the rear window, are becoming common. At cruising speeds a modern ventilation system will change the interior air completely in well under a minute.

Car heating systems nowadays are in many instances far superior to home central heating installations, in particular because they provide the warmth at foot level and cooler breathing air, which ensure comfort with minimum fatigue (Fig. 2.31). Considerable care is also taken in the best systems to keep the temperature reasonably constant, regardless of how the car is being

driven. Air intakes and outlets are normally so proportioned so that the forward intake generates slight "ram" pressure in the moving car, this preventing draughts and dust entering at other points such as around imperfectly sealed doors.

Cars are quietened in a great many different ways. Carburettor air intakes as well as the engine exhaust are fitted with silencers. Rubber is interposed between road springs, the engine and the main structure of the car. Panels which might vibrate are stiffened or have damping material glued to or sprayed on to them. Further noise reduction can be achieved by application of sound-absorbing material (felt or quilted glass-fibre, for example) to as many surfaces as possible—beneath carpets, inside doors, below bonnet lids and rear parcel shelves, and anywhere else where noise can be absorbed.

CHAPTER 3

FAULT TRACING AND TESTING

SEARCHING for an engine fault can be a frustrating experience for the novice, but the expert will often find a defect in minutes by testing at key points in a carefully planned sequence. His method, known in the trade as "area testing", divides the engine into four sections, and begins where the fault is most likely to be —in the ignition system. If he draws a blank here, he goes on to check the electrical, carburation, and compression areas in sequence.

The quest for unserviceability can arise in two ways: because the engine stops or will not start, when it is usually called *fault tracing*; and *testing* as a preliminary to overhaul or as part of the electronic diagnosis checks offered to motorists by some service stations. Obviously, the circumstances in which these two are made are likely to be very different. How to trace a fault in an emergency with few tools at hand is described first.

FAULT TRACING IN AN EMERGENCY

Before disconnecting anything, make sure there is enough petrol in the tank, then raise the bonnet and see if anything is loose or out of place. Feel for looseness in the coil, distributor and carburettor, and make sure the engine bonding strap is secure. This unlikely fault can cause intermittent engine failure because the ignition will not be properly earthed.

Refusal to Start. First switch on the lights to make sure the battery has a charge, then check the connections. Enough current can sometimes be conducted through a loose connection for the lights,

but not enough for the starter motor. The "crack" from the battery terminals when the starter is operated is usually plainly audible. Watch the side lights when checking for current; if these dim or go out when the starter is operated, trouble of the kind described on page 89 is indicated, and there is little one can do about this if the battery is to blame. A faulty starter motor or a battery flat through disuse can be overcome either by providing a push start or by connecting "jump" leads from a serviceable battery.

When the ignition light appears bright at first but fades, there is a short in the circuit, possibly a lead adrift from a terminal. The light going out and staying out, with no response from the starter when operated, indicates a short in either the feed or the starter itself.

If lights and battery terminals are all

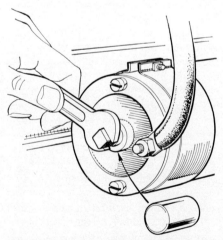

FIG. 3.1. A jammed starter motor can usually be freed by turning the armature shaft with a spanner, after removing the end cover.

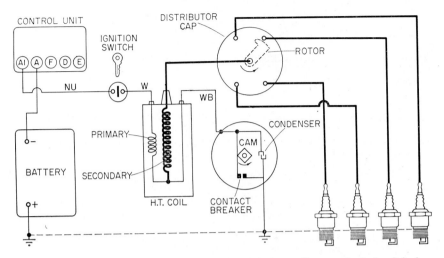

FIG. 3.2. Ignition circuit for a four-cylinder engine. The primary (low-tension) circuit is drawn in light line and the secondary (high-tension) circuit in heavy line. The firing order shown is 1, 3, 4, 2. The standardized coding for cable insulation colours is used, as on wiring diagrams: NU is brown/blue, W white, WB white/black.

right but there is no sound when the starter is pressed, the starter pinion may be jammed in mesh with the flywheel. Rocking the car with bottom gear engaged and the ignition switched off will often free it, or the square shaft on the end of the motor, accessible when the protecting cap is removed, can be turned with a spanner (Fig. 3.1). Failing this, the motor will have to be loosened at the flywheel flange.

When the starter is sluggish and the electrical system is known to be in good condition, the cause is dirty brush gear or poor electrical connections. Sometimes dirt on the helix prevents the pinion nut from running into engagement. This can often be overcome by tapping the starter casing with a heavy spanner, but a permanent remedy is to strip and clean the parts (see page 236). In cold weather, a frozen water pump will sometimes give all the indications of a jammed starter pinion. A cloth soaked in boiling water and wrapped around the inlet where the bottom water hose joins the engine usually cures this trouble.

Wet-weather Failure. Dampness on the high-tension leads can cause this trouble on cars such as the Mini where the distributor is directly behind the front grille, and the only permanent cure is to fit a boot over the distributor, treat the leads with silicone grease, and put rubber covers on coil and plug terminals. Meanwhile, moisture can be carefully wiped off with the leads still in place. Blanking off the radiator grille can help temporarily, although this may make the engine run hot.

When all these points have been checked, full-scale fault tracing can begin with the ignition system. A circuit for a four-cylinder engine is shown in Fig. 3.2.

IGNITION FAULTS

Plug Testing. One simple check can clear the whole of the ignition circuit— are the plugs sparking? To find out, take a plug from the cylinder, then lay it on a good earth (any bare metal surface will do) with its lead connected, and crank the engine with the ignition on (see Fig. 3.3). A good, "fat" spark will clear the system,

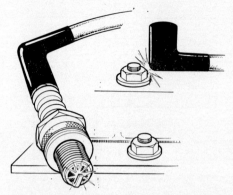

FIG. 3.3. To test the ignition system, a sparking plug removed from its cylinder is laid on bare engine metal. If the plug sparks when the engine is cranked with ignition switched on, this clears the ignition system. (*Inset*) Faulty insulation allows a spark to be obtained from a suppressor cap, detached from its plug.

but before moving on to look at the petrol supply, check on the insulation of the plug cap before replacing the plug in the cylinder. A hair crack in the plastics moulding can cause a high-tension leak that will be very difficult to detect since the ignition apparently functions normally in the test just described.

Hold the cap close to a good earth and repeat the sparking test; if the cap is defective, a spark will jump the gap. This test applies especially to persistent misfiring on the road. To find the faulty cap, stop the car and feel each plug lead in turn. The one that has been misfiring will be appreciably cooler than the others at

the plug end. Binding the cap with insulation tape makes a temporary repair.

If the test reveals no spark at the plug, first note whether the points are correctly gapped, and reset as described on page 109 if necessary. Dampness inside the plug indicates either too rich a mixture or oil in the cylinder. All plugs failing simultaneously in an otherwise serviceable ignition system is rare but not impossible, and fouling by oil or neat petrol could be the cause (Fig. 3.4). Check the other plugs if such fouling is present. Oil on the electrodes can only be cured permanently by overhaul, but a temporary stopgap might be hotter plugs that keep clear by burning off oil before it can accumulate. Service the plug or substitute one known to be good, repeat the test, then go on to checking the supply if no spark is obtained.

High-tension Supply. The first check if no spark appears at the plug gap is on the high-tension supply, the lead from the centre terminal of the coil to the distributor cap (Fig. 3.5). Release this from the cap by undoing the grub screw inside the cap enough to pull the lead out of place, then make a spark test with the ignition switched on.

Hold the lead about $\frac{1}{8}$ in. away from a good earth, and either crank the engine or flick the contact breaker points open a few times with the thumb. A spark will confirm that the coil and low-tension circuit are in order, and the defect must be in the distributor cover, the rotor or

FIG. 3.4. Much can be learned about the engine from the condition of its sparking plugs. (1) A dry, grey appearance indicates an engine in good condition, with a well-tuned carburettor. (2) Wet, black carbon results from oil reaching the cylinders past worn components. (3) Dry, soft soot: carburettor set too rich, or air filter blocked. (4) Burned appearance with dead-white insulator: carburettor set too lean, or induction air leakage.

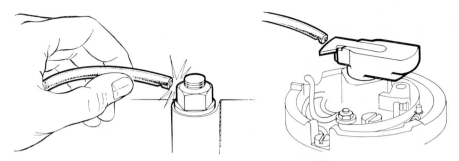

FIG. 3.5. (*Left*) To test the H.T. supply from the coil, remove the lead from the distributor cap and hold it close to earthed metal. A spark should appear when the contact breaker points are flicked open with the ignition on. (*Right*) If the insulation of the rotor arm is cracked, a spark will appear when this test is repeated on the brass pick-up.

the plug leads, all being part of the thick circuit shown in Fig. 3.2. After making the test, replace the centre lead in the distributor cap, making sure it goes fully home so that the grub screw when tightened pierces the same place in the insulation.

Rotor and Distributor Cap. Trouble here can be due to a cracked cap: electrical corrosion on the segments inside the cap and the rotor; a broken brush or spring inside the cap; a bad connection between the high-tension lead and the cap; or a defective rotor shorting to the distributor spindle. The rotor is easily checked by repeating the spark test with the H.T. lead held close to the brass section of the rotor (see Fig. 3.5). If the moulding is cracked and current is escaping through the rotor to the distributor spindle and back to earth, a spark will be obtained between lead and rotor when the contact breaker points are flicked open.

A crack in the distributor cap can often be seen after cleaning with a soft cloth. A remedy is to break the path of current tracking from the segments to the distributor body, and a small hole drilled through the crack is often enough to do this. Replacement is the only effective answer, though.

Electrical corrosion on the rotor and segments should be carefully cleaned off, but not scraped (Fig. 3.6). As good a way

as any to clean a rotor is to rub it on a tyre. A weak brush spring can be stretched as an expedient, and a broken brush can be temporarily replaced with a length of thin wire wound in the same direction as rotor movement (usually anti-clockwise) so that it is constantly tightened.

One other factor that might cause a break in the supply of high-tension current to the plugs is too high a resistance of the leads. Normally, this should be about 1,800 ohms, but deterioration can multiply this to the point where current is no longer conducted. The workshop checks described later reveal increasing resistance before unserviceability occurs, and the leads can then be replaced in good time.

Low-tension Circuit. Trouble in the upper half of the distributor must be suspected when the H.T. lead from the coil produces a spark on test. But if only a weak

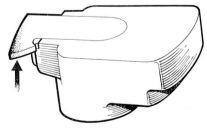

FIG. 3.6. Electrical corrosion on the rotor arm pick-up can cause intermittent misfiring. Rub the arm on a tyre to clean it.

83

spark or no spark at all is obtained, then the low-tension circuit indicated by the thin line in Fig. 3.2 and comprising the primary side of the coil, the condenser (Fig. 3.7) and the contact breaker points, is suspect.

An ammeter fitted to the car is useful but not essential for this next stage of testing. Assuming first that one is fitted, it ought to give a fluctuating reading between zero and 3 amps or so as the points open and close when the engine is turned over with the ignition switched on. No reading indicates an interrupted circuit, and a constant reading means that the points are not opening. On cars without an ammeter, switch on the ignition, turn the engine until the points are closed, then flick these open two or three times with the thumb. There should be a *weak* spark between the contacts.

First make sure that all connections are intact and the plastics insulation free from damp. If an interrupted circuit exists, it is most likely to be in the coil itself (Fig. 3.8), so make a test on the CB terminal when the points are open. If no spark is obtained when a screwdriver earthed on the engine is touched to the terminal, either the low-tension supply from the battery has failed or the coil is at fault. A spark from the CB terminal when the points are closed indicates failure in the low-tension circuit, most likely through dirty points.

The low-tension supply is the easier of the two to check, so pull off the Lucar connection from the SW terminal of the coil, pull back the insulation and flash the metal end

piece against a good earth with the ignition switched on (Fig. 3.9). If there is a spark, change the coil. No spark means that the low-tension supply from the battery through the control box and ignition switch has failed, and a look at the wiring traced from the wiring diagram in Chapter 10 might show a loose connection.

An emergency measure is to connect a lead direct from the A1 outlet on the control box to the coil SW terminal, or a lead direct from the battery if this is under the bonnet. Press the starter and make for home if the engine fires, but check the wiring over and rectify the fault as soon as possible.

The supply and coil will be suspect when there is no spark from the test on the CB terminal of the coil. But if a spark is present, then check for continuity in the thin wire running from the coil's CB terminal to the distributor (see Fig. 3.7). Disconnect at that end and try flashing it on the engine. A break in continuity in the wire itself is most unlikely, but it can occur and the cause will probably be a chafed insulation. A live lead now isolates trouble to the distributor, in either the points or the condenser.

Condenser. Failure in the condenser (or "capacitor") is unlikely to occur without some previous warning, such as misfiring or poor response when the throttle is suddenly opened on acceleration. If

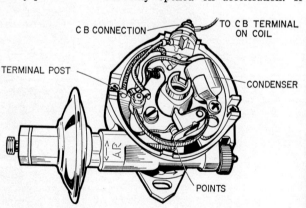

FIG. 3.7. Lucas distributor with cap and rotor arm removed, showing the components included in the low-tension circuit.

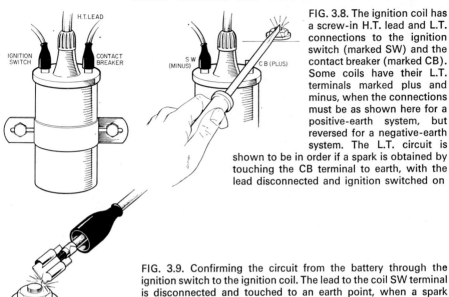

FIG. 3.8. The ignition coil has a screw-in H.T. lead and L.T. connections to the ignition switch (marked SW) and the contact breaker (marked CB). Some coils have their L.T. terminals marked plus and minus, when the connections must be as shown here for a positive-earth system, but reversed for a negative-earth system. The L.T. circuit is shown to be in order if a spark is obtained by touching the CB terminal to earth, with the lead disconnected and ignition switched on

FIG. 3.9. Confirming the circuit from the battery through the ignition switch to the ignition coil. The lead to the coil SW terminal is disconnected and touched to an earth point, when a spark should be given.

these symptoms have been prevalent before the breakdown, suspect the condenser. A fat spark obtained when the points are flicked open indicates an inoperative condenser, confirmed by disconnecting its lead from the points terminal post (see Fig. 3.7) and repeating the test.

No difference in the size of the spark means that low-tension current is bypassing the condenser internally although its insulation is intact. A short circuit between the condenser and earth (usually internally) can be expected if no spark at the points when flicked open becomes a fat spark after disconnecting the lead from the points terminal post. In both cases, changing the condenser is the only answer.

Contact Breaker. One of the most common causes of ignition failure, trouble at the contact breaker points (see Fig. 3.7), can be due to two main reasons. One is pitting, usually caused by a faulty condenser failing to control sparking as the points open and close, and the other is dirt or grease on the contact faces, often from over-lubricating the distributor.

Much less common is trouble caused by misalignment from wear or incorrect assembly.

First examine the contact faces for both gap and condition; most Lucas points are gapped at 0·015 in., but Delco Remy distributors have 0·020 in. (Vauxhall) and 0·015 in. (Triumph) gaps. A gap more than a few "thou" out should be reset if the faces are smooth and clean. Wiping off dirt or grease is a matter of moments, but pitting is another matter and the only really satisfactory remedy in this case is to replace the points. In an emergency on the road, the striker side of a matchbox folded lengthwise to make a double surface can sometimes serve to remedy points failure. The points are held open while the makeshift "file" is admitted, then held lightly together as the abrasive is moved gently backwards and forwards. All traces of dust must be removed afterwards.

Condensers and contact points cost only a few shillings, and substitution is the easiest way to confirm a diagnosis. A bubble pack containing both that is avail-

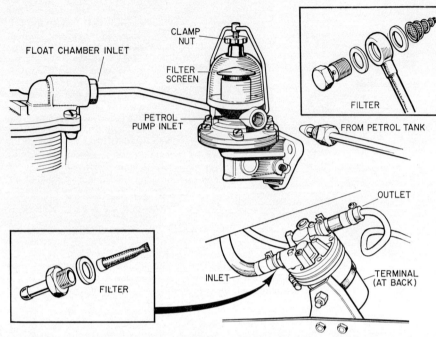

FIG. 3.10. (*Upper*) Mechanical petrol pump, showing its filter and pipe connections, and the form of pipe union in common use. To confirm the petrol feed, the feed pipe is disconnected at the carburettor inlet and the engine cranked. The spurting of petrol from the open pipe indicates that the pump is working and any carburation defect must lie in the carburettor. (*Lower*) Connections to the S.U. type SP electric petrol pump, and its filter. (*Top right*) The gauze thimble-type petrol filter located in the inlet of certain S.U. carburettors.

able from most accessory shops offers a convenient way of keeping these components in the car clean and handy for such an emergency. New contact points must be cleaned in petrol to remove the preservative that will otherwise act as an insulator, and the gap must be set after assembly.

Coil. Serviceability is confirmed by elimination at several stages in the tests on the ignition. Because the coil shares a circuit with the contact-breaker mechanism in the distributor, direct testing of this component in an emergency can be misleading, so the sequence followed in area testing is the surest way to discover a fault.

A coil will sometimes fail when it gets hot yet appear to be serviceable after cooling—a sign of impending failure. If diagnosis points to the coil yet the engine

starts after it has been standing for a time, change the coil at the first opportunity. Make sure to connect the SW and CB leads the right way round. The ignition will function either way, but with a drop in efficiency the wrong way round (Fig. 3.8).

CARBURATION FAULTS

Breakdown on the Road. Obvious faults to look for once the ignition has been exonerated and carburation is suspected are: broken or disconnected leads to an electrical petrol pump or a loose mounting on the mechanical type; a loose petrol pump cap causing an air leak; or a broken petrol feed.

The confirmatory test if all these appear to be serviceable is the supply of petrol to the carburettor. To make this, disconnect

86

the petrol feed pipe at the carburettor end (Fig. 3.10), then either turn the engine for a mechanical pump or switch on the ignition for an electrical type and watch the delivery from the pipe. Petrol spurting from here indicates that if there is a carburation fault it must be in the carburettor. The petrol supply ought to be clean and free from bubbles, with about half an egg-cupful delivered every second turn of the engine. No feed immediately suggests the petrol pump as the most likely cause of failure.

Carburettor Faults. Petrol delivery to the carburettor is governed by the float needle valve, so if the car stops suddenly on the road, but there is petrol in the tank, and the feed test shows the pump to be working, the most likely cause is the needle sticking on its seating or possibly a blocked inlet filter. To remedy this, take the top off the float chamber after releasing the petrol feed pipe, then carefully clean the needle and seating or the thimble filter sometimes installed.

The usual cause of sticking is the gummy deposit formed from evaporation of petrol when the car has been standing some time, but an obstruction can also be caused by dirt in the petrol blocking the inlet. The carburettor and petrol pump are also affected, and the only permanent cure is to clean out the entire petrol system from the tank to the inlet manifold at the earliest opportunity. Apart from blocking the feed, dirt may also cause the carburettor to flood by keeping the needle off its seating.

Having cleaned the needle and seating, fill the float chamber with clean petrol and watch for it flowing from the carburettor jet in the venturi. No flow indicates a blocked jet. An S.U. carburettor can often be cleared by cranking the engine and blocking the air intake momentarily with the palm of the hand. The jet on this carburettor is large enough to allow dirt to be sucked through by induction. Solex and Zenith types have a different feed arrangement, necessitating stripping and cleaning in most cases.

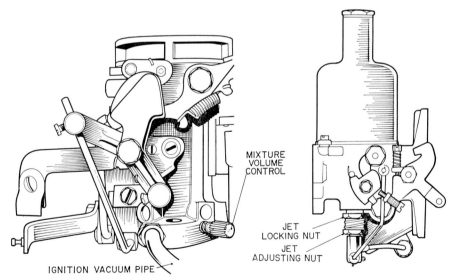

FIG. 3.11. (*Left*) Location of the slow-running mixture control on a Solex carburettor. A blocked jet can sometimes be cleared by removing this screw and blowing through the hole. (*Right*) The jet locking and adjusting nuts on an S.U. carburettor. Care must be taken to avoid moving the upper nut when making adjustments or the jet will have to be re-centred.

In an emergency, try removing the volume control screw (Fig. 3.11). First note its position by counting the number of turns required to fully tighten it (by hand), then remove the screw and blow air through the screw hole. If the screw setting is lost, about 1¼ turns out is an average adjustment.

When the petrol feed pipes are intact and there is petrol in the tank yet none is delivered at the carburettor, the petrol pump is most likely at fault.

Electrical Petrol Pump. Confirm the electrical supply by removing the "live" lead from the pump and striking it on a good earthing point. Then remove the pump cover and after making sure that the points now seen are closed, repeat the test against the terminal post. If no spark is obtained this time, the points need cleaning by pulling a piece of paper between the two contact surfaces while held lightly together (Fig. 3.12).

Next, crank the engine and watch the points make and break as petrol is drawn from the carburettor float chamber. Non-operation means either that the pump has an internal fault and must be changed or there is an obstruction between tank and pump, probably in the filter at the tank

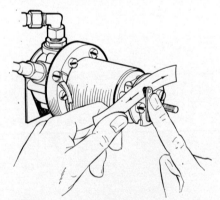

FIG. 3.12. The contact points under the moulded cover on an S.U. electrical petrol pump can be cleaned, if necessary, by pulling a strip of clean paper between them while the points are held in contact.

outlet. Try blowing through the suction pipe with air. When the points fail to close, check that the tips of the inner rocker are in contact with the magnet housing; an armature not returning to its normal position will prevent this. The pump must be changed in this case, or if cleaning the suction pipe fails to cure the trouble.

Generally speaking, electrical pumps seldom give trouble, but it is worth carrying a spare on an overseas journey.

Mechanical Petrol Pump. With a mechanical pump, first make sure that the sealing washer under the cover has not been damaged. A weak spring on the operating arm can reduce the output from the pump and cause petrol starvation; if the spring is broken, the delivery will cease. Starvation can also be caused by loose pipe unions or a distorted filter cover, or by the pump or petrol lines being too close to some hot part of the engine so that petrol vaporizes. A heat shield is the answer to the vaporizing problem. Damaged unions and gaskets can usually be spotted by petrol leaking.

A pump that has a slightly reduced output for some reason normally affects only high-speed running, and persistent trouble is best treated by removing it from the engine and overhauling it, using a repair kit that contains all the spares necessary. If the rocker assembly or pivots are worn, though, there will be no option but to change the pump.

All the defects in the petrol supply so far discussed apply to a breakdown on the road. In addition, a number of faults can occur that will make for both difficult starting and erratic running, but these are discussed in Chapter 4.

COMPRESSION FAULTS

Trouble on the compression side of the engine seldom arises as an emergency on the road. When it does, it will probably be a "blown" cylinder head gasket or a valve that has lost its collets and dropped into the cylinder with consequences that will be plain to see. As far as the home mechanic is concerned, looking for trouble in this section is mainly a matter of noting the fall-off in performance or the consumption of oil, then making some confirmatory tests before stripping the engine for a detailed examination of components. All this belongs to engine overhaul.

The garage man is in a different category since the equipment he can use in fault tracing can also be adapted to testing engine condition and performance, including its compression. The checks he can make, first with the conventional tools of the trade and then with modern diagnosis equipment are described here.

TESTING IN THE WORKSHOP

Looking for trouble so far has been confined to fault tracing when the car stops or will not start. The next stage is testing in the service station or (to some extent) the well equipped home garage.

Every mechanic uses some instruments to complement his own skill and experience in diagnosing engine faults, or to make the adjustments necessary for obtaining the engine performance specified by a manufacturer. These instruments are just as much working tools as a set of spanners, and usually comprise a voltmeter, ammeter, and ohmmeter to test electrical components, a tachometer to count engine revolutions, a compression gauge and its counterpart, the vacuum gauge, to measure the efficiency of the cylinder components, and perhaps a stroboscope to check engine timing. In addition to these, a dwell meter is sometimes used either separately or in conjunction with an oscilloscope to pinpoint ignition defects.

Electrical Efficiency. To test the efficiency of the battery and electrical circuits first make the checks on the battery described on page 80. Lights that dim or go out indicate either a "flat" battery or a faulty starter motor. A "flat" battery can be due to a defect either in the charging system or in the battery itself, and how to make the tests necessary to ascertain and correct such faults is described in Chapter 10. In very cold weather, unlikely but possible alternatives to electrical trouble are that either too thick a grade of engine oil is being used (check the sump) or the engine has seized (try to turn it manually). It should also be remembered that in very cold weather electrical efficiency generally is reduced, especially the capacity of the battery.

When the battery appears to be serviceable except for being under-charged, tests on the charging circuit (see Chapter 10) are made. Very often, an adjustment to the voltage control unit is all that is required to restore the system to perfect order. Battery condition during fault tracing is best checked by substitution with one known to be good.

The starter motor becomes suspect when the rest of the system—starter switch, solenoid switch, and leads—has been cleared, and it should then be removed from the car, serviced and bench-tested (see Chapter 10). The following simple tests can be made with instruments on the starter system.

Starter System. Three tests can be made on the starter control system installed in the car, using a voltmeter ranging to 20 volts and an ammeter reading up to 10 amps. If a click from the starter solenoid switch cannot be heard when the starter is operated, the contact bridge is inoperative. To find the trouble, connect a voltmeter between earth and the small terminal on the solenoid (Fig. 3.13). On most circuits, this has a white-red wire attached. No reading on the voltmeter when the starter is operated means that current is not reaching the solenoid, either because of a broken wire or a defective starter switch. Replace the wire and try again, then change the starter switch if no reading is obtained.

A reading of 12 volts on the meter confirms the supply, so the next test is on the solenoid windings, made with an ammeter connected between the white-red wire and the small terminal. Disconnect the white-red wire and insert the meter in the circuit to test the flow when the starter is operated. A reading of 4-6 amps will confirm a flow through the windings. The solenoid must be changed if there is no reading.

With the windings cleared, the last test is across the two main terminals, again with the voltmeter. A reading of 12 volts obtained on connecting up should fall to zero when the starter is operated if the solenoid contacts are serviceable. Renew the solenoid if it does not.

IGNITION TESTING WITH INSTRUMENTS

The instruments required to test the ignition system are a multi-range voltmeter and a high-resistance tester such as the well-known "Megger" instrument. An alternative is a universal electrical test instrument specially made for automobile work (Fig. 3.14). Tests will be misleading unless the battery is in good condition.

Low-tension Circuit. Connect the voltmeter between earth and the SW terminal (minus on Delco equipment) of the coil, then switch on the ignition and check for a reading of 11·5-12 volts on the meter (Fig. 3.15). No reading indicates a

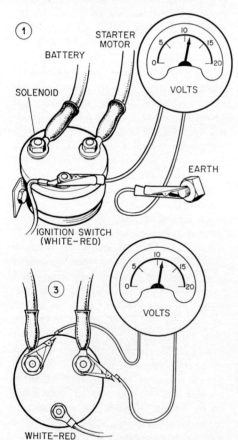

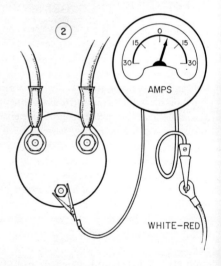

FIG. 3.13. Three tests that can be made with a voltmeter and an ammeter on a suspect starter solenoid switch. (1) The battery reading on the voltmeter when connected to the white/red terminal confirms the supply from the starter control. (2) The solenoid windings are checked with the ammeter connected between the white/red lead and its terminal on the solenoid. (3) The battery reading across the two large terminals will fall to zero when the starter is operated, if the solenoid contacts are serviceable.

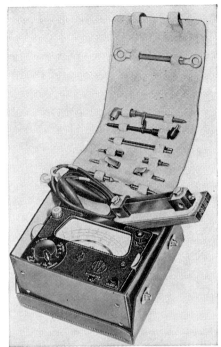

FIG. 3.14. The small "Megger" resistance-testing instrument shown left is widely used in the motor trade for testing insulation and continuity of circuits in a car's electrical harness (Evershed & Vignoles). The Avo Model 12 test set is designed for the comparatively small voltages in automobile electrical systems (Avo Ltd.).

break in the supply on either side of the ignition switch or in the switch itself. If the ignition warning light is also out, the trouble is in the feed to the switch, or in the switch. Look for a faulty connection. On cars such as Vauxhall that interpose a fuse between switch and warning lamp, check the No. 2 fuse.

Isolate the wires and check for continuity with the Megger or the ohms circuit of the tester, first on the brown-blue wire from the A1 terminal of the control box to the switch, then the white wire from the switch to the SW terminal on the coil. If these are cleared the break must be

between the battery and control box. Be careful when checking any wire or component for continuity or resistance that it is not already carrying current or the tester may be damaged.

Once the supply to the coil has been verified, disconnect the white-black wire

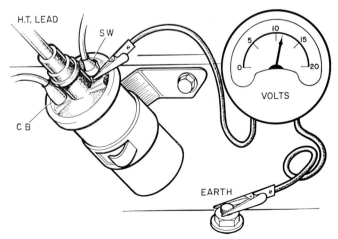

FIG. 3.15. Testing the ignition supply. The voltmeter should read the battery voltage when connected between the coil SW terminal and earth, with ignition on.

91

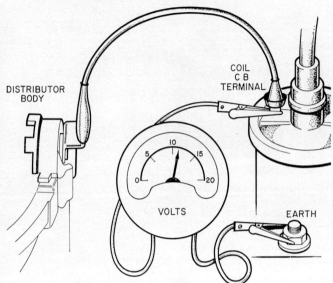

FIG. 3.16. Testing the ignition L.T. circuit. The voltmeter should read the battery voltage when connected between the coil CB terminal and earth, either with the contact breaker points open or the CB lead between coil and distributor disconnected.

from the CB terminal and check for a reading of 11·5-12 volts between the terminal and earth. If no reading is obtained, confirm a faulty coil by connecting an ohmmeter across the two terminals, and change the coil if anything substantially higher than the 1·5-2 ohms of a serviceable coil is recorded. Once the coil has been cleared or changed, reconnect the white-black wire to the distributor and coil and repeat the voltage test, CB terminal to earth, with the contact breaker points open to obtain the 12 volts reading (Fig. 3.16). A nil reading now indicates points or condenser trouble.

Condenser and Contact Breaker. The condenser can be shorting to earth through being wrongly connected or because of an internal fault or a bare lead; a low reading indicates a breakdown internally, and in both cases the condenser must be changed.

Now close the points and watch for the voltmeter to drop to zero. If it still gives a reading, there is trouble caused either by dirty or pitted contact breaker points, a broken white-black lead between the CB terminal on the coil and the distributor, or perhaps the contact breaker base plate. If there is an earthing lead on the distributor body, make sure this is intact. Make sure,

too, on distributors without this lead that the earth to the engine is satisfactory.

A direct test on the condenser in position for serviceability can be made with a Megger or similar tester. Before connecting the Megger, open the contact breaker points and disconnect the white-black lead from the coil CB terminal. Connect the Megger with one crocodile clip to the condenser terminal lead and the other to the distributor body (Fig. 3.17). A serviceable component will give a maximum leakage reading of 3 megohms.

The tester or the Megger can also be used to check the resistance of the contact breaker points. First switch it to the 0-1 volt scale, close the contact breaker points, then connect the Megger between the coil CB terminal and the distributor body. With the ignition switched on the reading should be zero. Anything more than 0·2 volts indicates the earthing defects in the contact breaker already mentioned.

Coil Secondary Circuit. A coil tester is normally used to test this component in a service station, but the rough-and-ready method of holding the lead near to the engine while the points are flicked open described earlier is a reliable guide to secondary (high-tension) circuit serviceability in the coil.

High-tension Leads. Serviceability of the high-tension leads is checked with an ohmmeter or the Megger, and the length of the lead must be taken into account in assessing the resistance when checking for continuity. The suppressor-type leads normally fitted in Britain have a resistance per foot run of from 4,000 to 8,000 ohms.

Dwell Meter. The dwell meter is in fact a combined voltmeter and ohmmeter that enables a mechanic to determine the condition of any part of the car's electrical circuit when the engine is stationary or running. It is often included as one of the interconnected instruments in the sophisticated electronic system used by many service stations for fault diagnosis. Coupled with a tachometer and an oscilloscope, for example, it can give a complete picture of ignition performance throughout the engine's operating range. Its name derives from its ability to measure the "dwell period" during which the operating arm of the contact breaker is out of contact with the distributor shaft and the points are closed, but it can be used to check any

part of the electrical system in much the same way as the Megger. The same instrument can usually double for an electric tachometer merely by switching from one scale to another.

A typical instrument will have a meter with several scales and a single needle. One scale is used for leakage tests, checking for continuity and resistance of circuits. Another is divided into degrees of a circle, from 0–60 on one side and 0–90 on the other. In use, the meter is first plugged in to a source of supply and its service leads connected to the component to be tested. As examples of the instrument's many uses, checking the resistance of the distributor and measuring the contact breaker points gap are outlined here.

With the engine stationary but the ignition switched on and the contact breaker points closed, the service leads are connected to the CB terminal of the coil and the body of the distributor. The resistance of the distributor can then be read off the meter's dial. Accept or reject limits on the meter decide whether the distributor low-tension circuit is serviceable. A rejection indicates earthing defects (as described already on page 92), and the instrument is then reconnected at various stages in the system to isolate the leak.

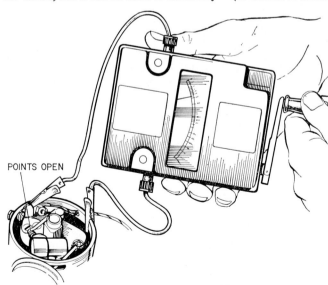

POINTS OPEN

FIG. 3.17. Testing the condenser for serviceability. The white/black lead is disconnected and the clips of the test instrument attached to the contact-breaker terminal post and the distributor body (earth). The contact points must be open when condenser leakage is measured.

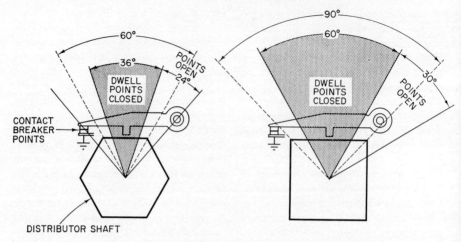

DISTRIBUTOR SHAFT

FIG. 3.18. Characteristic movement on the contact breaker arm for six-cylinder and four-cylinder engines. When the shaft is rotating, the points open as the contact breaker arm makes contact with the "corners" or cams of the shaft, and close during the "dwell" period when the arm is over the flats. A dwell meter connected to the distributor as the engine is cranked indicates whether the points are opening and closing through the permissible angular limits, and thus whether any adjustment is needed.

Measuring the contact breaker points gap with the dwell meter is done by cranking the engine and watching the action of the needle on the scale set for a particular engine. Taking a six-cylinder engine as an example, the distance between the apex of each cam on the hexagon of the distributor shaft is 60 deg. (Fig. 3.18). If the points are correctly set, the contact breaker arm will begin to make contact with each cam at a certain point, and will cease contact at an identical point on the opposite side of the cam. The arm will then be out of contact over the flats of the hexagon for a dwell period when the points are closed until it again makes contact.

On average, the dwell period for a six-cylinder engine is 36 deg. of rotation of the cam, the remaining 24 deg. being taken up with opening and closing. When the meter fails to indicate such a reading, the points are set too far apart if the dwell is below 36 deg., or too close if it is more. The degree of adjustment is easily ascertained in practice.

Oscilloscope. The oscilloscope is basically a cathode ray tube that is able to project as a "picture" on a screen the ignition system in operation, including the actual firing of the plug (Fig. 3.19). A skilled operator can thus quickly determine the condition of the coil, condenser, distributor cap and rotor, high-tension leads, contact points setting and condition, distributor mechanical condition and the overall ignition efficiency. So long as the engine is running and the instrument is connected, the information on the condition of these components is given continuously on the screen. An oscilloscope is therefore able to provide in a single test information that would require many separate tests with conventional instruments. Nevertheless, it complements rather than supersedes these since it gives an indication of *where* the trouble lies, and the meters already referred to are still required to find *what* the trouble is.

The firing of the sparking plug can be seen in detail on the oscilloscope screen (Fig. 3.20). The voltage required to fire the

FIG. 3.19. With its screen calibrated in kilovolts, an oscilloscope is able to measure the performance of the ignition circuit as the engine is running. A trace is flashed on the screen each time a plug fires. Both the L.T. and H.T. ignition circuits can be selected to isolate a source of ignition trouble.

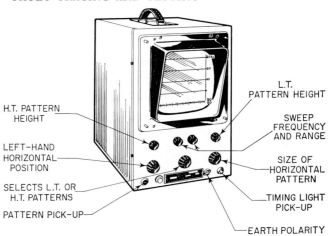

plug is measured in kilovolts which is then compared to a "norm". The condition of the plug itself can be seen as a shape on the screen. One advantage of the oscilloscope that cannot be matched by conventional instruments is its ability to measure the voltage requirements of the plug at the moment of maximum demand—when the accelerator pedal is suddenly depressed —and compare this to the potentiality of the ignition system, thereby indicating the reserve available. Other advantages it has are that performance at a specific engine speed can be tested if a flat spot exists, and it can be used to diagnose trouble on an engine that will not start.

Originally an oscilloscope was used merely to help to clear or indicate the ignition system as a source of trouble. The latest instruments are able by comparison with known "norms" of voltage demand from a plug to identify the behaviour of a sparking plug in a cylinder with poor compression or in which a weak or rich petrol/air mixture is fired. These "scopes" can differentiate between trouble caused by ignition, carburation or compression.

The influence of mixture strength on the voltage demand at the sparking plug enables an oscilloscope used in conjunction with an exhaust analyzer (see below) to balance carburettor adjustments on multiple-carburettor installations. Even such compression failures as valve float or

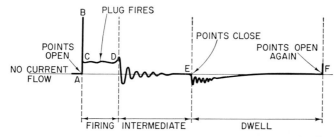

FIG. 3.20. Typical trace obtained on the oscilloscope when the sparking plug fires. The increase in voltage recorded at A-B as the plug fires drops immediately to the sustained firing voltage indicated by C-D, then tails off to point E when the contact breaker points close. The dwell section is the period when the points remain closed. Ignition system defects produce peculiarities in the trace that are easily interpreted by a trained operator.

95

bounce, impossible to pick up on the tests mentioned later in this section, can be identified by an experienced operator from the curious wave pattern created by such defects on the screen.

IGNITION TIMING

Setting the ignition timing is a job normally required only when the distributor has been taken off the engine for overhaul, and its initial setting following this is described on page 118. But checking the ignition timing in the workshop, perhaps as part of a tune-up, is a routine operation and it can be done in one of several ways.

Setting with a Vacuum Gauge. Before the gauge can be used, an adaptor must be fitted between the carburettor butterfly valve and the engine, away from the hot spot in the manifolds. The simplest way of doing this is to drill a hole in the carburettor flange that can be tapped to take the adaptor. This must be blanked off, of course, when the gauge is not in use. Although the gauge must not be fitted to the ignition vacuum control, it can be attached to the vacuum screen washing adaptor on cars such as Vauxhall.

Adjustment on the distributor is made by setting the throttle to give a fast tickover when the engine is running, loosening the clamp securing the distributor body, and then turning the body until the vacuum

gauge needle records its highest point without fluctuation (Fig. 3.21). Besides being simple, the adjustment obtained in this way is accurate because it takes into account every condition affecting combustion, including the octane value of the petrol.

Setting with a Timing Light. The timing light makes use of the stroboscope's ability to "stop" a mark on a rotating object by synchronizing an illuminating pulse of light with it. It does this by being linked to No. 1 sparking plug, on which ignition timing is normally set. When the engine is running, the timing light emits a flash of light each time the plug fires. The flash is directed through the timing aperture on the flywheel casing (or at the crankshaft pulley on vehicles timed in this way), so that it illuminates the timing mark on the engine flywheel each time it appears in the aperture, giving an illusion of "stopping" it (Fig. 3.22).

The result is that the timing mark can be seen stationary in relation to its pointer at any speed through the range of the engine, and checking and resetting ignition timing is merely a matter of adjusting the distributor body until perfect alignment of mark and pointer is obtained. The ignition must be in perfect condition to obtain a steady timing mark, and one of the subsidiary advantages of using the timing light

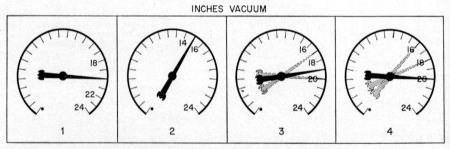

INCHES VACUUM

FIG. 3.21. Typical readings from the dial of a vacuum gauge. (1) While idling, an engine in good condition should record between 15 and 21 in. without flickering. (2) Consistently low readings indicate late timing or air leakage into the inlet manifold. (3) A carburettor out of tune is indicated by a "floating" needle. (4) Falling back of the needle over a period of ten seconds at medium throttle openings suggests valve defects such as a sticking valve.

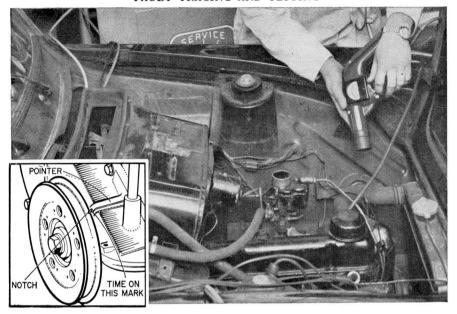

FIG. 3.22. Checking ignition timing with a stroboscope or timing light. The instrument is triggered to flash by the firing of No. 1 sparking plug, and at 900 r.p.m. illuminates the crankshaft timing mark so that its relation to the fixed timing pointer shows whether the timing is correctly set. A typical timing indicator on a Ford engine is shown inset.

is that defects in the contact breaker system are immediately apparent by a wavering mark. Defects in the advance and retard mechanism will also show up at varying engine speeds.

CARBURATION TESTING WITH INSTRUMENTS

Service-station tests on the carburation system will comprise a check on the petrol feed determined as a graduated measure delivered at a certain pressure; carburettor settings measured either with a vacuum gauge or with an exhaust-gas analyser; and the condition of the air cleaner.

Most petrol pumps operate at fairly low pressures (about 3 lb per sq in. is an average) and a high or low pressure will cause flooding or starvation respectively in the carburettor. The following two tests can be made on the pump with the same instrument, one for volume delivered and the other for pressure.

Testing the Petrol Pump. For really accurate testing, the gauge should be connected into the fuel line as close to the carburettor as possible so that the check can be made with the engine running. The gauge is therefore mounted on the carburettor inlet with the feed pipe connected to it, and the engine is set to run at idling speed (Fig. 3.23).

The instrument is a combined pressure gauge and fuel cock, with a rubber tube attached so that a quantity of petrol can be drawn off into a graduated jar while the pump is operating. As the engine idles, the cock is opened and the time taken for a pint of petrol to run into the jar is noted. Then the cock is closed and a reading taken off the pressure gauge. Both capacity and pressure are then compared with the figures quoted in the car manufacturer's manual. Air leaks in the system will show up as bubbles from the rubber tube while the capacity test is being made.

Carburettor Setting by Vacuum Gauge. The gauge is connected to the inlet manifold as described on page 96, but a prelude to testing and adjusting the carburettor is to ensure that the air cleaner is not obstructed. A blocked or partially choked air cleaner will restrict the flow of air into the cylinders and cause a rich mixture, producing the symptoms of an unbalanced petrol/air ratio. On a vacuum gauge, this will appear as a falling off of the needle reading when the engine speed is held at about 2,000 r.p.m. for ten seconds or so. The remedy is to clean or change the element. Once the air cleaner has proved to be serviceable, go on to check the carburettor setting.

Make sure on an S.U. carburettor that the hydraulic damper if fitted is correctly topped up, and slacken off the screw securing the choke wire. Then with the engine set to run at a slow tickover, either turn the air mixture control (Solex or Zenith), or adjust the jet position (S.U.) until the needle on the vacuum gauge records its highest figure without kicking, usually about 21 in (see Fig. 3.21). Multiple carburettors are adjusted on the gauge by first setting a uniform throttle opening for idling, reconnecting the throttle opening linkage, then making a preliminary adjustment on each carburettor in turn. After this, the gauge is connected by a multiple union to all carburettors simultaneously, and a final setting is made to obtain the highest reading.

Exhaust and Induction Systems. While the vacuum gauge test is being made, a note can be made of the condition of the exhaust system. A blocked silencer or pipe will cause a build-up of back pressure in the cylinders that will make it impossible for the gauge to hold a steady reading, and the needle will gradually fall back. An exhaust in good condition will give an immediate response to the gauge needle when the throttle is dabbed open and shut.

The vacuum gauge can also be used to test for induction air leaks, and if these are suspected, the test is best made before adjusting the carburettors or the work may be wasted. To make the test, slacken off the throttle stop screw so that the throttle is fully closed, then fully open the choke. Now turn the engine over on the starter while counting to fifteen and note the reading on the gauge. It should be a steady 15 to 17 deg. A low or unsteady reading indicates an air leak in the system. A sticky valve will also show up as a regular dropping back of the needle each time the engine completes a revolution (see Fig. 3.21).

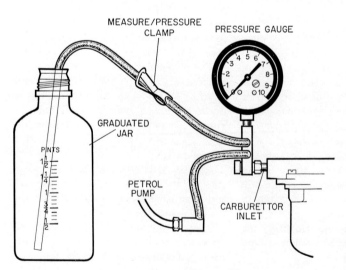

MEASURE/PRESSURE CLAMP

PRESSURE GAUGE

GRADUATED JAR

PINTS

PETROL PUMP

CARBURETTOR INLET

FIG. 3.23. Testing the output of a petrol pump. The time taken for a pint of petrol to run into the graduated jar and the pressure recorded are compared with the maker's specifications (Suntester).

Carburettor Setting by Exhaust Analyser. The exhaust or combustion analyser, as this instrument is variously known, makes use of the different levels of thermo-conductivity possessed by an exhaust gas depending upon mixture strength at the time of combustion. In use, a sample of the exhaust is passed over a balanced electrical circuit that responds to the presence of either hydrogen or carbon dioxide in the exhaust.

Although the instrument has been available for some time, its acceptance by the trade has not been as widespread as one might imagine, mainly because earlier models tended to produce a slow reaction to changes in carburettor setting and the operator found the process took too long. Present-day instruments have a motor-driven impeller to ensure that the reaction is almost immediate.

The exhaust analyser is largely used today as a very accurate method of making a final setting to the carburettor following overhaul, and many manufacturers carry out their carburation pre-delivery check with it. In practice, the instrument is connected to the exhaust and the carburettor is adjusted to give the optimum reading between limits throughout the engine speed range. At an idling speed of 500 r.p.m. the air/petrol ratio is set at approximately $10\frac{1}{2}$: 1 for normal motoring.

To enable vehicles under test to comply with legislation controlling smoke emission, exhaust analysers incorporate a scale that shows up the carbon monoxide content of the gas as a percentage, indicating when the crankcase ventilation valve needs servicing.

COMPRESSION TESTING

Several types of gauge can be used to determine the condition of those factors affecting engine compression. The vacuum gauge already mentioned can give a rough-and-ready indication of such things as cylinder balance (that is the degree of compression in each of the cylinders compared to the others), but for really accurate diagnosis, a compression gauge in the right hands is invaluable.

With a Compression Gauge. The check is made to ensure that there are no leaks from the cylinders part worn or broken parts, such as valves, piston rings and gaskets, that would prevent the engine developing full power. To do this, the compression gauge is substituted for a sparking plug in each cylinder in turn so that a reading in lb per sq in. can be taken on the compression stroke of the piston when the engine is turned over with the ignition off. The reading is then compared with that specified by the manufacturer of the vehicle.

Although many Continental and practically all United States car makers quote a compression figure, few of their British counterparts do. The reason is to be found in the qualifying statement made earlier, that a gauge *in the right hands* can be invaluable. A good deal of experience is needed to obtain an accurate reading and then to analyse its significance. For though such things as wear will lower the engine compression, other equally undesirable factors such as an accumulation of carbon or oil in the cylinder will raise it.

The figure for a particular engine is easily arrived at since it is based on the compression ratio and this is always quoted. The formula is: (Compression ratio × Atmospheric pressure) + Atmospheric pressure, and it is best demonstrated by a simple example. Pressure of air, although 14·7 lb per sq in. at sea level, rapidly diminishes with height, so an average of 14 lb per sq in. is taken. If the compression ratio is $8\frac{1}{2}$: 1, the compression reading taken from a cylinder in perfect condition should be ($8\frac{1}{2}$ × 14) + 14 = 133 lb per sq in.

To use the gauge, thoroughly warm the engine and remove all sparking plugs. Then either screw or press the meter on to its seal in the sparking plug hole and note the reading when the starter is operated with the throttle held wide open. The figure must be taken before the fourth or fifth engine revolution, or it will be misleading. For best results, position the piston in the cylinder to be tested half-way down its power stroke so that almost a full cycle is obtained. First take a reading from each cylinder in turn and compare results. One cylinder well below the average most likely indicates a broken compression ring or a burnt valve. Try injecting oil into the cylinder and repeating the test. If this brings the reading up considerably, the ring is at fault; if it does not, the valve can be suspected.

Sometimes a piece of carbon shaken loose when the plug was removed will lodge under a valve seat and give a misleading reading. Make sure this is not the case by removing the rocker cover and turning the engine so that both valves are free, then lever each valve open in turn and allow it to snap shut several times. An inlet valve affected in this way will also cause spitting back in the carburettor so it can readily be identified, but an exhaust valve can pass unnoticed, although compression in that particular cylinder will be well down.

Readings of 10 per cent more than can be expected for a particular engine indicate the need for decarbonization. Low readings on all cylinders where the engine is burning oil confirm that a remedy is necessary.

A defective cylinder head gasket between adjacent cylinders will give a low reading on the two cylinders affected. A low reading on a single cylinder, when not caused by valve trouble, may be due to a leaking cylinder head gasket or a crack in the cylinder block or head.

With a Leakage Tester. Another method of testing for leakage is to use a compressed air line connected through a specially designed meter. Engine prepara-

tion is exactly the same as for testing with a compression gauge, and is made with the air cleaner and crankcase filler cap (where fitted) removed and the throttle held wide open. The radiator is also topped up.

In use, the piston in the cylinder under test is placed at the point where the spark occurs, and the adaptor from the meter is connected to feed air into the cylinder while the pressure is read off the gauge. A check is then made for leaks by listening at the exhaust pipe, carburettor air intake, and crankcase filler. The radiator is also checked for air bubbles. Readings are taken on each cylinder in turn.

Such positive treatment gives more accurate results than a compression gauge and differentiates between the cause of loss in most cases. Air heard escaping from the exhaust pipe, for example, obviously indicates a defective exhaust valve. The major exception is air in the cooling water, which could be due to either a leaking cylinder head gasket or to a crack in the block or head allowing air to escape into the water jacket.

OTHER TEST INSTRUMENTS

Testing with a Tachometer. The tachometer is an instrument for measuring the speed of crankshaft rotation and many jobs in the service station workshop these days cannot be done accurately without it. The exhaust-gas analyser already mentioned is normally combined with or is coupled to a tachometer so that carburettor settings to achieve maximum performance can be made at varying speeds, and the precise points at which the automatic advance and retard operates on the distributor can only be checked with its use. But these are merely two examples, for testing the condition of an engine is usually made under five main headings—cranking speed, idling, 1,000 r.p.m., 2,500 r.p.m., and acceleration from that point.

The instrument mainly in use today is one that measures the ignition pulse and

FIG. 3.24. A twin-O.H.C. engine coupled to an electronic diagnosis tester by only three leads. Console testers of this type enable service stations to provide a serviceability check on all components that affect performance. Dozens of checks can be made by a skilled operator in a fraction of the time required to test the car on the road. The interconnected gauges show up defects as easily identified irregularities from known "norms."

records this as revolutions a minute (r.p.m.). After the instrument has been plugged in to a power supply, its pick-up is connected to No. 1 sparking plug and the selector then turned for a four-stroke cycle, if this type of engine is being tested.

Console Testers. So far, the instruments that a mechanic might regard as the tools of his trade have been discussed as individual instruments and only the barest mention has been made of using these interconnected in such a way that each confirms or rejects the possibilities suggested by the others. Such a system is now widely used in the console testers installed in those service stations that specialize in offering a fault diagnosis scheme.

As an example, a large console tester such as the Sun (Fig. 3.24) has an oscilloscope and all the metering equipment mentioned in this chapter. With only three connections being made to the

engine, the oscilloscope, tachometer, dwell meter, timing light, and exhaust-gas analyser all work simultaneously. Tachometer, timing light, and exhaust analyser are thus ready for adjustments to be made to ignition and carburation, while the "scope" is able to verify whether all other systems and components are operating satisfactorily. These testers are also being incorporated with a dynamometer of the "moving road" type to simulate road tests on the vehicle while connected to recording instruments in the garage.

In use, when the "scope" indicates the presence of trouble, the ohmmeter, voltmeter, cylinder leakage tester, and fuel pump tester, all previously described, are available in the console to pinpoint trouble. Such equipment reduces to the minimum the time taken to sort good from bad, which is after all the basis of all fault tracing and testing.

101

CHAPTER 4

ENGINE MAINTENANCE

MODERN engines are the result of constant development by designers, production engineers and fuel and lubrication technologists, working as a team to improve efficiency, reduce costs and to increase the life of component parts between overhauls. At the same time, the service and repair sides of the motor industry are developing the tools and equipment needed to keep today's ever-more complex power units and accessories in first-class condition.

The practical owner, therefore, scores all along the line. As explained in Chapter 13, today's fuels and lubricants and improved component design have enabled car manufacturers to specify considerably longer periods between routine servicing and major overhauls than used to be the case, and where figures are quoted in this chapter they are based on modern practice. It is always advisable, however, to follow the recommendations in the car instruction book.

When jobs are beyond the capabilities of an owner working in the home garage, it is possible to take advantage of the service-exchange schemes which now apply to almost all components, from a complete engine to a carburettor, fuel pump or ignition distributor, allowing the worn unit to be exchanged for a factory-reconditioned part or assembly.

The electronic testing and tuning equipment described in Chapter 3 also simplifies maintenance. The efficiency of the individual components of the electrical and ignition systems and of the engine as a whole can be quickly checked by a service station with such equipment, and faults which might otherwise have gone undetected are shown up with uncanny accuracy. The modest cost of a comprehensive check-up in this way—once a year or every 12,000 miles—is an excellent investment, even if it only confirms that conscientious servicing by the owner has maintained the engine in first-class tune.

It is logical to begin by considering the routine jobs that are needed to keep an engine running efficiently. The work is simple, calls for few tools, and should be within the scope even of the novice. Apart from the power unit, we shall deal here with attentions to the ignition components, cooling system and fuel system. Normally, of course, these will form part of a regular servicing schedule for the whole car (a typical complete maintenance chart is given in Chapter 12).

POWER UNIT: ROUTINE SERVICE

Engine Oil. The oil level in the sump should be checked at intervals of not more than 250 miles, and more frequently if the engine is worn and using much oil. Oil consumption will be higher than usual, too, in very hot weather or when high speeds are maintained—as on a motorway —since the oil will become thinner and will be more easily pumped past the piston rings and down the valve guides into the combustion chambers, where it will be burnt.

If the needle of the oil pressure gauge flickers or falls back when the car is driven fast round a corner, or the oil pressure warning light flashes momentarily under similar conditions, treat these as urgent danger signals. The implication is that the level of the oil in the sump is so low that when the oil surges to one side, the intake pipe or filter is temporarily starved.

When checking the oil level, remove the dipstick and wipe it clean before taking a reading so that oil splashed on it will not give a false impression. If the engine has been running or oil has just been poured into the filler, wait several minutes with the engine switched off before taking the reading so that all oil can drain into the sump.

Changing the Oil. The oil filter, however efficient it may be, cannot prevent the oil in the sump being diluted by condensed fuel which passes the piston rings when the engine is cold, nor can it remove the water which is a by-product of combustion (burning a gallon of petrol produces over a gallon of water). Most of this water passes out of the engine as steam, but some finds its way past the rings and some condenses inside the crankcase and valve chamber as the engine cools down. The mixture of oil and water forms sludge, and acids are formed by the burnt gases which are dissolved in the water. (This is further explained in Chapter 13.)

It will be evident, then, that although oil does not wear out, its effectiveness as a lubricant is progressively reduced. It is usually recommended that the sump be drained and refilled at intervals of about 3,000 miles, or more frequently if most of the running is in the form of short trips in cold weather. When multigrade oils are used, the mileage can often be doubled, however, as these lubricants are detergent and are able to hold impurities in solution for longer periods without the risk of excessive sludge formation. But when the engine and gearbox or automatic transmission share the same oil, changes at 3,000 miles or earlier are usually specified, even with multigrades.

The sump should be drained when the engine is really hot, preferably after a fairly long run, so that any impurities are thoroughly mixed with the oil instead of lying in pockets in the crankcase or on the bottom of the sump. Leave the drain plug out long enough for the last drips to cease. If the plug has a magnetic filter, clean this thoroughly.

Oil Filters. The lubrication system of the modern car is well protected against the entry of grit and sludge. In nearly every case, there is a suction filter which surrounds the intake to the oil pump. In some cases this filter can be removed by unscrewing a plug on the side or base of the sump, or by taking off a screwed-on plate (Fig. 4.1). It should preferably be cleaned at intervals of about 15,000 miles by swilling in petrol or paraffin, scrubbing it with a brush and allowing it to dry before replacing it; never wipe it with a fluffy rag.

Internal filters can be cleaned only after the sump has been removed. As this is not always a simple matter, the job is best left to a service station. These filters are usually of fairly generous area, however,

FIG. 4.1. Servicing this engine oil strainer entails washing it out in petrol and then installing with new paper gaskets, as a safeguard against leakage (Volkswagen).

FIG. 4.2. Fitting a replacement paper element in a full-flow oil filter (Tecalemit). A good seal must be made at the casing joint because oil enters the filter at full pump pressure.

and need be cleaned only at infrequent intervals. On the assumption that a detergent oil will be used, in fact, many manufacturers do not specify regular servicing of the primary filter.

The majority of engines also have an externally fitted filter (Fig. 4.2) through which oil is passed under pressure from the oil pump. This filter may be of either the full-flow type, where the whole output of the pump passes through the element, or the by-pass type in which only about ten per cent of the oil is diverted through the element.

Above the element in a full-flow filter is a spring-loaded safety valve which lifts when the restriction to the oil flow caused by a blocked element becomes excessive. Oil then passes directly from the inlet to the outlet side of the filter casing without being filtered, so the advisability of regular maintenance is evident. On some engines, a switch is operated by the excess pressure caused by a clogged filter, and a warning lamp on the instrument panel is illuminated. The filter element should then be changed within 300 miles.

The element of a full-flow filter is sometimes the washable felt type that is removed and cleaned in petrol every 3,000 miles, then renewed after 6,000 miles; but more usually it is an impregnated paper type that is discarded and replaced every 6,000 miles. The by-pass type of filter cannot be cleaned. Instead, either the complete assembly or the internal element must be replaced by a new one at specified intervals, usually 6,000 miles.

The filter is often rather inaccessible and it may be necessary to unscrew it from beneath the car. If a replacement sealing ring is provided with the new filter, it may not be easy to fit this to the recess in the cylinder block or housing, and it is advisable not to disturb the old ring if it was not leaking. After fitting the new filter and screwing the casing firmly in place, run the engine and check for oil leakage past the joint. If slackening and repositioning the filter casing does not cure leakage, the new ring must be fitted.

Screw-in type replaceable filters are often very tight and it may be necessary to use a hammer and punch to start to unscrew them. As the old filter will be discarded, of course, any damage done to it does not matter.

Crankcase Ventilation Valve. On modern engines, some form of ventilation system for the crankcase and valve gear is provided to prevent excessive condensation and the sludge formation already mentioned. In the simplest arrangement fumes are expelled through a vent pipe and fresh air is drawn in through the oil filler cap, which usually has a small air filter that requires cleaning every 6,000 miles.

In more elaborate ventilation systems, the fumes are drawn into the inlet manifold on the engine side of the carburettor, thus providing positive extraction even when the engine is idling with the throttle almost closed. Fresh air is fed into the rocker cover, valve chamber and crankcase, either through an air filter in the oil filler cap or through the carburettor air filter.

With this arrangement there is an emission-control valve—usually termed an "anti-smog" valve—in the pipe leading to the inlet manifold, which will restrict the amount of air drawn in under idling conditions and prevent excessive weakening of the fuel mixture. The valve is of the spring-loaded plunger or diaphragm type and should normally be serviced at 12,000-mile intervals (Fig. 4.3). Dismantling is quite straightforward, but a note should be made of the order in which the parts are assembled. The components should be thoroughly washed in petrol and any that are obviously worn or corroded should be renewed.

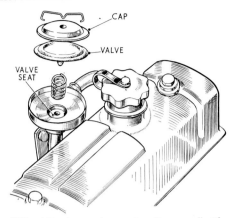

FIG. 4.3. A crankcase breather or "anti-smog" valve, shown dismantled for cleaning. Fitted between the rocker cover and the inlet manifold, it permits the burning of blow-by gases from the crankcase, thereby reducing oil sludging and air pollution.

COOLING SYSTEM: ROUTINE SERVICE

Modern cooling systems are of two types. In the simplest and most common, the radiator filler cap incorporates a spring-loaded valve which opens when pressure in the system exceeds the designed maximum figure, which may be about 4, 7, or 13 lb per sq in. Water and steam can then escape through the overflow pipe. A second, smaller valve in the cap operates in the reverse direction and allows air to enter the system as it cools down, so preventing the formation of a partial vacuum.

The more elaborate system is the fully-sealed type (Fig. 4.4), in which the overflow pipe is taken into the base of an expansion tank or reservoir which contains a small quantity of water, or a mixture of water and anti-freeze solution. A cap containing spring-loaded valves of the type just described is fitted to this tank. The radiator header tank has a plain cap, sealed by an air-tight washer. Thus, as the system warms up, steam and excess water can escape through the overflow pipe into the expansion tank, where the steam is condensed and the water retained. When the engine cools down, the partial vacuum which forms in the radiator header tank sucks sufficient water back from the expansion tank to restore the correct level in the radiator.

It will be evident that the two types of system require slightly different treatment in service. With the simpler arrangement, the water level should be just below the base of the filler opening when the engine is hot. There is no point in topping-up until the water reaches the filler neck; in fact, if this is done when the system is cold, the expansion which occurs as the engine warms up will result in coolant being lost through the overflow pipe.

When a sealed system is fitted, there should be no need to top-up the radiator header tank regularly. Leaks can develop, however, and it is as well to check the level at 3,000-mile intervals.

When the engine is cool, the water level should be almost up to the top of the filler neck. If necessary, top-up the level, replace the cap, run the engine until it is hot, allow it to cool down, then re-check the level. If the system has been drained, repeat the sequence three times to ensure that the system is full. There should

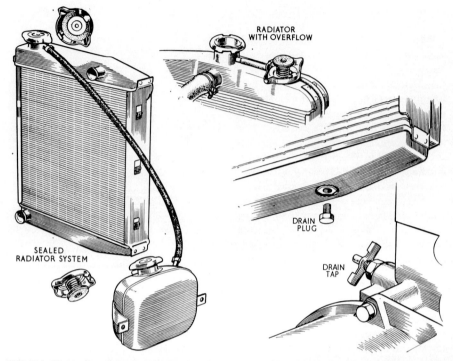

FIG. 4.4 The radiator can be of the open-overflow type, when the filler has a spring-loaded pressure cap, or the sealed type. In the latter case, a special solid cap is fitted on the header tank and a spring-loaded cap on the overflow tank. There is usually a drain tap on the cylinder block, and either a tap or a plug in the radiator base.

usually be about two or three inches of water in the expansion tank.

There are two points to bear in mind. First, do not interchange the filler caps on the radiator and expansion tank of the sealed system. The expansion tank cap has the spring-loaded valves in it. If this cap is substituted for the plain cap on the radiator tank, the system will behave like a normal pressurized system. Water will escape through the overflow pipe to the expansion tank, but it will not be drawn back into the header tank as the system cools.

Secondly, owing to the pressure which is maintained in both systems, the boiling point of the coolant is raised, but when the pressure is relieved by removing the cap, sudden and violent boiling may occur,

ejecting scalding water from the filler. The cap should, therefore, be removed only when the system is cool or with the cap wrapped in a cloth to protect the hands. Turn the cap part way until the pressure has been relieved, and then fully to disengage the bayonet catches.

IGNITION SYSTEM: ROUTINE SERVICE

Since experience has shown that a large proportion of roadside breakdowns are caused by ignition system faults, regular inspection and maintenance of the ignition components will pay dividends. In addition, it is advisable to have the various components and the system as a whole tested at intervals of 12,000 miles by a service station which has modern electronic test-tune equipment of the type described in Chapter 3.

Distributor Lubrication. The automatic advance mechanism, contact breaker cam, contact breaker plate assembly and contact breaker lever pivot require lubrication at 6,000-mile intervals (Fig. 4.5).

A trace of grease should be smeared on the faces of the contact breaker cam. Pull the rotor off the top of the spindle, or carefully prise it off with a screwdriver if it is tight, and put a few drops of engine oil on the exposed screw to lubricate the cam bearing. Do not remove the screw—there is a clearance through which the oil passes to the bearing. Replace the rotor correctly and push it on to the spindle as far as it will go; otherwise there is a risk of the moulded cap becoming burnt or cracked.

The automatic timing control should be lubricated by injecting a few drops of engine oil through the aperture in the contact breaker base plate, and a trace of engine oil should be placed on the pivot of the contact breaker lever. Above all, avoid excessive lubrication of the distributor. If too much oil is used, it is apt to get on the contact-breaker points and cause misfiring and difficult starting.

After this, the ignition components should be inspected and serviced. Wipe the inside and outside of the moulded distributor cap with a petrol-moistened cloth, paying particular attention to the spaces between the terminals. Dark lines between the terminals indicate that "tracking" has been taking place—the current has been jumping between the terminals instead of to the rotor—and renewal of the cap is necessary. Make sure that the small carbon brush in the top of the distributor cap works freely in its holder. Alternatively, if the contact is made by a spring arm on the rotor, check that this is not cracked or flattened.

Next, examine the contact breaker (Fig. 4.6). The contact points must be free from grease or oil. If they are burnt or blackened, smooth them with a fine Carborundum stone or a contact-breaker file, afterwards wiping them clean with a petrol-moistened cloth. Do not use glasspaper or emery cloth on the points as particles may become embedded and cause arcing.

Cleaning of the contacts is made easier

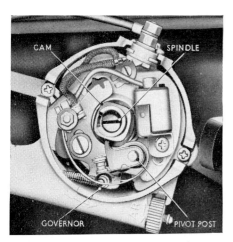
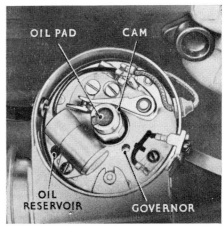

FIG. 4.5. Location of lubrication points on two modern distributors: (*left*) Lucas, (*right*) AC-Delco. Distributors of all types must be given very sparing but regular lubrication, as detailed in the text.

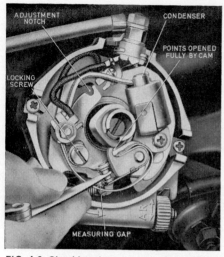
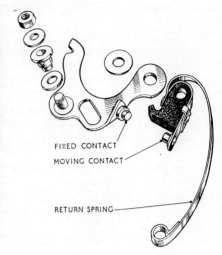

FIG. 4.6. Checking the contact breaker on a Lucas distributor. A feeler gauge is used to measure the gap with the points opened to their widest. Worn or damaged points are easily replaceable by a new set (*right*).

if the contact breaker lever and the fixed contact plate are removed. The method of detaching the arm, which is retained by the spring, or the Ford single-unit contact assembly, will be evident on examination. When removing an arm and plate, make a careful note of the position of insulating washers and bushes.

As removing the points entails a fair amount of work (it may be necessary to remo/e the distributor from the engine and to reset the ignition timing on re-assembly as described on page 118), there is a lot to be said for fitting a new set of points. They are not expensive and can revitalize the engine. In any case, they should be renewed when a new set of sparking plugs is fitted, at about 12,000-mile intervals.

Adjusting the Contact Breaker Gap. After cleaning or renewing the points, check the contact breaker gap. It is useless to do this before the points have been serviced, since a small "pip" forms on one contact and a "crater" in the other, as the result of normal slight sparking. If the blade of a feeler gauge is passed between

points in this condition, the height of the pip will render measurement inaccurate by several thousandths of an inch.

To set the gap in most types of distributors, turn the engine until the contact breaker lever is on the highest point of one of the lobes of the cam and slacken the screw or screws which secure the plate that carries the fixed contact. Move the plate until the gap is set to the thickness of the gauge and tighten the locking screw or screws. It is advisable to recheck the gap to ensure that no movement has taken place while tightening the screws.

In some distributors, an eccentric screw is fitted in the fixed contact plate and by turning this the contact breaker gap can be opened or closed. The fixed contact plate of another type of distributor is slotted at the edge and secured with a single screw. To set the gap, slacken the screw and move the fixed contact plate by inserting a screw-driver in the slot provided and twisting it clockwise or anti-clockwise as required.

A special combined screwdriver and contact breaker feeler gauge is often provided in the car tool kit. If this has been

108

mislaid, use a normal feeler gauge and set the gap to the figure given in the car instruction book.

Renewing High-tension Cables. Any oil or dust should be wiped off the ignition cables (and off the moulded top of the ignition coil), and the cables should be replaced when they show signs of perishing or cracking.

On the majority of recent cars, each sparking plug lead contains a built-in resistance which is intended to suppress interference from the ignition system with radio and television receivers. These leads should not be cut, and no attempt should be made to remove the terminals; otherwise, the effectiveness of the resistance will be destroyed. The leads are marked "suppressor cable" or are coloured red.

Sparking Plugs. The sparking plugs can make or mar the performance of the engine. There are three essential factors: the plugs must be of the correct type; they must be clean; and the electrodes or points must be set to the correct gap.

If a car is used mainly for short journeys or the engine is worn and using a lot of oil, so that the plugs tend to soot-up or oil-up quickly, a "softer" or "hotter" grade of plug than that normally specified may prove more satisfactory, as such plugs operate at a higher temperature and burn off the fouling. Conversely, if the car is usually driven hard and the plugs have a short life, a "harder" or "colder" type will give better service. Plug manufacturers' lists give comparative charts from which a selection can be made.

Generally speaking, however, the standard grade specified by the car manufacturer will give the best results. Oiling-up or sooting-up should be tackled at the source, either by an engine overhaul or by ensuring that the carburettor mixture and ignition timing are correct, as the case may be. Plugs of the correct type, cleaned and reset to the correct gap at intervals of 3,000-6,000 miles (depending on the engine

and running conditions), should have a useful life of about 12,000 miles. At this stage it will pay to fit a new set. Keeping old plugs in service is false economy.

Servicing the plugs is quite straightforward. The only efficient method of cleaning the internal insulators is to use the abrasive-jet type of plug cleaner which is a familiar feature in virtually every service station. Makeshift methods such as swilling the plugs in petrol are ineffective.

When the plugs are clean, the gaps must be set (Fig. 4.7). For most cars a gap of 0.025 in. between the central and the side electrode is about right. Some modern engines (usually sports cars) need a gap of 0.032 in. when a special high-voltage ignition coil is fitted. If the car instruction book is not available, the correct gap can be found in the plug manufacturer's chart, or the local agents for the car will be able to advise. Do not be tempted to experiment with wider or closer gaps than those specified.

The gap must always be adjusted by bending the outer electrode. Never bend

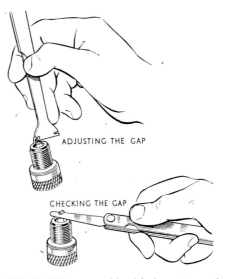

ADJUSTING THE GAP

CHECKING THE GAP

FIG. 4.7. Using a combined feeler gauge and gap-setting tool to check and adjust sparking plug points.

the central one as this will result in the insulator being cracked or fractured. The gap should be measured by a feeler gauge. A combined gap-gauge and setting tool is available quite cheaply from most garages or accessory shops. Before refitting the plugs, clean the threaded portions and smear them with graphite grease. Make sure that the sealing washers are in place before screwing the plugs home. If the washer is badly flattened, fit a new one.

It should be possible to screw the plugs in by hand, only using the tommy-bar of the plug spanner for the final half-turn to tighten down firmly. Excessive tightening will distort the plugs, whereas if they are loose, they will overheat and probably cause pre-ignition and pinking. If the plugs are too tight to screw in easily, have the threads in the cylinder head cleaned up by a garage, using a plug-thread tap.

OTHER ROUTINE ATTENTIONS

Valve clearances may require adjustment as described on page 115 if the engine sounds "tappety", although if properly adjusted, the clearances should not need attention until about 6,000 miles have been covered. On a few models, no provision is made for adjustment once the engine has been assembled.

The petrol pump and carburettor filters will benefit from examination and cleaning every 6,000 miles, as described on page 120, and the air filter may require cleaning or renewal.

Carburettor Air Filter. There are four basic types of air filter (Fig. 4.8). The simplest is the oil-wetted wire-mesh type, incorporated in one end of the combined air cleaner and silencer. This is cleaned by swilling the mesh in paraffin, allowing it to dry and lightly re-oiling it with engine oil to trap the dust, before fitting it to the engine (Fig. 4.9).

A polyurethane-foam filter can be cleaned by removing it from the housing, swilling it in a detergent solution, gently

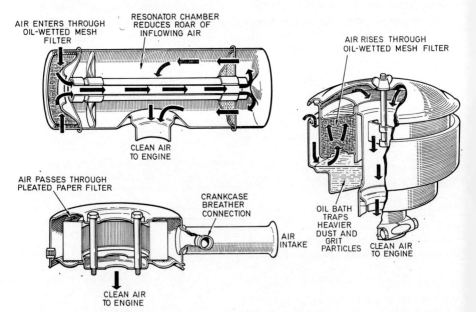

FIG. 4.8. Three forms of carburettor air cleaner: wire mesh or gauze type (*upper left*), pleated-paper type (*lower left*), and oil-bath type. The cleaner filters the inflowing air to remove dust and grit, and also dampens "power roar" caused by the rush of air.

110

FIG. 4.9. (*Right*) A pleated-paper air cleaner element and a dry-gauze element, fitted in the same casing on the same series of cars, but requiring different servicing. (*Below*) When an oil-bath cleaner is serviced, the element is washed in paraffin and the reservoir thoroughly wiped out. Fresh oil is then poured in up to the level mark. Oil-wetted mesh cleaners are usually cleaned by swilling in paraffin, and re-oiled after being drained off. Paper elements are simple to replace, but if joint rings are fitted these must be in good condition.

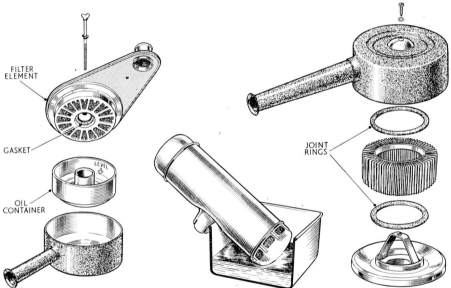

FILTER ELEMENT

GASKET

LEVEL

OIL CONTAINER

JOINT RINGS

squeezing it dry and allowing it to dry out completely before re-oiling it with engine oil and replacing it in the cleaner.

Oil-bath air cleaners have a wire-mesh filter element mounted above a shallow bath of oil in which the heavier particles of dust are trapped before they reach the element. This type of filter can be dismantled by undoing the central nut and lifting out the element. Pour away the oil, clean any sediment out of the bowl and refill it with clean engine oil up to the level mark. Clean the filter mesh in paraffin and fit it dry—do not re-oil it.

Paper-element cleaners have filter elements made of pleated paper. The life of a paper element is about 12,000 miles in normal service, but it should be cleaned after 6,000 miles by lightly tapping it to dislodge the dust.

The carburettor fuel filter in the carburettor inlet or in the fuel pump (or in both) should not need cleaning at this stage, but the hydraulic damper in an S.U. or

Zenith-Stromberg CD carburettor may need topping-up with engine oil as described on page 126.

Fan Belt. The fan and generator driving belt will require occasional adjustment as slackness develops, usually by loosening the pivot bolts and the bolts on the strut and swinging the generator away from the engine (Fig. 4.10). Do not overtighten the belt or there will be a risk of overloading the generator and water pump bearings. It should be possible to depress the belt by about $\frac{1}{2}$ in. at the centre of its longest run.

Water Pump. The water pump located on the front end of the engine should not need any attention unless a lubrication nipple or a removable plug is fitted to its shaft bearing housing. In such cases a small amount of water-pump grease should be injected. Avoid over-lubrication: if excess grease reaches the pump seal it may cause leakage, and if it mixes with the cooling water it will form a soapy scum that may clog the radiator passages.

FIG. 4.10. The generator bracket bolts provide a means of adjusting the tension of the fan belt. Maximum belt movement should be about $\frac{1}{2}$ in. with the type illustrated, or up to 1 in. where there is a longer run between pulleys.

SEASONAL SERVICING

In addition to the routine jobs that must be done at regular mileage intervals, a general check-over should be carried out in the spring in anticipation of warm-weather motoring, and again in the autumn to forestall cold-weather starting and running troubles.

Hot-weather Motoring. During the spring engine check-over, particular attention should be paid to those points which are likely to cause trouble during warm weather: mainly to be expected are overheating and fuel-vaporization troubles.

The engine cooling system is obviously the most important consideration. The radiator and water passages should be de-scaled and flushed out as described on page 131. It is best to refill the system with anti-freeze solution as this will protect it against corrosion, and the anti-freeze will slightly raise the boiling point of the water. Make sure that the filler cap on the radiator header tank or on the expansion tank is maintaining the correct pressure in the system. A leaking cap will allow coolant to escape if the system is not of the sealed type, and it can also cause overheating. Most well-equipped service stations can test the cap with a combined pump and gauge. If in any doubt, renew the cap; it is not expensive. Check the thermostat (see page 132) and renew it if there is any doubt about its condition or if it is two years old, and then go over the radiator and heater hoses and renew any that have softened or perished. Again, renewal after two years is a sound rule.

Next, carry out the normal servicing of the ignition, carburettor and fuel supply systems. A slightly weak mixture or retarded ignition timing can cause overheating in hot weather, while pre-ignition —caused by unsuitable sparking plugs or detonation due to over-advanced ignition timing—will also cause overheating. If severe detonation occurs at high speed and with a wide throttle opening, it may damage the pistons.

Fuel-starvation can be caused in hot-weather by vapour locks forming in the petrol pipe. This is a fairly common trouble on some models and can be cured only by re-routing the pipe so that it is well clear of the exhaust manifold, exhaust pipe and silencer; or, if this is not possible, by wrapping the vulnerable sections of the pipe with asbestos string. If fuel vaporizes in the float chamber of the carburettor when the engine is idling or is switched-off after a fast run or after a hard climb in low gear, an asbestos-faced heat shield, fitted between the carburettor and the exhaust manifold, may cure the trouble.

Winter Precautions. The first essential when preparing for cold weather is to drain the sump and to refill it with the grade of oil recommended by the car manufacturer for winter conditions. This may be the same as that recommended for summer running, especially if a multigrade oil is used; otherwise a thinner grade may be specified. In extremely cold conditions it may be necessary to use a very thin oil, such as S.A.E. 5W.

The modern car fares quite well in an unheated garage and will not come to much harm even if it must stand outdoors in all weathers. If weather protection and warmth can be provided, however, the life of the engine will inevitably be prolonged, and the battery will have a much easier time if it does not have to turn over a half-frozen engine. Methods of heating the garage and engine, and obtaining a start when the engine is reluctant, are discussed in Chapter 12 (page 283).

Use of Anti-freeze. Even having a heater in the garage does not entirely rule out the risk of a frozen radiator or cylinder block. Frost strikes quickly and often without warning, so if there is the slightest risk that the car may be left for some time without heat, or if it is to be driven in frosty weather, a reliable anti-freeze agent must be added to the cooling water.

Of the possible anti-freezing compounds,

the choice can be narrowed down to two—ethylene glycol and alcohol. The latter has the disadvantage of a low boiling point, so most proprietary anti-freeze agents sold today consist of ethylene glycol mixed with inhibitors which prevent any risk of corrosion of the cooling system. Ordinary commercial glycol is very corrosive, but the mixtures sold under well-known brand names are perfectly safe to use. Some are claimed to be satisfactory for two years, but there is a lot to be said for draining the system in the spring, flushing it out thoroughly and refilling it with fresh anti-freeze to give protection during the summer months, as mentioned earlier.

In the autumn, the specific gravity of the mixture should be tested (most service stations have a special hydrometer for this purpose) and fresh anti-freeze should be added, if necessary, to bring the mixture up to the strength specified for the winter temperatures likely to be encountered. Fortunately, there is a useful safety margin. For example, if, with a recommended percentage of anti-freeze added, the solution will freeze at, say, 20 deg. C., no damage will be done to the radiator or cylinder block even if 50 deg. of frost is experienced.

This is because the solution does not turn solid at its freezing point as does plain water; instead, small crystals form, and the mixture becomes increasingly mushy. Such a consistency in the radiator on a freezing morning, therefore, need not cause alarm, but the engine should be run slowly until it has warmed up, as the coolant will not circulate properly and overheating may occur. If it is necessary to drive the car away immediately in very cold weather, equal parts of anti-freeze and water will probably be required.

Before putting in anti-freeze, the radiator hoses must be examined and replaced if perished, and all joints in the system checked for signs of leakage. This is because anti-freeze has the property of

113

searching out the smallest leaks in the cooling system. The radiator cap should then be removed and both taps opened fully. As anti-freeze also tends to loosen scale and dirt in the cooling passages, the taps may become choked and should be kept clear by probing with wire. Reddish-coloured water indicates the presence of rust, and the system should be flushed continuously by means of a hose until the water leaving the taps is quite clean.

After flushing, close the taps, half-fill the system with fresh water and add the anti-freeze. The instructions on the container should be followed for best results. In general, a 25 per cent solution of anti-freeze (1 part anti-freeze to 3 parts water, by volume) is sufficient to provide full engine protection throughout the winter, but more anti-freeze should be added in abnormal conditions. Run the engine for a few minutes before finally topping-up.

Correct operation of the radiator thermostat is important for satisfactory winter running, particularly where an interior heater is fitted. In many cases a special "winter" thermostat is available as an alternative to the standard unit, giving a higher engine operating temperature. This will result in improved fuel consumption and a better heat output from the car heater. Sometimes it is recommended that the original thermostat be replaced for summer running, but nowadays a unit having a higher operating temperature is often fitted as standard if the car has a heater. This point would be worth checking, if in doubt, with the local agents for the car.

PREVENTIVE MAINTENANCE

We now come to work which is a little more ambitious than that so far described, although it should still be within the scope of a practical owner. It aims at checking the slow deterioration in efficiency which inevitably occurs as the mileage mounts up, restoring lost performance and at the same time forestalling trouble which might develop if minor faults had been allowed to go undetected. This work is commonly known as a tune-up—not to be confused with super-tuning for extra performance which is dealt with in Chapter 14.

Most car manufacturers recommend that these jobs should be carried out at 6,000-mile intervals. A complete tune-up is likely to occupy the better part of a full weekend, but there is no reason why the jobs should all be done at one time.

It is a good plan to begin the check-over by getting the engine thoroughly clean with paraffin or a proprietary engine cleaning fluid. Apart from being more pleasant to work on a clean power unit, there is less chance of causing subsequent trouble by transferring dirt to components such as the ignition system or the carburettor, and any oil, fuel or water leakages will show up immediately.

MECHANICAL CHECKS

With the engine clean and warmed-up (but not hot), the next step is to check over all external nuts, bolts, electrical leads and connections. Particular attention should be paid to the nuts or bolts which secure the inlet and exhaust manifolds. Air leaks past the inlet manifold flanges will make it difficult or impossible to obtain satisfactory idling, and many hours can be wasted on carburettor and ignition adjustments if this is overlooked.

Do not over-tighten the carburettor flange nuts, however, or there may be a risk of distorting the flange, making it impossible to obtain an airtight joint. A surprisingly large number of carburettors returned in part exchange are found to have a distorted flange. This can be rectified by rubbing the flange down carefully on a sheet of emery cloth laid on a flat surface such as a sheet of thick glass.

A second word of warning is necessary at this stage. Do not tighten the cylinder head nuts indiscriminately, especially if some are external and others are under the valve cover. It is essential to tighten the nuts progressively, each a little at a time, working outwards diagonally from the centre and following, if possible, the diagram printed in the car instruction book or workshop manual. Typical sequences are shown in Fig. 4.11 for a four- and six-cylinder engine, respectively.

If in doubt, it is better to leave the cylinder-head nuts well alone and to ask the local agents to tighten them, using a special torque spanner to measure the load evenly on each nut. If the nuts are tightened in the wrong sequence or unevenly, a gasket failure and possibly distortion of the cylinder head can be expected.

One problem which troubles some owners who wish to carry out a tune-up is how to rotate the engine while making adjustments, when the car has no starting handle. The best plan is to remove the sparking plugs so that the engine can be turned easily, and to rotate the crankshaft by one of the following methods: (a) engage top gear and push the car backwards or forwards; (b) jack up one driving wheel, engage top gear and turn the wheel (this is a particularly useful method with front-wheel-drive cars); (c) turn the crankshaft by pulling on the fan belt or dynamo pulley—*not* on the fan blades.

Adjusting Valve Rocker Clearances. After the preliminary check-over, the valve rocker cover can be removed and the rocker clearances checked. Because the components of the valve gear expand at different rates as they warm up, a small clearance must be left between the tip of each valve stem and its rocker. No general rule can be given regarding the correct clearance, which will depend on the design of the cams and the operating gear. The only safe plan is to ascertain the figures

FIG. 4.11. Sequences for tightening or slackening the cylinder-head nuts on Triumph four-cylinder and six-cylinder engines. To avoid the risk of distorting the cylinder head, similar sequences are specified by most manufacturers and should be followed where possible.

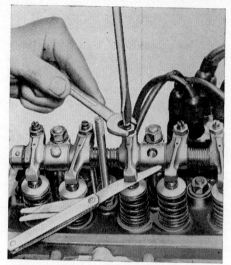

FIG. 4.12. Valve rocker adjustment. With a feeler gauge of correct thickness slipped between the valve stem and rocker pad, the adjusting screw is set accurately and then secured by its locknut.

specified by the manufacturer and to work to them.

Do not be tempted to use a smaller clearance because the engine then runs a little more quietly than with the correct gap. If the clearance is too small, there will be a risk of the rocker holding the valve slightly off its seating when the engine is hot, leading to loss of compression and rapid burning of the valve face and seating. The clearance affects the valve timing, too: a smaller clearance than normal will result in the valves opening too early, while too great a clearance will cause late timing.

On overhead-valve engines with push-rods, the clearance is generally adjusted by means of a ball-ended setscrew locked by a nut (Fig. 4.12). When checking, a feeler gauge is inserted between the other end of the rocker and the tip of the valve stem.

A different arrangement, however, is used on some engines. The rockers are not carried on a rocker shaft, but each rocker is located by an individual ball-shaped pivot on a stud which is a press-fit in the cylinder head (Fig. 4.13). A self-locking nut allows the position of the rocker to be adjusted in relation to the valve stem and push-rod. Adjustment of the clearance simply entails screwing this nut upward or downward on the stud.

The nut must be a stiff fit on the stud to maintain the self-locking effect. When the nuts become slack they should be renewed. Some manufacturers recommend that only hypoid gear oil should be used to lubricate the threads of the nut and the stud. If the threads on a stud become worn or if a stud becomes loose in the cylinder head, fitting a replacement is a job for the local agents for the car, as special tools are usually required.

It is essential to measure valve clearances when the tappet is on the base of the cam—that is, when the valve is fully closed. To ensure this, adjust the valves in the sequence quoted in the instruction book, or rotate the engine until the valve to be adjusted closes, and then give the engine a further half-turn.

It is sometimes recommended that the gaps should be checked when the engine is hot, but there is a growing tendency to specify clearances with the engine cold. In one or two instances the clearances must be checked and adjusted while the engine is running.

In the latter case, the idling speed should be set to a slow tick-over by unscrewing the carburettor slow-running (not the mixture) control, and the spanner and screwdriver must be allowed to ride up and down with the rocker while adjusting the clearance. The knack of synchronizing the movements is not difficult to acquire. As the blades of a normal feeler gauge will soon be damaged by being nipped between the rocker and the end of the valve stem, the cheapest plan is to purchase strips of feeler gauge material from the agents for the car. After setting and locking the tappet adjusting screws, it is essential to restore the normal idling speed.

Remember that when the valves are operated by push-rods, tightening the cylinder head nuts will upset the valve clearances, as the rockers will be brought closer to the ends of the rods. A further point to be watched on this type of valve gear is that the clearances will increase slightly when the engine begins to warm up, since the cylinder block expands and lifts the rockers away from the push-rods. As the valves become hot and the rods also warm up and expand, the clearances

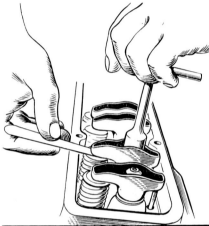

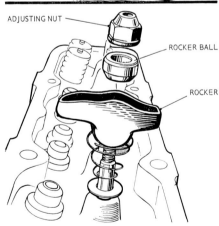

ADJUSTING NUT

ROCKER BALL

ROCKER

FIG. 4.13. On some Ford and Vauxhall engines each rocker is pivoted on a separate stud which makes a push fit in the cylinder head. The valve clearance is adjusted by turning the nut on the threaded end of the stud.

decrease again. Adjustment must, therefore, be carried out with the engine cold or thoroughly hot: never when warm.

IGNITION CHECKS

The ignition timing—that is, the instant at which the spark occurs in a combustion chamber—influences the whole of the engine performance, including starting, power output and fuel consumption. If the spark occurs too early, "pinking" and detonation may occur but modern premium and super-premium fuels have such high octane values that these symptoms may not be audible, especially if they occur when the engine is pulling hard at high speeds. Serious damage to the engine bearings and pistons can result; indeed, it is not unknown for detonation to cause such severe local overheating that holes are burnt in the piston crowns.

Retarded ignition timing, on the other hand, will reduce power output and maximum speed, increase fuel consumption, and cause the engine to overheat. It is important, therefore, to set the timing accurately in accordance with the car manufacturer's instructions.

The action of the centrifugal- and vacuum-advance controls in the ignition distributor can be checked only with special test equipment, and this emphasizes the value of a visit once a year or at 12,000-mile intervals to a service station equipped with modern electronic test-tune equipment.

Provided that these controls are functioning satisfactorily, however, it only remains for the owner to check the static setting from time to time—for example, whenever the contact-breaker points have been cleaned or renewed—as any variation in the gap between the points will slightly alter the timing. A change in the grade of fuel used, or the slow accumulation of carbon inside the engine, will also call for re-adjustment of the timing.

On the majority of modern distributors

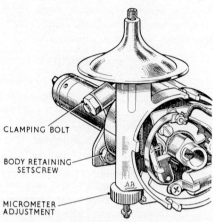

CLAMPING BOLT

BODY RETAINING
SETSCREW

MICROMETER
ADJUSTMENT

FIG. 4.14. The ignition timing can be set by turning the distributor in its mounting after slackening the clamping bolt. The Lucas type provides an additional fine adjustment by means of the micrometer control.

it is possible to advance or retard the firing point over an appreciable range by rotating an adjusting knob which forms part of the vacuum-advance unit. Generally speaking, the timing should not be altered by more than about six clicks of the knob at a time, as this usually represents about half a degree of crankshaft rotation. Turning the knob towards "A" advances the ignition and towards "R" retards it (Fig. 4.14).

When this type of micrometer timing control is not fitted, the bolt in the split clamp at the base of the distributor, or else the setscrew or setscrews which secure the distributor clamping plate to the cylinder head or crankcase, must be slackened just sufficiently to allow the distributor body to be turned to adjust the timing. It must be turned in the opposite direction to the rotation of the rotor in order to advance the ignition, or the same way as the rotation of the rotor in order to retard it.

The method of indicating the correct firing point varies (Fig. 4.15). For example, top-dead-centre of No. 1 cylinder may be shown by a line stamped on the rim of the flywheel, visible through an inspection opening in the crankcase or clutch housing,

or by a notch or hole in the flange of the crankshaft pulley at the front of the engine which registers with a pointer on the timing case. Sometimes alternative timing marks, at 5 deg., 10 deg. and possibly 15 deg. before top-dead-centre, are stamped on the flywheel, or there may be additional pointers on the timing indicator.

Timing Adjustment. To set the timing, rotate the crankshaft until the timing mark is lined-up with the indicator. Always make the final adjustment after turning the engine forward to take up backlash in the timing chain and distributor driving gears. Remove the distributor cap and check that the contact-breaker points are just about to open by slightly turning the rotor. If the ignition is switched on, a spark can be seen and heard as the points separate.

If the timing does not appear to be correct, advance or retard the setting by means of the micrometer timing knob. If this is not fitted, slacken the distributor clamping bolt, turn the distributor body in the same direction of rotation as the rotor until the points are closed, and then gently ease it in the opposite direction until the points are just opening.

The most accurate method of checking the exact moment when the circuit is broken is to connect a side-lamp bulb across the two low-tension terminals on the coil. When the points are closed and the ignition is switched on, the lamp will light up. At the instant that they open, it will go out. Apply light finger pressure to the rotor in the opposite direction to normal rotation while making this check, to take up any backlash in the drive. The test lamp could also be connected across the contact breaker, in which case it will light when the points *open* (Fig. 4.16).

When the distributor has been removed from the engine and refitted, the same method of retiming can be used, but it will be necessary first to turn the driving spindle so that the rotor is pointing in the direction of the contact in the distributor cap which connects to No. 1 sparking plug. At the base of the spindle is an offset driving dog. When the rotor is correctly aligned, this should engage with a similar dog on the upper end of the driving shaft in the crankcase or cylinder block. Retiming a modern engine is thus quite a straightforward job.

After the initial setting has been obtained, it should be checked by a series of road tests. Small adjustments may be needed to obtain the best performance and to suit the grade of fuel in use. The simplest plan is to time the acceleration in top gear between, say, 30 m.p.h. and 50 m.p.h., making several runs over the same stretch of road. The ignition setting which results in the shortest time to accelerate through this range will give the best all-round performance and the minimum fuel consumption.

FUEL SYSTEM CHECKS

Only after the engine has received a general check-over should attention be turned to the carburettor and fuel system. It is useless to attempt to set the carburettor

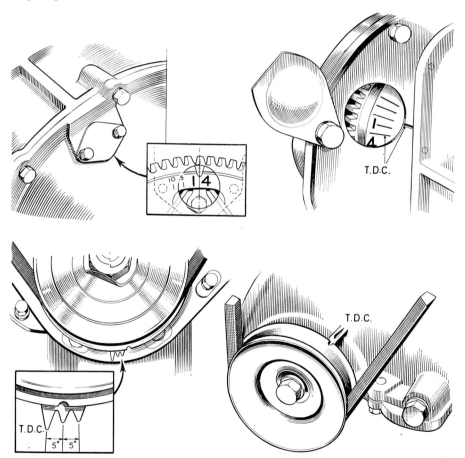

FIG. 4.15. The usual methods of indicating top-dead-centre (T.D.C.) of No. 1 piston, for ignition timing purposes. The timing marks may be on the flywheel rim, visible through a hole in the clutch housing, or there may be a groove or notch in the rim of the crankshaft pulley which aligns with a pointer or a mark cast on the timing chain cover.

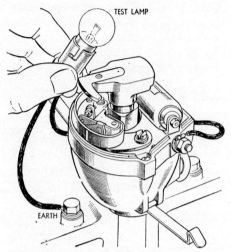

TEST LAMP

EARTH

FIG. 4.16. Basic ignition timing can be accurately set with the aid of a test lamp connected between the distributor low-tension terminal and an earth point. The lamp lights as the contact points open.

slow-running controls, for example, if there are air leaks in the induction system, if the clearances on several of the valves are incorrect, or if the ignition timing is too far advanced or retarded. The sparking plugs, of course, must be clean and set to the correct gaps, as described earlier in this chapter.

It should perhaps be emphasized that carburettor tuning in the strict sense of the word, which implies changing the jets, the size of the venturi and similar alterations to the standard settings, is beyond the scope of the amateur. It calls for skill, experience and, preferably, the use of special equipment such as a dynamometer on which the engine power output can be measured and an exhaust-gas analyzer which indicates whether the carburettor mixture is correct at different engine speeds and loads (see Chapter 3).

Cleaning the Fuel Filters. It used to be general practice to incorporate a small gauze filter in the inlet union of the carburettor, but in the majority of cases nowadays only the filter in the fuel pump

requires cleaning. When a mechanical pump is fitted, this takes the form of a gauze disc, fitted beneath a domed metal or transparent filter cover or above a filter bowl (Fig. 4.17). The cork washer between the bowl or cover and the pump must be in perfect condition, as an air leak here will reduce the output of the pump or put it out of action altogether. When a metal cover is fitted, do not forget to fit the fibre washer beneath the retaining screw, and do not overtighten the screw and risk distorting the cover.

In some cases, the petrol tank is at a higher level than the pump, and petrol will flow from the pump as soon as the filter cover is taken off. A tap may be fitted in the fuel line but when this is not provided disconnect the inlet pipe from the pump and either pinch the pipe (if it is of rubber) or block the end with a tapered wooden plug before removing the filter cover.

When an S.U. electrically-operated pump is fitted, the method of cleaning the filter depends on the type of pump (Fig. 4.18). Again, it will probably be necessary to disconnect the fuel inlet pipe at the pump and to plug it to prevent loss of fuel. Electrical pumps are often fitted below the car, and mud and grit must be carefully cleaned off before dismantling begins. Even a minute particle of grit can put the pump out of action.

Servicing Petrol Pumps. Apart from cleaning the filters, petrol pumps require little or no attention during their normal service life. It often used to be recommended in car instruction books that the cover should be removed from the contact-breaker mechanism of an electrical pump at intervals of about 6,000 miles, and the contact points cleaned by passing a piece of fine glasspaper between them. Experience suggests, however, that a pump usually functions best if left alone. When it begins to give trouble, it is better to fit a reconditioned replacement under the service-exchange scheme rather than

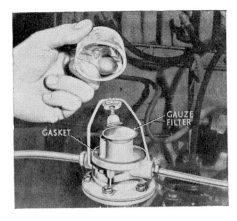

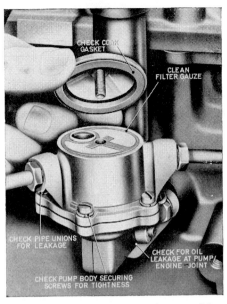

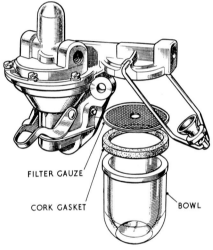

FILTER GAUZE

CORK GASKET

BOWL

FIG. 4.17. The only routine servicing required by a fuel pump is to clean its filter. Three types of filter on mechanical pumps are illustrated. After replacing the filter, a check should be made for signs of leakage at joints (see above).

amount of know-how, and the rate of flow and the pressure developed should be checked after overhaul with special test equipment (see page 98). A works-reconditioned unit is therefore likely to be the most satisfactory proposition in the long run.

attempt to overhaul it in the home garage.

Fault-tracing on an electrical pump, therefore, should be confined to checking for leakage around the unions in the pipelines between the tank and the pump and between the pump and the carburettor, and making sure that the electrical connections including the earthing wire are clean and sound.

A service-exchange unit is also the best proposition when a mechanical pump begins to give trouble. Although pump overhaul kits containing a diaphragm, a pair of valves, the necessary gaskets and other small items can be purchased, rebuilding the pump calls for a certain

CARBURETTOR SERVICING

Many modern carburettors, including Solex, Zenith, Zenith-Stromberg, Weber and similar types are fairly complex units. Figs. 4.19 to 28 illustrate typical examples. The amateur should therefore confine himself to simple servicing and should not dismantle the unit more than is necessary to clean out the float chamber, remove and blow through the jets, and to check the action of the acceleration pump when this is fitted.

A thermally-operated automatic choke should not be disturbed because it is necessary to reset the tension of the thermostat spring correctly on re-assembly and also to check the action of the vacuum-kick piston, when fitted. But the pipe that supplies heat to the thermostatic spring should be cleaned out.

When a manual or automatic choke is linked to the throttle lever to give a higher idling speed when the choke is in action, the linkage must not be disturbed unless full instructions are available for resetting it. This information is usually available only in a workshop manual. Straight-forward servicing and adjustment, how-ever, are almost invariably covered in some detail in the car instruction book.

Fixed Jet Carburettors. Considering

first the Solex, Zenith, Zenith-Stromberg, Weber, and similar "static" carburettors, the float chamber can be inspected either by removing the upper cover from the carburettor or by slackening the retaining screws and lowering the float chamber assembly. The float can then be lifted out. A certain amount of fine reddish sediment will almost certainly be found in the base of the bowl, and this should be flushed out, taking care not to swill it into any of the fuel passages.

If the float is dented or has shown any sign of collapsing (a fault which does occur on some carburettors), fit a replace-ment. Next, unscrew the needle valve

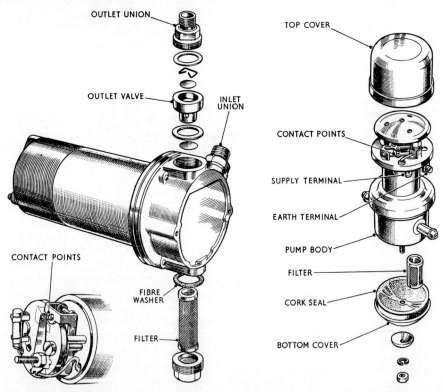

FIG. 4.18. (*Left*) This type of S.U. fuel pump has been widely used for many years. The filter is removable for cleaning, while the valve parts are accessible by disconnecting the outlet union. The contact points may be cleaned by passing a strip of paper between them while they are held open. (*Right*) The S.U. type PD pump is hermetically sealed and cannot be serviced except by replacement of the parts illustrated. Normal attention is confined to cleaning the filter and replacing it together with a new cork seal.

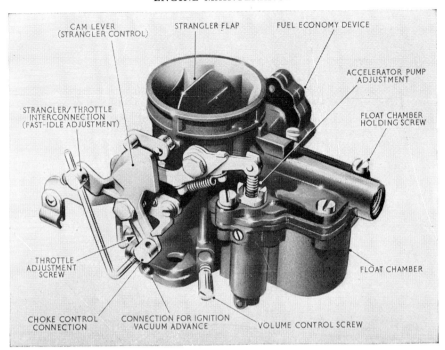

FIG. 4.19. The Zenith VN is typical of modern fixed-jet downdraught carburettors and used on a number of British cars. It is fitted with an automatic strangler for cold starting, an economy device to reduce fuel consumption under part-throttle cruising conditions, and an accelerator pump to enrichen the mixture with a spurt of petrol whenever the throttle is suddenly opened.

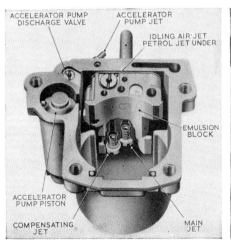

FIG. 4.20. (*Left*) Zenith VN float chamber, showing the locations of the jets and accelerator pump. (*Right*) Normal setting of the accelerator pump is when the pump arm makes contact with the higher of the two "ears". Turning the block round so that the arm contacts the lower ear lengthens the stroke for operation under very cold conditions.

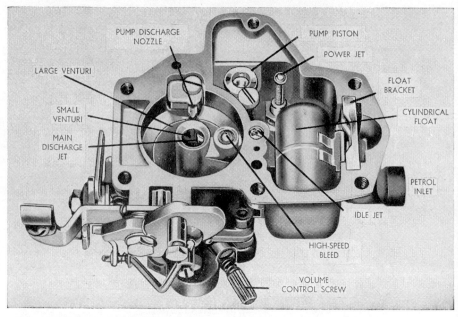

FIG. 4.21. The Zenith W-type carburettor is used on some larger cars, and this illustration shows the float chamber and jets. An interesting feature is the power jet which provides an extra supply of petrol at wide throttle openings or when engine depression is low, permitting maximum power under conditions of high speed or heavy load.

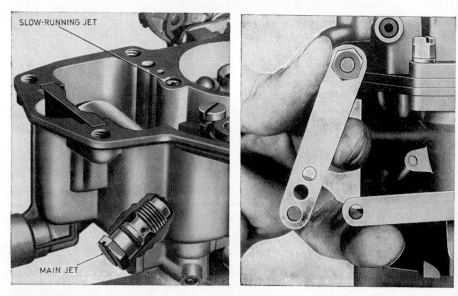

FIG. 4.22. (*Left*) The main jet of the Zenith W-type carburettor is removable by unscrewing the hexagon-headed jet carrier under the bowl. (*Right*) The middle hole in the accelerator pump adjustable arm is the setting normally used.

which controls the flow of fuel into the float chamber, swill it in petrol and blow through it to make sure that it is not sticking. It is a sound plan to renew this inexpensive assembly at about 12,000-mile intervals. On some carburettors, the valve becomes ridged and does not control the flow of fuel as effectively as it should. This results in an abnormally high petrol level in the float chamber, which can cause heavy fuel consumption and may even result in the petrol flooding when the engine is idling, rendering it difficult or impossible to achieve satisfactory slow-running.

Flooding can also be caused by incorrect setting of the float lever. The method of adjusting the height of the float in relation to the needle valve is usually explained in the car workshop manual, and entails gentle bending of the float lever. Do not alter this adjustment unnecessarily.

The next step is to remove and blow through the jets. On some carburettors, these can be taken out by unscrewing external plugs. On others, some of the jets are in the base of the float chamber or in the spraying-block assembly, and can be reached only when the carburettor has been dismantled, as just described.

When an accelerator pump is fitted, the small non-return ball valves should not be overlooked. If they stick, the pump will not operate and there will be a pronounced flat-spot in the acceleration when the throttle is opened quickly. Do not operate the pump with petrol in the carburettor bowl when the bowl or top cover is removed or one of the balls may be ejected and fall into the carburettor intake. It might then be necessary to remove the inlet manifold and perhaps the cylinder head to retrieve it.

When re-assembling the carburettor, make sure that the various gaskets and washers are in good condition. The gasket between the float chamber and the carburettor body or top cover is particularly

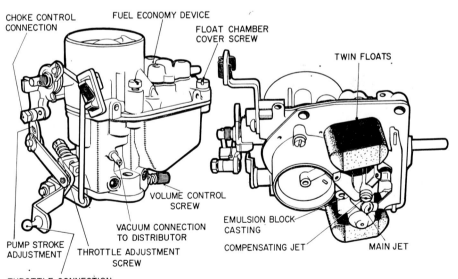

FIG. 4.23. The Zenith IV is a recent design in the series of V-type carburettors. All the jets and the accelerator pump are in the detachable emulsion block casting (*right*). Features include a strangler for cold starting linked to the throttle to provide a fast idle, diaphragm-operated economy device, and leak-proof float chamber with twin floats.

important, as air leakage past it can completely upset operation of the unit. When the carburettor has been re-assembled, warm up the engine and reset the idling speed and mixture controls as described on page 127.

Variable Choke Carburettors. The various types of S.U. carburettor, and the Zenith-Stromberg CD design, differ from those just described in having a single jet of relatively large diameter through which the flow of petrol is metered by a tapered needle which rises and falls in response to differences in engine speed and throttle opening. These carburettors, therefore, are virtually immune to troubles caused by sediment or water which may clog the fine jets and fuel passages of static carburettors.

Servicing is normally confined to cleaning out the float chamber at 6,000-mile intervals, and dismantling is quite straightforward. The earlier remarks concerning the needle valve and the correct height of the float apply also to these carburettors.

A further job that must be done on the S.U. and Zenith-Stromberg CD at about 6,000-mile intervals is to top-up the small hydraulic damper in the top of the suction chamber with engine oil, to just below the top of the hollow piston rod. If the damper is allowed to become dry, difficult starting, hesitation and misfiring during acceleration can be expected. To check the oil level, unscrew the nut at the top of the carburettor, lift out the damper—being careful not to bend the rod—add oil if necessary,

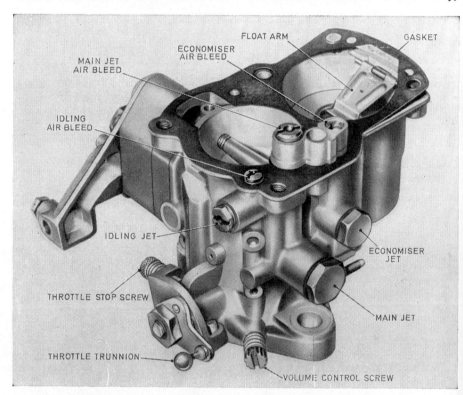

FIG. 4.24. The Solex PSEI carburettor, with cover removed to show the choke tube and float chamber side by side. Features include a strangler for cold starting, an accelerator pump, and an economy device operating automatically at cruising speeds.

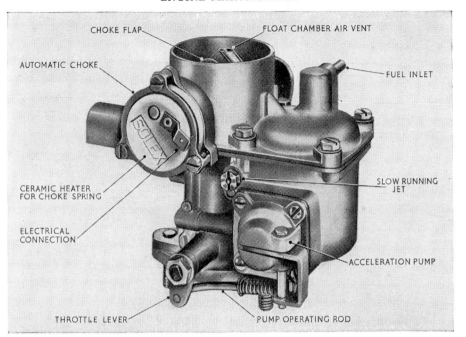

FIG. 4.25. The Solex PICT carburettor, used on recent Volkswagen cars, incorporates an automatic choke control—basically a spiral bimetal spring which responds to small changes of temperature. Fitted on the choke valve shaft, the spring is heated by a ceramic cover and opens the choke valve as the engine warms up. The device is non-adjustable.

and gently press the damper back into position before tightening the nut firmly.

CARBURETTOR ADJUSTMENTS

As has been suggested earlier, the amateur should not attempt to tune a carburettor, but re-adjustment of the idling speed and slow-running mixture strength will be needed from time to time. The engine must be at its normal running temperature. The throttle-stop screw and the screw which controls the strength of the petrol-air mixture in a static carburettor when the engine is idling must be identified. These will be shown in the car instruction book.

First set the throttle-stop screw to give a fairly fast idling speed. If the idling speed is too low, the engine is likely to stall when the throttle is suddenly closed or when it is not fully warmed-up. Now the mixture-

control screw must be adjusted. If the screw is mounted fairly high on the carburettor, it probably controls the proportion of air in the slow-running mixture: screwing it inwards will enrich the mixture, and outwards will weaken it. If the screw is low down on the carburettor near the mounting flange, it usually controls the volume of mixture entering the engine, and its effect is reversed.

The object is to find a point at which the engine runs at its highest speed with an even exhaust note. If the mixture is too weak, there will be an occasional misfire in the exhaust. If it is too rich, the engine will slow down and run unevenly with a rhythmic beat (termed "hunting"), and black smoke may be visible in the exhaust gas. Having found the best position for the screw, re-adjust the mixture so that it is very slightly rich. This will give improved

127

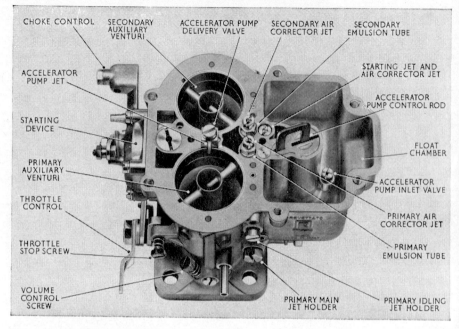

FIG. 4.26. The Weber DCOE is an advanced twin-choke carburettor used on certain British high-performance cars. The primary choke is used for idling and medium speeds, the secondary choke coming into operation at higher speeds. In effect, the instrument consists of a pair of single-choke carburettors with two venturis in each choke.

acceleration from low speeds. Some engines are particularly sensitive to the slow-running mixture strength in this respect.

As a final check, speed up the engine once or twice and snap the throttle closed to make sure that the slow-running remains stable. Also check the idling with the clutch pedal depressed. This will usually slow the engine down, and if the idling speed or mixture strength are not correct it may stall.

The only other adjustment likely to be required in normal service on static carburettors is to reset the accelerator pump linkage for winter or summer running. When the pump is operated by a linkage from the throttle lever, there are usually two alternative holes for the link pin. One gives a longer stroke than the other, and the pin should be inserted in this hole during cold-weather running.

The shorter pump stroke will give better fuel economy during the summer.

Another arrangement is to provide an adjustable stop beneath the pump lever. By rotating this, either a long or a short projection can be positioned beneath the lever, thus regulating its stroke (Fig. 4.20).

Adjusting Variable Choke Carburettors. On the most widely used types of S.U. carburettor, the mixture strength is altered by turning the jet adjusting nut shown in Fig. 4.27. Screwing the nut upwards allows the jet to move closer to the needle and thus weakens the mixture, while screwing it down has the reverse effect. Otherwise, adjustment is carried out as just described for static carburettors.

On an S.U., disconnect the mixture control rod or wire from the jet-operating arm on the carburettor, and keep the jet against the nut while carrying out the adjustment. Afterwards, reconnect the wire or rod, allowing a small amount of slack so that the throttle interconnecting mechanism can be used to speed up slow-running slightly during the first half-inch of movement of the dashboard knob, before the lever begins to lower the jet. If the fast-idling screw interferes with the setting of the normal idling-speed adjustment, slacken it off while setting the slow-running adjustment, and then screw it down so that there is a very small gap between the screw and the lever or plate which is linked to the jet.

On the S.U. diaphragm-jet (HD) type of carburettor, the jet assembly is enclosed within the base of the carburettor, and the height of the jet is controlled by a small screw beside the suction chamber. Screwing this adjustment downwards enriches the slow-running mixture.

On some HD carburettors the amount of mixture reaching the engine is governed by a screw at the side of the carburettor, the tapered end of which projects into a by-pass passage through which the mixture passes when the throttle is closed. The slow-running speed is therefore increased by unscrewing this screw, and decreased by screwing it down. On other HD models a throttle-stop screw is used to regulate the idling speed. If a by-pass screw is also provided, this should remain closed (fully screwed down).

On the Stromberg CD carburettor, in which the mixture strength during normal running is controlled by a tapered needle as already described, the throttle-stop screw is of the normal type, and the height of the jet in relation to the needle is regulated by a screw which projects from the base of the carburettor (Fig. 4.28).

Multiple Carburettors. When two or

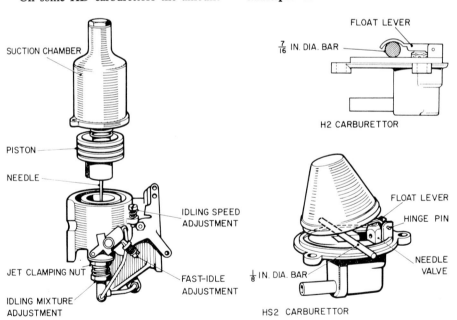

FIG. 4.27. S.U. carburettor adjustment. The adjustable controls are shown left, also the metering needle which is replaceable for tuning purposes by needles of different profile. (*Right*) Methods of checking for correct fuel level in the float chambers of earlier and later models. With the chamber inverted so that the needle valve is closed, it should just be possible to slide a bar of diameter shown between the cover and float lever. If necessary, the fuel level can be corrected by carefully bending the float lever.

more carburettors are fitted to an engine, it is necessary to synchronize the slow-running speeds and mixture strengths. If this is done correctly at idling speed, the carburettors will supply a balanced mixture to the engine at all other speeds. Synchronization, however, is a somewhat tricky job and it is essential to follow the instructions in the car handbook or workshop manual. It is easy to get twin or triple carburettors hopelessly out of synchronization, and the job should therefore be left to an expert—and this does not mean the average garage mechanic, who may be enthusiastic but seldom has the experience needed to achieve the fine edge of tune which makes all the difference to the smoothness, performance and fuel consumption of a multiple-carburettor engine.

Fortunately, normal cleaning and servicing can be carried out without disturbing the basic settings. It is even possible, in many cases, to remove the carburettors from the engine without altering the idling speed, mixture strength and throttle interconnection adjustments.

This completes the work on the fuel system which the average owner should tackle, but there is a further job which is worth doing at intervals of about 12,000 miles on S.U. carburettors. Remove the piston damper, undo the screws that secure the suction chamber to the body of the carburettor, and carefully lift off the chamber. Lift out the piston, taking care not to bend the needle, and put the spring on one side. Do not be tempted to stretch it. If there are closed coils at one end of the spring, these go towards the piston.

Clean any oil or carbon from the inside of the suction housing and from the lands and grooves of the piston. Do not use metal polish or emery paper. There is a carefully controlled air leak between the piston and the suction housing, and the parts must be assembled dry. Only the piston rod into

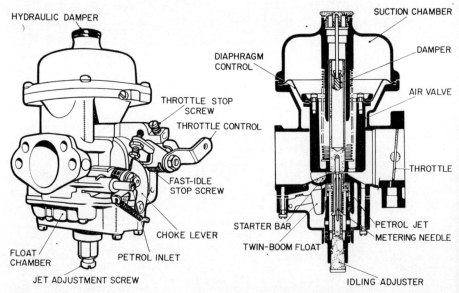

FIG. 4.28. The Zenith-Stromberg CD carburettor is a constant-vacuum instrument working on the same principle as the S.U. type. Its metering needle working in the single petrol jet is raised and lowered by a flexible diaphragm. For cold starting a starter bar is partly rotated, lifting the needle to pass more petrol but also preventing the entry of more air. The float chamber is concentric around the jet, with twin solid floats.

FIG. 4.29. A bellows thermostat contains a volatile liquid
which vaporizes at running
temperature, expanding the
bellows and opening the valve.
It is being superseded by the
wax element type, which is
insensitive to pressures in the
cooling system; the diagrams
explain its operating principle.
The hole with a jiggle pin
prevents the formation of air
locks when the system is being
refilled and the valve is closed
(Western-Thomson).

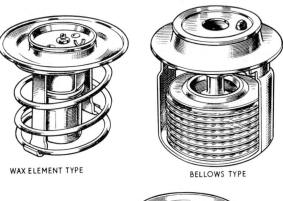

WAX ELEMENT TYPE   BELLOWS TYPE

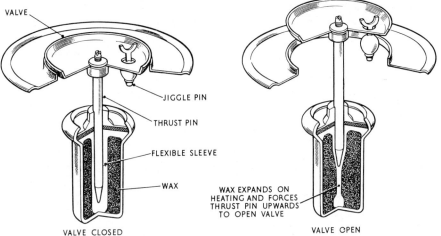

VALVE

JIGGLE PIN

THRUST PIN

FLEXIBLE SLEEVE

WAX

WAX EXPANDS ON
HEATING AND FORCES
THRUST PIN UPWARDS
TO OPEN VALVE

VALVE CLOSED   VALVE OPEN

which the damper fits requires a drop or
two of engine oil.

Before refitting the piston, check that
the needle, which is retained by a setscrew,
is correctly positioned. The narrow end of
the tapered shoulder should be just flush
with the underside of the piston. After
re-assembling the carburettor, refill the
damper with engine oil and refit the
damper piston and cap.

COOLING SYSTEM CHECKS

After this, attention can be given to the
cooling system. Surprisingly often, owners
will spend much time making carburettor
and ignition adjustments in an attempt to
cure faults such as heavy fuel consumption,
detonation (or "pinking"), and "running

on" when the ignition is switched off,
without realizing that the cooling system
can cause or substantially contribute to
these troubles.

Once a year, then, it is advisable to flush
out the system to remove any deposits of
sludge or rust. The best time to do this is in
the spring so that the system will be clean
and operate at maximum efficiency during
the summer months.

The most effective method is first to run
the car for several days with a proprietary
de-scaling compound added to the cooling
water in order to remove any deposits of
lime and rust which may have built up.
Then, immediately after a run when the
engine is hot and any sludge will still be in
suspension in the water, open the drain

taps or remove the drain plugs from the cylinder block and radiator, probe the openings with a wire to ensure a full flow, and allow sufficient time for the system to drain completely. If an interior heater is fitted, open the water valve or select "hot" on the heater control to make sure that the heater matrix is also drained.

When the system has emptied, leave the taps open and run clean water through the system, preferably using a garden hose, until the water flowing from the taps is quite clear. Then close the taps, slacken the water-return hose from the interior heater at the engine connection, and run water into the system until it begins to flow from the heater hose, thus making sure that there is no air-lock in the heater.

This process should be all that is required if the cooling system has been well maintained. If, however, it has been neglected, it would be advisable to have the work done by a service station which possesses reverse-flushing equipment.

Once every two years it is as well to renew the radiator hoses and the interior heater hoses. Often a hose will appear to be in perfect condition on outward inspection, but the inner lining may have become softened and sections may have become partly detached, acting as flap valves to obstruct the water flow; the hoses connected to the suction side of the pump may collapse under the partial vacuum created when the engine is running at a fairly high speed, again seriously restricting the flow of coolant.

Remember, too, that the hoses may be subject to a fairly high pressure, with the result that pin-hole leaks may allow a considerable amount of water to escape when the engine is running at maximum speed, or when it twists on its mountings under load, although no leakage may be evident when the engine is idling. Often wire-type hose clips can start this sort of trouble, especially if they are over-tightened.

Radiator Thermostat. The last item to check but nevertheless one of the most important is the thermostat. This is a heat-operated valve, fitted usually beneath the outlet union on the engine to which the upper radiator hose is connected, which prevents circulation of water through the radiator until the engine has attained its normal running temperature (Fig. 4.29). The valve may be operated by a bellows filled with a volatile liquid which vaporizes when the correct temperature is reached, expanding the bellows and opening the valve.

Nowadays, however, it is more usual for the valve to be controlled by a wax-filled capsule. This type of thermostat gives more precise control over the temperature of the coolant and, unlike the bellows, is not affected by changes in the pressure in the system. For example, if the valve in the radiator filler cap is not holding the correct pressure, a bellows-type thermostat will open too early and the engine will run too cool.

Wax-capsule and bellows thermostats, although normally reliable, can fail in either the open or closed position. The former fault results in the engine running at less than its most efficient temperature, and the latter causes severe engine over-heating. It is good practice, therefore, to inspect the thermostat once a year when the system is flushed out. A doubtful unit can be tested by immersing it in a saucepan of water which is slowly brought to boiling point. If the valve opens when the water is lukewarm or has not opened by the time the water is boiling, the thermostat is obviously faulty.

If it appears to be satisfactory and is free from scale or corrosion, it can be put back for another year's use, but it is advisable to replace a thermostat after two years in view of the vital influence it has on the efficiency of the engine—apart from fuel consumption and the effectiveness of the interior heater.

CHAPTER 5

ENGINE TROUBLES AND OVERHAULS

TROUBLES should be rare in an engine that is carefully maintained on the lines laid down in the last chapter, but naturally they cannot always be avoided. Apart from breakdowns usually due to ignition or carburation faults (see Chapter 3 for systematic fault diagnosis), the power unit may develop running troubles through wear or neglect. The chart on pages 134 and 135 indicates the more common troubles of this kind.

Experienced mechanics can diagnose a good deal about the state of an engine from unusual noises that emanate from it while running. The chart on page 136 gives a guide to knocks and noises that may be encountered—again with particular reference to worn engines—but it must be emphasized that experience is needed to be able to locate troubles successfully by sounds alone, and amateurs should beware of misinterpreting engine noises.

The overhaul of engines is a subject that concerns the motorist much less frequently than used to be the case. As mentioned in the last chapter, improvements in engine design and materials, in fuels and in lubricants, have combined to give modern engines a greatly extended life before any kind of reconditioning is required. When an overhaul must be considered, most owners will prefer to entrust the work to professional hands, but some overhaul operations are well within the scope of the home mechanic.

TOP OVERHAUL

Sooner or later, even the most carefully maintained engine begins to lose power, although the process may be so gradual that the owner fails to notice it at first. After perhaps 20,000 miles have been covered, a "top overhaul" will probably be found necessary.

Many engines will, in fact, run for greater mileages than 20,000 before a top overhaul is needed. On the other hand, a high-performance power unit may need attention at less than 15,000 miles. If the compression is low in one or more cylinders when the engine is tested with a cylinder compression gauge (as described on page 99), the time for a top overhaul has arrived. If compression is normal, however, and the engine is running well, it is better not to disturb it unnecessarily.

After about 30,000 miles, engine oil consumption often begins to increase. Symptoms of cylinder and piston ring wear sometimes appear at an earlier mileage, but other engines will run for 50,000 miles or more before poor compression and excessive oil consumption indicate that attention is required. It is thus impossible to lay down any hard-and-fast rule regarding overhaul periods.

A systematic series of checks, as outlined in the chart showing running troubles on pages 134 and 135, should determine fairly conclusively whether a top overhaul, partial overhaul or a complete overhaul (or alternatively a works-reconditioned engine) will be needed to restore efficiency in any given case.

Partial and complete overhauls are discussed later in this chapter. To start with we must consider a top overhaul, which can be tackled quite successfully by any practically-minded motorist. Only the upper part of the engine is affected, the

ENGINE RUNNING TROUBLES

Trouble	Cause	Remedy
REDUCED POWER, POOR ACCELERATION, MIS-FIRING	Ignition system faults.	Have checked with electronic test-tune equipment. Service distributor (page 107), check timing (page 117), clean, regap, or renew sparking plugs (page 109).
	Carburation faults.	Service carburettor float chamber, jets, acceleration pump and petrol pump (pages 120-131). Check oil in carburettor damper (page 126). Check that throttle valve and choke valve are opening fully.
	Carburettor icing-up.	In winter adjust air intake to warm-air position (when provided). Blank-off radiator. Try different brand of fuel.
	Dirty air cleaner.	Service the cleaner (page 110).
	Overheating.	Carry out checks under "Over-heating."
	Low compression.	See under "Low Compression."
LOW COMPRESSION	Incorrect valve clearances.	Check clearances and re-set (page 115).
	Sticking, pitted or burnt valves.	Carry out top-overhaul (page 133).
	Leaking cylinder-head gasket.	Fit new gasket. Check cylinder head for distortion and skim if necessary. Tighten cylinder-head nuts to specified torque loading (page 143).
	Worn cylinders and piston rings.	Carry out partial overhaul (page 145). or rebore cylinders or fit liners (page 146).
HEAVY FUEL CON-SUMPTION	Poor engine tune.	Have checked with electronic test-tune equipment. Check particularly: sparking plugs, contact-breaker points, ignition timing.
	Over-rich carburettor mixture.	Check exhaust gas for black smoke and exhaust pipe for sooty deposits. Service carburettor float and needle valve (pages 122, 125). Check: fuel tank, pump, pipelines and carburettor for leaks, jets for correct sizes (page 125), setting of acceleration pump (pages 123, 124), economy device (when fitted), and choke for correct operation (may be remaining in action when engine is warmed-up).
	Overcooling.	See under "Overcooling."
OVERHEATING	Low water level in radiator.	See under "Loss of Coolant."
	Cooling passages clogged by scale or rust.	De-scale and flush out (page 131).
	Fan belt slipping.	Adjust (page 112) or fit new belt.
	Radiator filler cap not holding pressure.	Pressure-test or renew (page 105).
	Thermostat faulty.	Remove and test, or renew (page 132).
	Ignition timing retarded.	Check timing (page 117).
	Leaking cylinder-head gasket.	See under "Low Compression."

ENGINE RUNNING TROUBLES

Trouble	Cause	Remedy
LOSS OF COOLANT (RADIATOR NEEDS FREQUENT TOPPING-UP)	Faulty filler cap. Leakage from hoses. Leakage from radiator or cylinder block. Leaking water pump. Leaking cylinder-head gasket.	Test or renew (page 105). Tighten clips, check condition of hoses, renew if necessary (page 132). De-scale, flush out (page 131). Add leak-stopping compound. If ineffective, fit reconditioned radiator. Fit service-exchange replacement. See under "Low Compression."
OVERCOOLING	Faulty or incorrect thermostat. Trouble may be characteristic of engine.	Check thermostat (page 132). Fit "winter" type in cold weather if not fitted as standard (page 114). Fit radiator blind or blank-off part of radiator. Remove fan blades, *but check for overheating in traffic.* Fit thermostatically-controlled fan.
HIGH OIL CONSUMPTION	Piston rings not bedding properly. Oil leakage into combustion chambers past valve stems. Worn cylinders and piston rings. Worn connecting-rod bearings and/or crankpins. Leakage from engine joints, pipe unions or bearing seals. Excessive oil pressure.	Engine may not be fully run-in. Consumption is sometimes high for first 2,000-5,000 miles. Check valves and guides for wear. Fit new oil seals to valve stems (page 142). Carry out partial overhaul (page 145) or recondition cylinders (page 146). Carry out partial overhaul (page 145) or major overhaul (page 144). Clean engine thoroughly, warm-up and check carefully for leakage, which may occur only under running conditions on the road. Have pressure checked by accurate gauge. Service pressure-relief valve if necessary.
LOW OIL PRESSURE	Wrong grade of oil in use, or oil excessively diluted by condensed fuel during cold-weather running. Too little oil in sump. Choked oil filter. Faulty pressure-relief valve. Worn engine bearings. Leakage at filter flange or other joints on suction or pressure side of pump. Worn or damaged oil pump.	Drain sump and refill with correct grade of oil (page 103). Top-up to correct level (page 103). Clean or fit new filter element (pages 103, 104). Remove, clean and inspect valve. If necessary renew valve and recondition seating. Fit new spring and adjust correctly. Carry out partial or major overhaul (page 144). Check gaskets, seating of filter, tightness of unions (this may entail removing the sump to inspect internal components). Fit replacement pump.

135

ENGINE KNOCKS AND NOISES

Sound	Cause	Action
Light metallic tinkling when engine is pulling	"Pinking" caused by detonation or pre-ignition	Change to fuel having higher octane value, *but check:* sparking plugs for correct type (page 109), ignition for over-advanced timing (page 117), distributor for faulty automatic timing mechanism (with electronic test set), engine for overheating (page 134). If these checks are ineffective, carry out top-overhaul (page 133).
Tapping or clicking from top of engine	Incorrect valve clearances or worn valve gear	Remove valve rocker cover and check clearances (page 115).
Hollow metallic tap or clatter from cylinder block	Piston slap, caused by worn pistons and rings	If noise disappears as engine warms up, it may not indicate serious trouble. Some engines are more prone to this noise than others.
Light tapping from top of cylinder block	Worn gudgeon pin	Check by short-circuiting sparking plugs in turn. Noise will often disappear when plug in affected cylinder is shorted-out.
Metallic clatter from base of engine	Worn connecting-rod bearings	Check by speeding engine up without load. Noise may disappear when engine is pulling, if clearances are not excessive.
Thumping or rumbling noise when engine is pulling	Worn main crankshaft bearings	Check for oil leakage past front and rear crankshaft bearing seals, which often accompanies this fault. Some engines are prone to "main-bearing thump" when in good condition.
Rattle, whine or chatter from front of engine	Worn timing chain or defective tensioner	This noise is often more noticeable at a fast idling speed when the engine is thoroughly warmed-up.
Squeak or squeal from front of engine at high speeds or when accelerating and decelerating	Worn or glazed fan belt, worn belt pulley, worn water pump, defective dynamo bearings	Check tightness of belt. Smear with brake fluid or rubber lubricant. If noise does not cease, disconnect belt to verify that trouble is in dynamo or water pump. A squeaking pump gland can often be cured by adding soluble oil to coolant.
Irregular knock from front of engine when idling	Crankshaft pulley or vibration damper loose on keyway	Check for free movement with engine stopped.

work being restricted to cleaning carbon deposits from internal parts and (of greater importance nowadays) reconditioning the valves in order to restore compression. The various components that should receive attention during a top overhaul are illustrated in Fig. 5.1.

A reasonably comprehensive tool kit of the type found in most home workshops will suffice for a top overhaul, but it must be supplemented by one or two special items. A valve-spring compressor, suitable for the particular design of valve gear, and a suction-type valve-grinding tool will be needed, and possibly one or two special spanners to deal with nuts that are difficult to reach. The local agents for the car will be able to advise on these items.

Another tool that should really be regarded as essential is a torque wrench. Car manufacturers specify the force that must be used when tightening the cylinder head and other vital nuts, and a torque (or torsion) wrench is required to obtain the correct force.

Few private owners are able to afford the cost of one of these expensive tools, but a service station might be prepared to hire one out for a week-end, especially if the parts needed for a top overhaul are pur-

chased from them. If this is not possible, have the tightness of the nuts checked by a service station as soon as possible after the work has been completed.

A small tin of valve-grinding paste containing both coarse and fine grades will be needed, also a plentiful supply of clean, non-fluffy rags, and some jam jars, tins and boxes to hold the various bits and pieces as they are removed. Parts that will be required include a set of gaskets and sealing washers, a set of valve springs, a set of valve-stem oil seals, and a spare inlet valve and exhaust valve so that a hold-up will not occur if a valve is found to be bent or badly burnt.

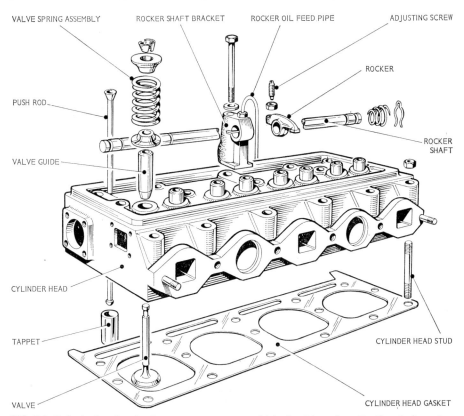

FIG. 5.1. Cylinder head and valve gear components which should receive attention during a top overhaul. One complete valve assembly is shown. Some engines have bolts retaining the cylinder head instead of studs and nuts as shown, and on some each rocker is mounted on an individual stud which is a press fit in the head.

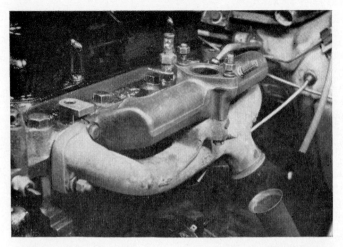

FIG. 5.2. Stages in dismantling an engine for top overhaul. (*Top*) The carburettor is removed, and it is advisable to detach both manifolds in order to lighten the head assembly and improve access to the retaining nuts. (*Centre*) The rocker shaft assembly can be lifted off complete after undoing the bracket nuts which retain it. (*Bottom*) The cylinder head must be lifted straight off after removing the nuts or bolts which secure it to the cylinder block

Dismantling the Engine. A survey of the engine before starting work will indicate which items must be removed to give access to the cylinder-head and inlet- and exhaust-manifold nuts. Before starting to dismantle, disconnect the battery and drain the cooling system. The upper water hose and the heater hose, if it is connected to the cylinder head, can now be taken off. As the hoses generally stick to the metal, it is probably better to cut them away and to fit new hoses on re-assembly. With many modern engines the thermostat by-pass hose between the cylinder head and the water pump has also to be freed.

If the ignition distributor has to be removed, undo the set-screw or screws which secure the split clamping plate to the cylinder head or crankcase. Do not slacken the split clamp itself, as the timing will be lost if the distributor is allowed to rotate in the clamp. (Sometimes a second set-screw engages with a groove in the spindle of the distributor.) The pipeline which connects the vacuum ignition timing control to the carburettor must be disconnected. Be careful not to bend or kink the tube.

After the petrol pipe, throttle and starting controls have been disconnected, the carburettor can be unbolted from the inlet manifold (Fig. 5.2). Sometimes the manifold retaining nuts can be reached without removing the carburettor, but as this should in any case be detached from the manifold later, there is no advantage in deferring the operation. On small engines, the manifolds can often be left on the cylinder head and subsequently dismantled on the bench. They may, however, mask the cylinder-head nuts, and on larger engines they add considerably to the weight of the head and are best removed. The exhaust pipe should now be freed from the manifold.

The valve gear is then dismantled. After uncoupling any oil pipes which supply the valve gear, the rocker shaft and brackets can usually be unbolted from the cylinder head as an assembly and lifted off the push rods (Fig. 5.2). But first link the push rods together with string before the rocker shaft is lifted, so that there is no possibility of them dropping into the sump. After removal, lay out the push rods in sequence on the bench, so that each will subsequently be refitted in its original position. It is as well to check each push rod by rolling it on a flat surface to detect any which may be bent; these should be renewed.

Cylinder Head Removal. The cylinder-head nuts or bolts should now be unscrewed a little at a time in rotation, following a sequence similar to that given in Fig. 4.11. This is to avoid distortion of the head. Often the nuts which secure the valve rocker brackets also serve as cylinder-head nuts.

On larger engines, it is best to enlist the help of an assistant when lifting the head. It may stick, but by tapping it lightly with a mallet the joint can generally be broken. Sometimes lugs are cast on the head and cylinder block so that the head may be levered up with a pair of screwdrivers or tyre levers. Never be tempted, however, to drive a screwdriver or other tool between the head and the block to break the joint, as this will damage the mating surfaces.

If the engine has removable cylinder barrels, the crankshaft should not be rotated when the cylinder-head nuts have been removed, owing to the risk of the barrels being lifted by the friction of the piston rings. This will disturb the joints at their bases and may cause water leakage into the crankcase when the engine is re-assembled. The cylinder head must be carefully withdrawn, therefore, and small clamps—short lengths of tube or even several large nuts and washers will do—should be fitted to the studs adjacent to the edges of the barrels to keep them in place. A cylinder head must be lifted squarely, to prevent it binding on the studs.

139

FIG. 5.3. A wire brush operated by a power tool is a useful tool for decarbonizing the cylinder block, head, and the mating surfaces of the manifolds. If the valves have first been removed, as shown left, care must be taken not to damage their seatings.

DECARBONIZING AND VALVE RECONDITIONING

We can now start the work of decarbonizing, which involves the removal of carbon from the piston crowns, combustion chambers, and manifolds. The hard carbon may be scraped off with suitably shaped tools, followed by the use of a wire brush (Fig. 5.3). Particular care must be taken not to scratch or score the relatively soft surfaces of the aluminium pistons, or the combustion chambers when an aluminium cylinder head is fitted. It is best to decarbonize the head before the valves are removed to avoid any risk of damaging the valve seatings.

When decarbonizing the cylinder block, the cylinders on which work is not proceeding and the water openings in the cylinder block and head must be plugged with clean rags to exclude carbon chips and dust.

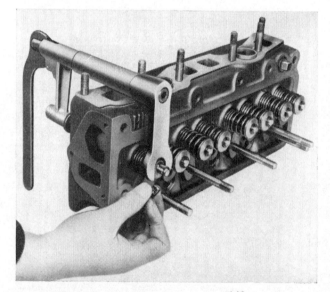

FIG. 5.4. Compressing the valve springs with a compressor tool of the type shown allows the valve-retaining split cotters to be removed, after which the tool is released and the remaining valve parts can be dismantled.

140

It is always a good plan to leave a ring of carbon, about ¼ in. wide, around the circumference of each piston crown and around the top of the cylinder bore. These rings will act as oil seals and will prevent an increase in oil consumption during the first few hundred miles following de-carbonizing. If an old piston ring is available, this should be laid on the piston crown to protect these "ring" areas from the scraper.

When the combustion chambers in the cylinder head are clean, the valves can be removed. As their spring tension is powerful, this requires the use of a valve-spring compressor tool to allow extraction of the spring cotters, as shown in Fig. 5.4. If this is not available, shape a block of wood to fit inside the combustion chamber and place the cylinder head on the bench with this block beneath the heads of a pair

FIG. 5.6. When valves are removed they should be kept in their original fitting order. The simplest method is to push the stems through a piece of card as shown.

of valves. Each spring can then be compressed by downward pressure exerted by a pair of screwdrivers on the valve collar. Hold the collar down with one screwdriver and remove the cotters or other retaining device (Fig. 5.5.).

Keep the valves in sequence so that they can go back into the same guides (Fig. 5.6), but discard the old valve springs. A new set is not expensive and should be fitted whenever a top overhaul is carried out.

The exhaust valves usually have deposits of hard, scaly carbon which is sometimes difficult to remove, whereas the carbon on the inlet valves is generally soft and oily or sooty. Do not clean the stems of the valves with emery cloth, as this may reduce their diameter. Make sure, however, that all carbon is removed by careful scraping, and that the stems are perfectly clean (Fig. 5.7). The valve guides will also need cleaning, although carbon will only accumulate at the necks. The guide bores may be cleared of gummy oil by drawing a petrol-soaked rag through them.

When the valves and guides are clean, insert each valve into its own guide and check it for sideways shake. If there is any appreciable slackness repeat the test with

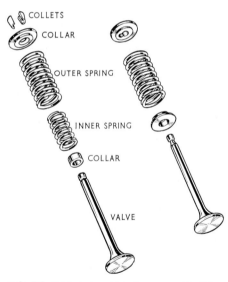

FIG. 5.5. Two types of valve assembly. The dual-spring type (*left*) is sometimes used on high-performance engines. The Triumph single-spring assembly (*right*) uses a "button-hole" spring retainer instead of split cotters or collets; after fitting it is moved sideways to allow the valve stem to engage in the smaller hole.

141

a new valve inserted in the guide, and if this shows that the guide is worn, take the cylinder head to the local agents for the car to have new guides pressed in. While it is not beyond the capabilities of the amateur to insert new guides, the valve seatings in the cylinder head should be recut after this has been done, and this calls for the use of special equipment. The best plan, therefore, is to let a service station carry out the work. This also applies if the seating faces of the valves are found to be badly pitted. They should be trued-up in a special machine.

On some engines the valves work directly in the cylinder head. When wear has occurred in their guides, the local agents for the car will be able to bore out the openings in the head to take oversize valves or, alternatively, will open them up sufficiently to allow conventional valve guides to be fitted.

Grinding-in the Valves. Assuming that the valves and seatings are in reasonably good condition, each valve must be lapped on to its seating with valve-grinding paste to ensure a gas-tight seal. Some inlet valves have an aluminium coating which increases their resistance to high-temperature oxidation by forming a hard, wear-resistant surface on the seating area, and

such valves should not be ground-in as this will remove the aluminium. If their faces are worn or pitted, new valves must be fitted and the seatings in the cylinder head should be recut by a service station. If the seatings are only slightly pitted, however, they can be cleaned up by grinding them with fine paste, using a discarded valve for the purpose.

To grind-in a valve, smear the face with a little of the fine grade of paste (the coarse grade should be used only if the valve is pitted, and then only when refacing cannot be done by a service station). Insert the valve in its guide and, using a suction-cup valve-grinding tool to hold it, rotate it a dozen or so times, a half-turn in each direction. Apply only light pressure while spinning the handle of the tool between the palms of the hands (Fig. 5.8).

A light coil spring fitted under the head of the valve will allow it to be lifted from its seating at frequent intervals, so as to redistribute the grinding paste. The valve should be given half a turn before grinding is resumed. Continue the operation until an even, matt grey ring exists on the valve and seating.

Clean both the valve and the seating and make a series of radial pencil marks across the seat, then replace the valve and rotate it through a quarter of a turn. All the pencil lines should have been erased at the centre. If lines are still visible, grinding must be continued. Prolonged grinding, however, is a waste of energy and is detrimental to the seatings. If good results cannot be obtained with light grinding-in, the valves, and possibly the seats, will require reconditioning by a service station as already mentioned.

Re-assembling the valves is a reversal of the dismantling process. Do not forget to fit new valve stem oil seals. To keep the split cotters in place on the valve stem as the collar is lowered, coat the groove on the stem liberally with thick grease. Some engines are fitted with valve springs which

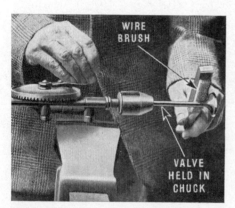

FIG. 5.7. Cleaning a valve by rotating it in a breast drill while a wire brush is held against the underside of the head.

142

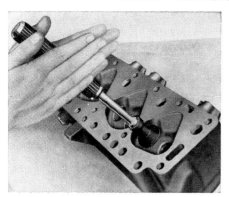

FIG. 5.8. The correct method of using a suction-cup valve grinding tool. The handle of the tool should be spun to and fro between the palms of the hands.

give a progressive resistance when compressed. These springs must be fitted with their closely-spaced coils nearest to the cylinder head.

Fitting the Cylinder Head. When all is ready for refitting the cylinder head, the gasket should be eased down over the studs. Make sure that it is the correct type and is being fitted the right way up. Care must be taken not to buckle the edges of the stud holes, and a good plan is to press the gasket over the studs with a box spanner. It is not advisable to use a jointing compound. If the car manufacturer does not specify that the gasket should be fitted dry, smear both sides with a thin film of high-melting-point grease.

Make sure that the cylinder head slides down easily on its studs. A bent stud can be carefully straightened but a badly damaged stud is best renewed. Screw two cylinder-head nuts on to it, lock them against each other and then unscrew the stud by using a spanner on the lower nut. The same principle can be used to screw the new stud into place. If a stud is broken, however, replacement may be a job for the service station, unless a special stud extractor is available.

If the cylinder head is retained by bolts instead of studs, it may be necessary to fit temporary locating studs at each end of the cylinder block to position the head and the gasket correctly while the remainder of the bolts are inserted. The local agents for the car can probably supply these, or they can be made by buying a couple of spare bolts, cutting off their heads and slotting their upper ends to take a screwdriver blade.

The cylinder-head nuts should be tightened progressively in the order shown in Fig. 4.11 in at least three or four stages, beginning with the nuts finger-tight, and ending with them pulled down as tightly as possible with a spanner of normal length for the nut size. Never use an extension on the spanner to obtain additional leverage as the studs may easily shear. The car handbook or workshop manual usually specifies the correct tightness (in lb/ft), and if a torque wrench is available this recommendation must be followed. Otherwise, as recommended earlier, have the nuts checked as soon as possible by the local agents for the car.

It only remains to complete the assembly of the engine, the operations being a reversal of dismantling, but before the inlet and exhaust manifolds are fitted, the mating faces must be thoroughly cleaned and carbon scraped out of the ports (Fig. 5.3). Do not forget to fill the radiator. The engine should be allowed to warm up gently until normal running temperature is attained, and the cylinder-head and manifold nuts, valve-cover nuts and similar items can then be checked over.

Remember that tightening the cylinder-head nuts on a push-rod-operated, over-head-valve engine will alter the valve clearances. Also, if the valve clearance quoted by the manufacturers applies to a hot engine, the clearances must be reset at this stage.

It may be necessary to check the ignition timing as described on page 117 and the carburettor idling adjustments must be reset (page 127). When the car has covered about 200 miles, a further check should be made on the tightness of the nuts and on the carburation and ignition settings.

MAJOR OVERHAUL

When an engine overhaul is needed, it may be cheaper in the long run to fit a works-reconditioned power unit, which can usually be obtained in exchange for the worn engine. The advantages of this scheme are that the replacement engine carries a guarantee and a fixed price is quoted, but to this must be added the labour charge for removing the old engine and installing the reconditioned unit, plus the cost of any reconditioned auxiliaries such as a clutch,

carburettor or distributor and, usually, the sparking plugs. Normally the car need not be out of service for more than a day.

If, on the other hand, you are in a position to carry out most of the dismantling and re-assembly yourself, have a workshop manual for the car, and can borrow or hire such service tools as may be needed, then a substantial saving in cost may be possible, for labour charges form a very high proportion of present-day repair bills.

It is often possible, for example, to obtain, either from the car manufacturer or from a specialist repairer, a "short engine". This consists of a completely

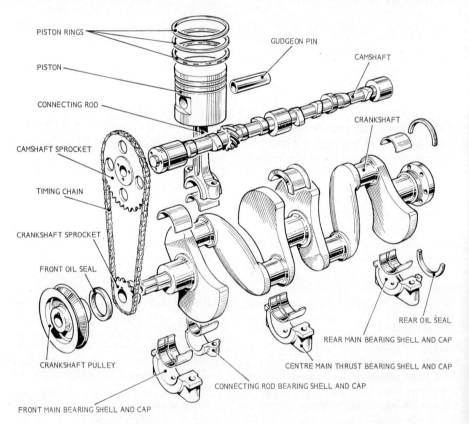

FIG. 5.9. The components which are involved in a partial or major overhaul. Attention to the pistons, rings, connecting-rod bearings and the timing chain may be sufficient to restore efficiency if the work is done at a suitable stage in the life of the engine.

FIG. 5.10. Piston fitting. (*Left*) On most engines pistons are removed and refitted through the top of the cylinder block. A piston ring clamp is used to compress the rings before the piston is entered into the bore, or a worm-drive Jubilee clip may be used for the purpose. (*Right*) It is usually necessary to tap the piston and ring assembly through the clamp with a mallet, but once the piston has entered the bore it should slide freely.

reconditioned cylinder block and crank-case assembly, incorporating rebored or sleeved cylinders, new pistons and rings, a reground crankshaft, new main, connect-ing-rod and camshaft bearings, and other essential items such as a new timing chain and sprockets, a reconditioned oil pump and so on. It remains for the owner to remove and refit the engine and to carry out a top overhaul on the cylinder head, thus obtaining a virtually new power unit for the minimum outlay.

A third possibility is to carry out a partial overhaul, often very effective when a modern engine has covered not more than about 30-40,000 miles. Cylinder wear, once the main factor in deciding when a major overhaul was required, is nowadays of less consequence than crankshaft bearing wear, the latter often determining whether a partial overhaul is likely to be an economic proposition.

Engine reconditioning firms supply standardized reconditioning kits, which include new pistons fitted with special oil-control rings that normally render a rebore unnecessary, a set of connecting-rod bearing shells, new exhaust valves, a set of valve springs, a timing chain, a set of gaskets, gasket cement, and graphite assembly compound. Using such a kit, a partial overhaul will often enable an engine that has had a life of about 30-40,000 miles from new to cover another 30-50,000 miles before a complete overhaul is required. The situation, therefore, is very different from that existing some years ago, when no responsible automobile engineer would have considered fitting new pistons to worn bores.

Fig. 5.9 shows the components that may be reconditioned in a partial or major overhaul, and which are referred to in this section.

145

FIG. 5.11. Measuring the piston-ring gap at a point just below the unworn section of the cylinder bore, as a first step in assessing the amount of bore wear.

Cylinder Wear. Before any decision is made regarding the probable effectiveness of a partial overhaul, the degree of cylinder wear must be determined. This wear takes two forms: the cylinders become oval, and are also worn more at the top than at the bottom of the bores, that is, they become tapered. On modern engines, however, it is unusual to find any appreciable degree of cylinder wear until 40-50,000 miles have been covered.

New, standard-size compression and oil-control rings will give satisfactory results if oval or taper wear does not exceed about 2 to 3 thousandths of an inch. If the wear exceeds this, several special types of piston ring are available which will compensate for ovality up to about 15 thousandths. When the wear exceeds these limits, the cylinders should be rebored and fitted with a set of oversize pistons and rings (Fig. 5.10).

Accurate measurement of the cylinders calls for the use of a special type of micrometer, but a fairly good idea of the amount of wear can be obtained by this rough-and-ready method (Fig. 5.11): Square-up a piston ring in the bore with a piston,

measure the gap in the ring at the top of the bore, push the ring to the bottom of the bore, and again measure the gap. Divide the difference between the two measurements by three.

When the degree of cylinder wear calls for a rebore, the work will, of course, be beyond the scope of the average owner. The engine can be stripped completely and the cylinder block rebored or ground oversize in a rigid machine tool. Alternatively, the work can be carried out with the engine in the car by using a portable boring machine. Provided that adequate precautions are taken to clean all foreign matter from the crankcase, and that the boring bar is operated by a skilled mechanic, "in situ" rebores are quite satisfactory.

If the engine has already been rebored and too little thickness of metal remains in the cylinder walls for further reboring, cylinder liners can be installed. Some engines have these fitted as standard, or removable cylinder barrels are used. These,

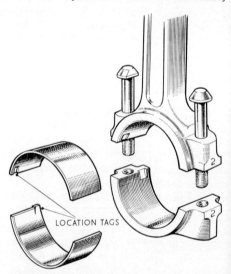

LOCATION TAGS

FIG. 5.12. Pair of half-liners for a big-end bearing; the locating tags must meet on the same edge. The connecting rod and bearing cap are numbered to ensure correct reassembly when new liners are fitted.

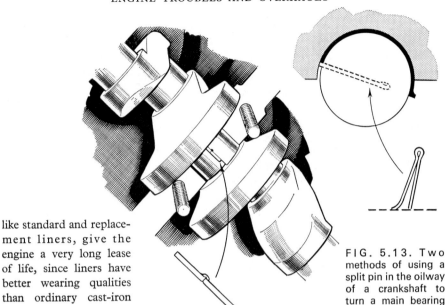

like standard and replacement liners, give the
engine a very long lease
of life, since liners have
better wearing qualities
than ordinary cast-iron
bores.

FIG. 5.13. Two
methods of using a
split pin in the oilway
of a crankshaft to
turn a main bearing
shell from its seating.

Crankshaft Wear. As indicated earlier,
the condition of the crankpins and journals
is a vital factor in determining whether a
major overhaul is needed. If the engine has
seen considerable service, these will be
worn oval to a considerable extent in
the case of the crankpins, and to a lesser
degree where the main-bearing journals
are concerned. To fit new bearings to
journals in this state is a waste of time. The
crankshaft journals should be reground,
and undersize bearings fitted. This is
obviously a job for the specialist. At the
mileage at which a partial overhaul is
carried out, however, crankshaft wear is not
usually excessive, and renewal of the
connecting-rod bearing shells is probably
all that will be required.

Thin steel shells faced with bearing
alloys are used almost exclusively nowadays,
although ball or roller bearings may be
used in some engines such as two-stroke
or racing designs. In these cases, replacement usually calls for special equipment
and is beyond the scope of the owner. Thin-
shell bearings, however, can be clicked into
the connecting rods without the need for

any filing of the caps, fitting of shims or
scraping the bearing metal, and do not
require running-in (Fig. 5.12).

Although main bearing replacements
are usually beyond the scope of the
owner, the bearing shells can sometimes
be renewed as follows: each bearing cap is
taken off in turn and the upper shell is
removed by fitting a split-pin in the oil
hole of the journal and giving the crankshaft a half-turn so that the bearing is
pushed round and displaced by the split
pin (Fig. 5.13). The new upper shell is
slid round into place in a similar manner.

When attention to the engine bearings
is required, it may be as the result of
general wear over a large mileage or may
be caused by oil starvation. If the bearings
have broken up or melted, it is essential
to clean out the oilways in the crankshaft
by forcing air or oil through the oil supply
passages under high pressure. If this fails
to dislodge the obstruction, it may be
necessary to remove the sealing plugs and
pass a wire or a drill through the passages.

147

CHAPTER 6

TRANSMISSION SYSTEM

A CAR'S transmission system comprises the whole of the components concerned with transmitting engine power to the road wheels—that is, the clutch and gearbox (or automatic transmission), the propeller shaft and final drive gearing, and the axles and bearings for the driving wheels. The first requirement for trouble-free operation of this system is obviously correct lubrication and maintenance. Beyond this, there are certain tasks which are within the scope of the more skilful home mechanic.

Serious trouble in the transmission system can prove expensive but is fortunately rare. Generally, it is best rectified by taking advantage of the makers' exchange replacement scheme. A replacement unit can easily be fitted by the local agents for the car, but both off-road time and expense will be saved if the owner himself is able to undertake removal of a faulty unit, and subsequent assembly of the replacement.

CLUTCH

The single dry plate type of clutch is in universal use on cars today, although multi-plate clutches are used for racing engines. Its basic design has remained largely unchanged for many years, but there have been constant detail improvements. However, the long-established use of coil springs to apply the necessary pressure between the driving and driven elements of the clutch is now giving way to the diaphragm principle (described later under "Diaphragm Spring Clutch"). Another difference is that on some cars the clutch is actuated mechanically, but the majority today employ hydraulic control between the clutch pedal and the withdrawal mechanism.

Construction. The driven plate is

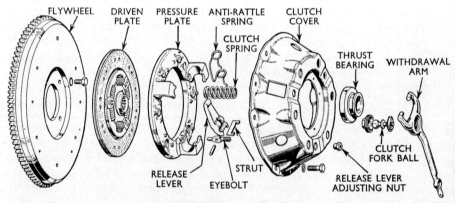

FIG. 6.1. The component parts of a standard coil-spring single-plate clutch. For clarity, only one of the three release-lever assemblies and one of the six coil springs are illustrated, together with the carbon-ring thrust bearing and withdrawal mechanism. This type of clutch is made in several sizes.

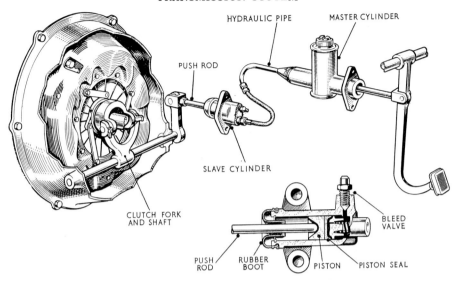

FIG. 6.2. Lockheed hydraulic clutch control system, in which fluid pressure is developed in the master cylinder and applied to the piston of the slave cylinder (shown inset).

faced on both sides by friction material known as the lining (Fig. 6.1). The withdrawal mechanism comprises a self-lubricating graphite block, ring-shaped and carried in a housing. The graphite surface forms the actual thrust face taking the withdrawal loading, and has considerable wearing depth. The clutch disc is flexible, and is not riveted directly to its splined hub but incorporates at the centre an assembly of coil springs which form the actual driving medium between plate and hub.

The result is that when the clutch is engaged, the springs have a degree of resilience as the load passes from the disc to the hub, while the flexibility of the plate as a whole ensures that as the pressure plate applies its "squeezing" effect the whole of the lining is in equal contact.

The driven plate, pressure plate, springs and related components are all housed inside a steel cover which is bolted on to the flywheel periphery, the assembly being known as the "pressure unit." This can be removed and refitted as a whole, and is

available as a service replacement unit in case of trouble. This is a very good feature, since the balance and adjustment of the pressure unit is a matter requiring special equipment. When assembled on the flywheel, the appearance with the gearbox removed is simply that of the unit cover bolted to the flywheel, having a large central aperture through which a circular machined face is visible. This face is the thrust pad, which is contacted by the separate carbon-graphite withdrawal block when the pedal is depressed.

The availability of the pressure unit as a service assembly has eliminated many of the problems formerly associated with clutch trouble. For instance a common source of complaint used to be uneven pulling-back of the pressure plate, this being caused by faulty adjustment of the levers transmitting movement from the thrust pad to the plate, or even by distortion of the levers. The former trouble is taken care of by "works adjustment" on the pressure unit, and this automatically makes the latter very improbable, since

149

levers properly adjusted can hardly be overloaded. Nowadays, therefore, clutch trouble is rare, and if it does occur is not likely to be due to some simple cause which can easily be rectified.

The graphite release bearing is actuated either by a mechanical linkage or hydraulically. With a mechanical system, the carrier locating the graphite ring is held in a fork which is pivoted on a cross-shaft in the main housing. An extended lever outside the housing is coupled to the pedal by a rod, chain or cable, so that pedal movement causes the lever to actuate the fork, bringing the graphite face up against the thrust pad on the pressure unit.

With hydraulic operation this withdrawal principle is unchanged, but the operating lever of the fork is coupled by a rod to the piston of a hydraulic "slave" cylinder, usually mounted externally. Fluid pressure is applied via a short pipeline from a master cylinder, whose piston is worked directly by the clutch pedal (Fig. 6.2). The required "leverage" is obtained by suitably pro-portioning the piston areas in the two cylinders.

Diaphragm Spring Clutch. This type is now coming into general use, having the advantages of being light in weight and able to exert a very even pressure around the edge of the pressure plate (Fig. 6.3). As manufactured, the one-piece diaphragm spring has a conical shape, but when assembled in the clutch it is strained to the shape of an almost flat disc, pressing against the pressure plate. Withdrawal of the clutch by means of a conventional graphite thrust bearing causes the inner portion of the spring to be pushed inwards, while the outer portion moves outwards as the diaphragm attempts to regain its conical form. Pressure is thereby released from the pressure plate.

In this case also the pressure assembly forms a self-contained unit which should be exchanged for a replacement assembly in the event of trouble. The general requirements for overhaul are the same as for a coil-spring clutch.

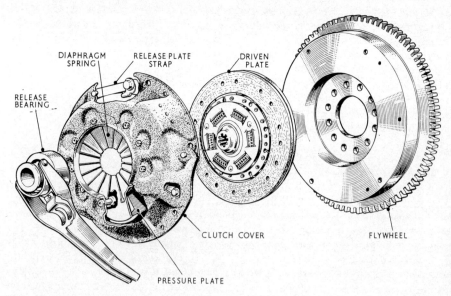

FIG. 6.3. Component parts of a diaphragm-spring clutch, with the clutch cover partly cut away to show how the rim of the one-piece diaphragm spring bears against the pressure plate. A conventional driven plate is used.

Routine Clutch Service. On most modern cars, the only regular attentions needed by the clutch are to inspect the level of fluid in the master cylinder reservoir, where hydraulic control is used (normally every 3,000 miles), and to check the adjustment of the clutch release mechanism at intervals specified in the car instruction book. However, a number of cars are now fitted with self-adjusting diaphragm-spring clutches which do not require the latter attention.

CLUTCH ADJUSTMENT

On all clutches except the self-adjusting type just mentioned, the matter of maintaining correct adjustment is of vital importance, as will be explained.

When the clutch is fully engaged the graphite face of the thrust bearing must be clear of the pressure pad by at least $\frac{1}{16}$ in. If the faces are touching (even without sufficient pressure to cause clutch slip by taking the load off the springs) the graphite will wear quickly, though it is easily up to the job if used intermittently, as intended. The careful driver will thus avoid waiting in traffic with the clutch held out by the pedal for unduly long periods, but get into neutral to release the thrust.

A few makers have up to recently used a metal bearing of the sealed ball-thrust type, to which the above comment applies. These bearings, while noisier than the carbon-graphite block, are equally reliable.

For a modern vehicle in good condition, clutch maintenance involves nothing more than ensuring that there is clearance at the thrust bearing, that the withdrawal mechanism is operating properly, and that the clutch withdraws far enough to ensure silent and free gear engagement, but without "binding" or closing-up the clutch springs to an extent which could overload the components.

In the case of mechanical linkage, the $\frac{1}{16}$ in. free movement at the thrust pad is usually "converted", in the car instruc-

tion manual, to free movement at the clutch pedal pad. For example, it might be specified that the pedal should move $\frac{3}{4}$ in. before resistance is felt, indicating that the pressure is being applied to the springs. This free motion of $\frac{3}{4}$ in. actually represents the $\frac{1}{16}$ in. multiplied by the leverage.

As far as ensuring clearance for the withdrawal mechanism is concerned, too much lost motion does no harm; the disadvantage—apart from the "sloppy" feel of the pedal—is that the remainder of the available movement might be insufficient to ensure complete freeing of the friction al faces. In some cars, quite a nice balance has to be struck between the extremes. It w ll be obvious that so long as the pressure plate is pulled back clear of the driven plate, so that the latter in turn can free itself from the flywheel face, all will be in order; any further pull-back is superfluous, and may over-compress the springs.

Some assemblies have an adjustable stop for limiting the amount of withdrawing movement, but this is hardly ever altered unless the clutch refuses to withdraw properly and all other possible faults have been investigated.

Assuming that adjustment all round is correct, we can consider what happens in the course of normal usage. Wear takes place on the two friction-lined faces of the driven plate, reducing its overall thickness. The clutch pressure unit ensures that the plate is still firmly gripped between the pressure plate and flywheel face, irrespective of wear, but in order to do this the former will have moved slightly closer to the latter when fully engaged. If therefore the pedal is pushed to the usual limit as when new, the subsequent withdrawal travel will give more clearance to the "thinner" plate. This is of little moment, far more important being the effect on thrust bearing clearance.

When as a result of lining wear the pressure plate moves forwards, this naturally moves the pressure pad *backwards*,

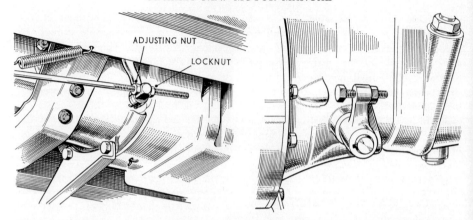

FIG. 6.4. (*Left*) The method of adjustment for a clutch linkage operated mechanically. (*Right*) An adjustable stop for limiting the amount of withdrawal movement, as used with some mechanically operated clutches.

that is, nearer the graphite block. In these circumstances, the $\frac{1}{16}$ in. clearance may gradually be reduced to zero. When that occurs, it is no longer possible for the pressure plate to exert its full "squeezing" effect, the clutch may slip, and the graphite block will be adversely affected.

Of course, there is a gradual reduction of the free pedal travel because of this wear; this will be noted by the alert driver, who will readjust the linkage to restore the necessary clearance (Fig. 6.4). The rule must be not only to ensure that pedal clearance is present but that the amount is correct as specified by the makers.

Hydraulic Operation. With a hydraulically controlled clutch the foregoing adjustments are eliminated. The only requirement is a very small clearance between the end of the hydraulic operating (slave) piston, and the push-rod taking the motion to the graphite block. Because of the inherent flexibility of the hydraulic system, there is no need for a large amount of free pedal movement. At the same time, as the fluid is not under any pressure when the clutch is fully home, there can be no damaging thrust-block contact.

Some makers suggest checking the adjustment at intervals of about 3,000

miles, others at 6,000 miles or more. The usual adjustment is by means of a nut and locknut on the threaded push-rod shaft (Fig. 6.5). As already mentioned, the hydraulic reservoir should be inspected at the same time. If the fluid level has dropped, the two cylinders and pipeline should be carefully checked for leakage, and this must be put right.

If air enters the hydraulic system through some defect, this will cause spongy operation of the pedal. The defective parts (often rubber piston cups) must be replaced and all air bled out of the system after it has been refilled. For this purpose a bleed nipple is fitted to the slave cylinder, the procedure being the same as that described for hydraulic brakes (see page 212).

CLUTCH MAINTENANCE

Trouble with the clutch is apt to be a nuisance because of the general inaccessibility of the components. It most commonly takes the form of either slipping under load or a refusal to free properly.

Slip can be caused by two things, assuming the mechanism is otherwise in good order: either inability of the springs to exert full pressure, or else a badly worn lining. In the first case, proper adjustment will ensure full spring pressure being brought to bear, but slip can still be induced sometimes by indulging in fast gear-changing on an open throttle—especially on engines that have been "converted" to produce more than standard power. It is important when considering any such engine modifications to include the clutch. A change of pressure unit for a more powerfully sprung type, plus different linings on the plate, may be desirable to give an adequate margin of grip to cope with the extra power.

Worn Linings. If the linings of the driven plate are much worn, impending trouble may be shown by a tendency to slip on fierce acceleration, which at first can easily be mistaken for wheel-spin, particularly on wet roads. Once it is established that wheel-spin is not in fact taking place, it is essential that attention is given to the clutch; otherwise the first time it has really to be "used" (in, for example, a hill-restart with a full load), it may give up altogether.

To obtain access to the clutch, it is normally necessary to split the flywheel clutch housing (or bellhousing) and to remove the engine or gearbox from the car.

Unless the former is due for overhaul any-way, it is usual to take out the gearbox, as being a simpler operation, but on "power-package" vehicles having front-engine/front-drive or rear-engine/rear-drive and transaxle units, the complete assembly usually has to come out. The method of parting the housing flange is detailed later in this chapter, in connection with gearbox removal.

Having gained access to the clutch pressure unit, the first thing to do before dismantling is to mark the pressure unit and flywheel with paint to ensure that it is replaced in the same position, so that correct engine balance is maintained. (There may be dowel location at the pressure-unit edge, in which case this precaution is unnecessary.) The pressure unit can be removed by taking out the bolts securing it to the flywheel rim, when the driven plate can be lifted out; it may tend to adhere to the flywheel face.

It is necessary to examine all the components closely to ascertain the actual cause of slip. If this was due to legitimate wear the lining will show clear evidence, as there will be considerable "thinning". In this case there are two courses open.

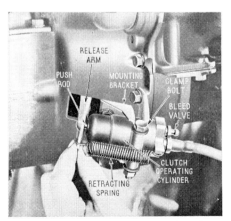 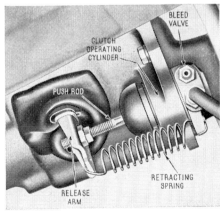

FIG. 6.5. Two methods of adjusting hydraulically operated clutches: Moving the operating cylinder bodily in its mounting bracket (*left*), and altering the effective length of the push rod by adjusting the position of its nut against the release arm (*right*).

153

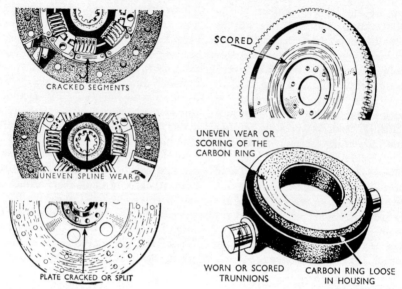

CRACKED SEGMENTS

SCORED

UNEVEN SPLINE WEAR

UNEVEN WEAR OR
SCORING OF THE
CARBON RING

PLATE CRACKED OR SPLIT

WORN OR SCORED
TRUNNIONS

CARBON RING LOOSE
IN HOUSING

FIG. 6.6. Some possible clutch troubles. The three faults in the driven plate shown on the left can result from misalignment of the clutch. Heavy wear on the driven-plate friction facings may develop through scoring on the flywheel face. Also illustrated are some release bearing faults which can lead to unsatisfactory clutch operation.

The plate can be taken to a repairer to be relined, or a complete replacement plate can be fitted. The latter, while more expensive, is probably best in the long run; apart from the linings, the cushioning springs at the plate centre come in for heavy loading, as do the shaft splines. With a replacement plate complete, all such parts are renewed as well and give a good return for cost, in terms of smoother take-up and reduced backlash in the transmission.

In the ordinary way, plate replacement would be all that is required to restore full efficiency, but while the clutch is dismantled it is a good idea to carry out an examination to make sure that the new plate is going to have a fair deal. The flywheel and pressure plate faces should be scrutinised closely; these may be scored radially if clutch usage has been more than normally incompetent, or if the linings have been allowed to wear right down to their rivet-heads. A badly-scored pressure-plate is best dealt with by an "exchange"

replacement of the whole pressure unit. Defects of the flywheel face are obviously more serious, necessitating removal of the wheel and a skimming operation, but fortunately such cases are rare.

Before re-assembling, all parts should be thoroughly cleaned. It is also a good idea to replace the graphite thrust bearing if this has seen a lot of service, as it is inexpensive and may save a job later on.

Clutch Defects. So much for the situation where, as expected, the lining is found to be worn out. We can now consider the occasions when after dismantling, the plate is obviously in good condition as far as this point is concerned. In such cases slip can only be caused by foreign matter—usually oil—being present on the friction surfaces. In normal use the linings take on a polish, giving very smooth engagement with adequate transmitting capacity, if the spring pressure is sufficient. This polish is easy to see, but does not affect the colour of the linings, which

154

together with the natural grain of the material can be seen quite clearly through the glaze. Darkening of the surface denotes that small quantities of oil have been present, but have been burnt off as a result of heat generated during starting.

A momentary defect of this kind has little effect on performance, and in fact is more likely to make the clutch fierce when engaging than to cause slip. Larger quantities of oil may not only give a much darker appearance to the linings but will only burn off in part, leaving a definite deposit on the surface. This then becomes glazed, but unlike the "natural" polish gives a coating to the face which will spoil the frictional grip. To some extent also it causes the plate to stick on engagement, so that the clutch will not free properly when the pedal is depressed but will at the same time slip when driving.

The more oil present the worse the effects, so that any discolouration of the linings must be suspect, and a check made for the source of possible oil leakage into the housing. The most obvious place is the rear main engine bearing. This, however, is normally provided with fully adequate oil-return arrangements. Even with the sump grossly overfilled, it is most unlikely that the oil (in defiance of all the obstacles in its path) will run completely out of the housing in preference to taking its simpler designed path back to the sump. Excessive bearing wear might be a cause, but this would become audible before clutch slip intervened.

Further possible sources are from oil-pressure points which may be incorporated in the crankcase housing behind the flywheel, such as blanking plugs of oil galleries. Evidence of leaks is usually found in the presence of oil at the bottom of the flywheel housing, and the only method of ascertaining the facts is to remove the flywheel. The gearbox input shaft at the point where it emerges from the box is another possible source of leakage, any oil creeping along the shaft from this point being in an ideal position to get straight on to the plate. Overfilling of the box, together with a blocked breather, might give rise to such a condition even if the oil seal is sound.

Finally, there is the situation whereby with the clutch faultless, there is still difficulty in obtaining a smooth take-off in certain circumstances. The remedy often lies in giving attention to the engine mountings and rear axle assembly. The former sometimes settle down and become excessively flexible, while if a torque reaction link is fitted to limit the degree of engine movement on the mountings, this may need adjustment. Judicious tightening can often help but must not be overdone, as the flexibility is there for a purpose.

The rear axle assembly also must be firm on its suspension, otherwise its "wind-up" due to torque reaction will introduce judder, particularly on hills. Springs that have settled down, or shock absorbers in need of servicing, can aggravate these faults.

The pressure unit should be left alone, apart from examining the face of the pressure plate as mentioned. If weakening of the clutch springs or uneven withdrawal (due to inaccurate setting of the levers) is suspected, the unit should be examined by an expert equipped with the necessary gauges, and a replacement fitted if advised.

The gearbox input shaft locates in a bearing at the flywheel centre. In order to facilitate uniting the engine and gearbox after refitting the clutch, it is necessary to centralise the driven plate by means of a mandrel through the centre of the pressure unit. This ensures that when the unit is in position the gearbox input shaft can be entered into the unit, without any trouble from misalignment of the driven plate. The pressure unit with the driven plate thus aligned is offered up to the flywheel, noting the position of the balancing paint

155

marks on pressure unit and flywheel rim. Push the pressure unit over the dowels if any are used, insert the bolts and tighten.

Automatic Clutches. Clutches of automatic or semi-automatic type have appeared from time to time, but since their constructional details differ widely, the makers' advice should always be sought in case of trouble. The advent of automatic transmissions suitable for cars of all sizes suggests that such clutches are unlikely to be revived in the future.

THE GEARBOX

The standard type of gearbox has its input and output shafts respectively at the front and rear of the housing, and gives a straight-through drive in "top gear" (Fig. 6.7). Beneath this main-shaft assembly, a layshaft is mounted parallel to it. Synchromesh mechanism is invariably provided at least on the upper three ratios,

and often on all four. Designs incorporating a power unit combined with gearbox and transmission, whether mounted at front or rear of the car, often use an all-indirect gearbox in which there is no direct drive. This meets better the requirements of the mechanical layout, as the input from the clutch is fed to one shaft, and the output (final drive) pinion is mounted on the other.

Trouble inside the gearbox is unlikely so long as the car is handled intelligently, but in any case dismantling is an involved operation generally calling for the use of special equipment. In the event of internal trouble, specialist advice should be sought. Normal maintenance is highly important, but in recent years this has been greatly minimized because of the long intervals now permissible between oil changes. In fact, certain makers have gone so far as to omit the drain plug altogether, in which

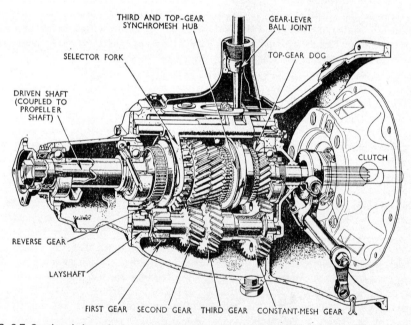

FIG. 6.7. Sectional view of a four-speed Austin gearbox. This shows how the clutch is located in a bellhousing forward of the unit, while the gearbox output shaft is coupled to the propeller shaft by way of a sliding joint in the rear extension housing. The gears run in an oil bath and are engaged by the sliding movement of selector forks.

FIG. 6.8. An oil drain plug and a combined filler/level plug are usually fitted to the gearbox. (*Left*) Drain and filler plugs on a Ford gearbox installed with an overdrive unit. (*Right*) The Volkswagen transmission unit has separate drain plugs for the gearbox and the final drive, although these components share a common oil supply.

case inspection of the oil level, and topping up if necessary, is all that needs to be done.

It is important always to use the correct grade of lubricant and to check the level as called for, however infrequently this may be. The filler plug is usually mounted at such a height on the casing as to form an effective level gauge, the box being filled until it overflows. However, separate level plugs may still be found, also dip-sticks, the function of which is self-explanatory (Fig. 6.8). When replacing gearbox plugs, check that their washers are in good condition, and the plugs tightened firmly but not excessively.

Oil leaks or undue gear noise should be investigated by removal of the box. No attempt must be made to rectify these by using thicker oil than specified, as in that case the lubricant may not reach important bearing surfaces when starting from cold, and rapid wear will be caused.

GEARBOX REMOVAL

If internal trouble is experienced with the gearbox, the assembly should be removed from the car for expert rectifica-

tion. Such trouble may show as refusal of gears to engage, failure of synchromesh mechanism, slipping out of mesh, or unusual and particularly intermittent noises. Most manufacturers include the gearbox assembly in their exchange replacement scheme, which means that however serious the trouble is found to be after dismantling, the car need be off the road only for the time taken to effect the changeover.

In normal layouts, the gearbox can readily be removed leaving the engine in position. The important point is that throughout the operation, the engine and gearbox must be supported properly, so that when parted at the flywheel housing flange, the clutch shaft (gearbox input shaft) is kept parallel. If it is subjected to any bending this will damage the clutch plate, and quite possibly the shaft itself.

The arrangement must first be investigated to decide the amount of preliminary dismantling necessary; in this, the maker's instruction manual will be of assistance. Components likely to impede access should be removed, and it is preferable to take off too many rather than to leave something *in situ,* which becomes a nuisance at a critical time when manhandling weighty parts.

Items such as the speedometer drive cable and battery earthing strap are often overlooked; it is advisable to disconnect the battery so as to make all circuits dead, in case odd wires have to be moved. The rear drive coupling flanges on propellor shaft and output shaft should be marked with paint so that they can be re-assembled in the same original position, and the flange uncoupled, when the propeller shaft can be telescoped along its splines and lowered to the floor.

All the bolts may now be removed from the flywheel housing flange except the lowermost one or two, after ascertaining that the unit is still firmly supported. If it is necessary to remove the top of the gearbox for convenience, make sure that the springs and balls of the selector shaft locks do not fly out; these are sometimes retained by the cover flange. The bolts can now be removed from the rear frame mounting on the gearbox, the final bolts taken out of the bellhousing flange, and the gearbox pulled backwards and lifted out. With the box removed, full access is obtained to the clutch, and this can be dismantled from the flywheel quite readily with the engine in position. When replacing the gearbox take great care in entering the input shaft to the clutch centre, keeping everything parallel and supporting the gearbox from underneath. Insert a few bolts into the bellhousing flange and tighten them finger-tight. Line up the rear mounting and insert the fixing bolts. When all is secure, fit all the bellhousing bolts and tighten them firmly; finally, secure the rear-mounting bolts.

A few older cars may have all the mountings on the crankcase, the gearbox being completely overhung at the bellhousing. In this case the job is rather simpler, but the same care is necessary to ensure that the gearbox is not allowed to drop and hazard the clutch plate.

Gear Controls. Gear-shift levers working directly on to the box give little trouble and are usually non-adjustable, as far as actual selection of ratios is concerned. Slipping out of gear with this type may be due to weak or broken selector-lock springs, usually accessible as mentioned from the lid of the box. Otherwise, trouble can almost certainly be rectified by replacement of worn components.

In the case of steering-column gear-change systems, adjust-

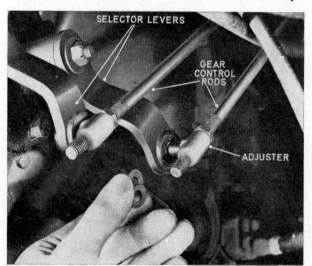

FIG. 6.9. A Ford steering-column gearshift arrangement with two linkages, one to select high and intermediate gears and one to select low and reverse gears. Adjustment is provided in each linkage in the form of an adjuster sleeve secured by a lock-nut which alters the effective length of the gear control rod.

ment is generally provided (Fig. 6.9). There are two movements involved: an up-and-down motion in line with the steering column, to engage the selector required for the particular ratio; and movement of the selector itself so as to mesh the gear. As the shift linkage merely actuates the selector rods, which have their spring-loaded locks of normal type, adjustment is not as a rule provided here.

The selector linkage, however, may have an adjustment to ensure that the correct selector is engaged for the ratio concerned. When out of adjustment, it is generally found that while two ratios, say 1st and 2nd, can be selected, the lever cannot then be moved to the other selector, to engage 3rd and 4th. Adjustment involves striking the correct balance between the two positions, and may be done by means such as the provision of threaded rods with lock-nuts at some point in the selector linkage.

OVERDRIVE

The usual electrical operation of overdrive units is very reliable, but requires a good deal of skill and experience to carry out adequate checks in the event of faulty working. It is, of course, quite feasible to examine the wiring so as to ensure that there are no visible short-circuits, particularly at terminals.

In the case of the Borg-Warner overdrive, failure to release can be due to defects in the governor or solenoid, and is shown by the refusal of the car to be pushed backward with the ignition off and the gearshift in neutral; but it can be pushed forward quite readily. Defective kickdown implies a fault in the kickdown switch or the solenoid. Faults may also cause the engine to cut out when kickdown is attempted.

As far as mechanical controls are concerned, the lockout cable must be correctly adjusted, as otherwise it is possible for the overdrive to lock itself out of action because of excessive rock on flexible engine mountings. However, this can also be seen by the fact that the facia control will move inwards from the lockout position during running.

When an overdrive is fitted to an existing car, the gearbox is modified by adding components to provide a lockout condition when reverse is selected. If, when an overdrive has been installed, the car will not reverse unless the facia lockout control is operated, it indicates that such parts have been omitted or fitted incorrectly. Accurate alignment of the overdrive unit with the gearbox is also important, as misalignment can cause a variety of troubles.

Fitting an Overdrive Control Switch. Automatic electrical control of the overdrive is highly satisfactory, but nevertheless there are motorists who may prefer a manual switch. It is possible to wire the Borg-Warner unit to provide such a feature, but the makers naturally take no responsibility, nor supply parts for such modification.

One method consists of fitting a switch within the driver's reach, one side being earthed and the other connected to the governor terminal. When the switch is open, or "off", normal automatic operation is maintained. When "on", the overdrive ratio will be maintained regardless of road speed when the accelerator is momentarily released. Kickdown gives the usual direct ratio, but the freewheel is inoperative, and the overdrive cannot be locked out by the normal facia control. Also, reverse gear cannot be obtained with the switch closed. Objections to the modification might be liability of the driver to hang on to the overdrive ratio at unduly low speeds, with wastage of fuel due both to excessive throttle opening and the unavailability of the freewheel.

If the switch is a two-way and off type, such as a turn indicator switch, this can be wired as shown in Fig. 6.10. Here, the two end positions provide the equivalent

159

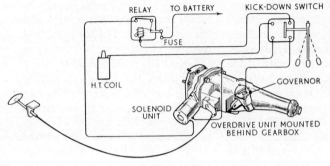

FIG. 6.10. (*Upper*) Installation details of a Borg-Warner overdrive unit, showing the parts mentioned in the text. (*Lower*) Wiring of an auxiliary switch to permit manual control of a Borg-Warner overdrive.

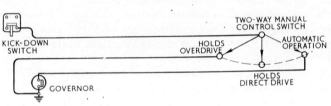

withdrawn. The clamp is left in position until the coupling is refitted (Fig. 6.11). The power package is usually lifted out by a hoist when front-mounted, but rear-engined cars may require a different technique. On the Hillman Imp again, the unit is supported from underneath and the car wheeled forwards clear of it, after removal of the rear body member and engine mountings, etc.

of the ordinary switch just described, while at the centre, overdrive engagement is prevented regardless of accelerator pedal release, above cut-in speeds. In this position, the freewheel action is available, but there is no engine braking, and of course no overdrive.

"POWER-PACKAGE" TRANSMISSIONS

When access is required to the clutch or gearbox on cars having unitary construction of engine and transaxle, and mounted appropriately for front- or rear-wheel drive, the complete unit must be removed from the vehicle. (Examples are front-wheel drive B.M.C., Hillman Imp and Volkswagen.) This involves uncoupling the drive shafts to the road wheels. It is usual for these to incorporate some form of vibration-absorbing coupling in addition to the universal joints, and these may require special care.

On the Hillman Imp, for example, it is necessary to restrain the couplings in the working position at all times, this being done by encircling the couplings by a readily-made clamp, before the bolts are

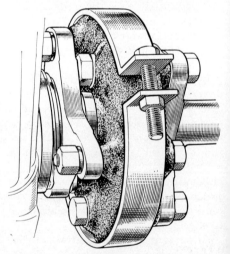

FIG. 6.11. Clamp in position to restrain the anti-vibration rubber coupling on a drive shaft of the Hillman Imp, prior to unbolting the coupling.

FIG. 6.12. This automatic transmission by Automotive Products is designed to fit into the sump of the smaller B.M.C. transverse engines, taking up little more space than the normal manual gearbox.

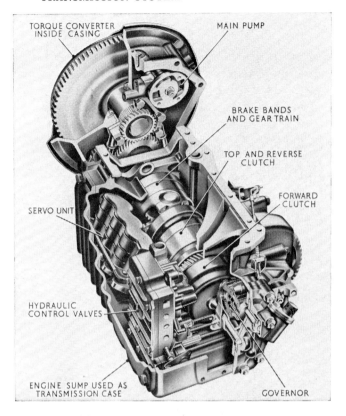

TORQUE CONVERTER INSIDE CASING

MAIN PUMP

BRAKE BANDS AND GEAR TRAIN

TOP AND REVERSE CLUTCH

FORWARD CLUTCH

SERVO UNIT

HYDRAULIC CONTROL VALVES

ENGINE SUMP USED AS TRANSMISSION CASE

GOVERNOR

AUTOMATIC TRANSMISSIONS

Various types of automatic transmission have been introduced in recent years. They include the Borg-Warner Model 8, used on larger cars such as the Jaguar Mk. 10 and Vanden Plas Princess R, and the basically similar Model 35 on a wide range of medium-size cars. The Hydra-Matic design is used on larger Vauxhall models, with a modified version on Rolls-Royce. No longer in production are the Roverdrive used by Rover and the Smiths Easidrive used on certain Hillman and Singer models. A more recent introduction is the Automotive Products transmission developed for small B.M.C. front-wheel drive cars (Fig. 6.12).

The established type as represented by the popular Borg-Warner Model 35 consists basically of a hydraulic torque converter and an epicyclic-type gearbox providing a series of ratios, on conventional principles. The equipment is necessarily complicated and specialized, in comparison with a normal friction clutch and manual gearbox, but experience shows that it is remarkably trouble-free and will normally outlast the life of the car.

Routine maintenance of these units is very simple but must never be neglected. On Borg-Warner equipment, the oil level should be checked and topped-up as necessary at intervals specified in the car instruction book (usually every 3,000 miles). After a run to bring the gearbox up to normal operating temperature, keep the engine idling, clean the dipstick fitted to the transmission, then check the oil level shown on it (Fig. 6.13). No oil changes are necessary.

On Hydra-Matic units, the oil and an oil filter must be changed every 24,000 miles or two years. The Roverdrive had separate oil supplies for its torque converter and gearbox, using S.A.E. 20 engine oil. Other transmissions employ specially developed lubricants and it is *essential* to use only the oils specified by the maker.

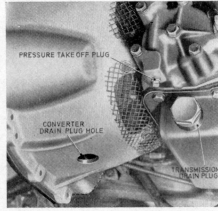

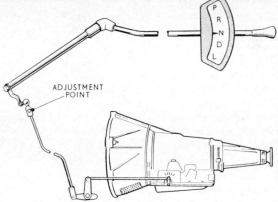

FIG. 6.13. Maintenance of automatic transmissions. (*Upper left*) A dipstick is provided on the Borg-Warner unit, and the oil should be topped up when necessary. (*Upper right*) Separate drain plugs are fitted for the torque converter and the gearbox, though oil changes are not normally required. (*Lower*) Borg-Warner selector lever and linkage, showing where adjustment is made for correct operation.

It is also of absolute importance to ensure that the smallest trace of dirt or grit is kept out of the system, so scrupulous cleanliness must be observed when removing the filler plugs and topping-up. Take care not to overfill with oil.

Apart from attending to lubrication, the owner should not tamper with an automatic transmission. The normal method of dealing with trouble is to fit an exchange service unit, and this work should be left to the local agents for the car. It is, however, possible for trained mechanics to make adjustments and replace some parts on a faulty unit. Before any dismantling is done it is useful to be able to give adequate information regarding the trouble symptoms as shown up by a road test. The same

road test should be carried out after a replacement unit has been fitted, to ensure that all is correct.

Road Test. Referring to the Borg-Warner units, first check that the starter operates only in positions P and N; also that when R is selected the reversing light (if fitted) operates. Apply the brakes, and with the engine idling, select in the sequence N to D, N to L, N to R. At each engagement, there should be a distinct "feel" in the transmission. The next test must be done in a maximum of 10 seconds to guard against overheating of the transmission. All that is required is to select L, check the engine stalling speed, and repeat for R; also note any signs of "clutch squeak" or slip.

162

The gear-changes in position D should next be checked, at normal running temperature. Then at a car speed of slightly over 30 m.p.h. coast the car with the ignition off. Let the speed drop to 30 m.p.h. and select L, when the engine should start, being driven by the car. This shows correct working of the rear oil-pump in the gearbox. Now do a stop-restart with the accelerator as normally and check for upward-change speeds.

The down-change speeds can next be tried. At 25 m.p.h. in top, apply nominal full throttle (i.e. not kickdown). There should be no down-shift. Repeat this using kickdown at 30 m.p.h. and a down-change should occur to 2nd. Repeat this kickdown at 15 m.p.h.; the down-change should be into 1st. Then try a stop-restart with the throttle hard down through the button, and check the up-change speeds.

Next check the braking effect. At 40 m.p.h. in top, let back the throttle and select L. Note if there is correct down-change to 2nd, with engine braking. Try this also on the 2nd to 1st down-shift at appropriate speed. Stop the car, and with L still engaged release the brakes and accelerate on full throttle to 20 m.p.h. There should be no upward change, but also no clutch slip or squeak. Finally, face the car downhill on a good gradient and select P. With the brakes off, the pawl in the gearbox should hold the car. The brakes must be put on again before the pawl is disengaged; then repeat the test facing uphill.

It must be noted that for the actual speeds at which the changes are required, the driving instructions issued with the car should be followed.

Automotive Products Transmission. Fitted to certain B.M.C. Mini and 1100 models, this transmission is incorporated in the engine sump, as in the case of the manual-change gear system. The torque converter is of conventional type, but the epicyclic-gear unit is interesting in that it uses bevel gearing instead of spur wheels. By this means, the overall diameter is kept to a minimum, facilitating installation in the confined space. The gear system also enables an overdrive to be included in the main unit (Fig. 6.12).

The selector control also differs from convention, in that separate positions are provided for each individual box rattle. Thus manual changes can be made if desired as in ordinary hand operation, the difference being that there is no clutch pedal movement and the changes can be extremely rapid. For automatic working, a D position is selected. In the event of trouble developing, specialist attention must be sought, the complete engine and transaxle unit being removed.

TRANSMISSION SHAFTS

The central propeller shaft from front engine to rear axle is still the standard method of power transmission, being a standardized component, with Hooke-type universal joints at each end (Fig. 6.14). Some universal joints are provided with a lubricator and require regular greasing or oiling, but the trend nowadays is towards sealed joints. Where the gearbox output shaft is located axially, the propeller shaft is arranged with a telescoping member, to allow for the variation in length consequent on its up-and-down movement. When the output shaft can float axially to allow this movement, the propeller shaft is a one-piece type, but similar universal joints are used. These joints are of needle-roller type, grease-packed and usually requiring no attention.

Telescoping shafts have sliding splines at the front end which are arranged for grease-gun lubrication. The position of this single nipple is inconvenient, as it is accessible only from underneath the car or through a hole in the gearbox tunnel, and also requires the shaft to be turned (by wheeling the car) to bring it to a suitable position for attack. It is thus liable to

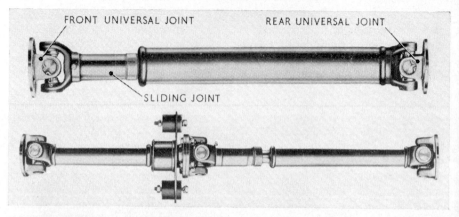

FRONT UNIVERSAL JOINT   REAR UNIVERSAL JOINT

SLIDING JOINT

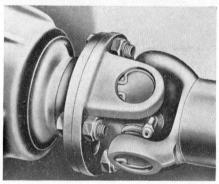

FIG. 6.14. Propeller shafts. (*Top*) The standard type of Hardy Spicer propeller shaft, with two universal joints to accommodate variations in alignment at the axle and gearbox, and a sliding joint to accommodate variations in shaft length due to flexing of suspension springs. These three joints need greasing on some cars, but not on others. (*Centre*) A divided propeller shaft used on cars having a long wheelbase; in effect, an extension shaft is fitted to the normal one. (*Bottom*) A universal joint, with needle roller bearings which require periodic greasing through the nipple shown. Many modern universal joints are pre-packed with grease.

neglect, but this can be serious; loading on the splines is heavy, and although the axial movement is relatively slow and small, wear on the splines causes transmission backlash and unpleasant noise. It is far better therefore to be generous with lubrication, rather than the reverse.

With independent rear suspension systems, the final drive unit is mounted on the frame and the propeller shaft joints have little movement, merely catering for relative movement between the gearbox and final drive. Universal joints are of course necessary in this case on the axle shafts taking power from the final drive to the road wheels, to cater for suspension motion. With transaxle units the latter also applies, while additionally, front-wheel drive cars require a special wide-angle joint at each steering knuckle (Fig. 6.15).

When a Hooke-type universal joint is operating at any angle, the speed of its output end varies cyclically, to an extent depending on the angle. This effect is cancelled when two joints are used on the same shaft, provided they are phased properly. It is important to appreciate this point in the case of telescoping shafts, where the two joint assemblies may be completely separated during overhaul; they must always be lined-up correctly.

Universal Joint Overhaul. The standard Hardy Spicer universal joint is nowadays of sealed type. When the bearings are worn to their practicable limits, the shaft may vibrate and the joints become noisy. It is quite feasible to replace the worn parts, which are available from service stations; the set comprising needle-bearing assemblies and snap rings, and

164

centre journal complete with gaskets and retainers. These are the only parts subject to normal wear in service (Fig. 6.16).

The snap rings or circlips are of the type dealt with by using circlip pliers to avoid damage, and are withdrawn by pinching their ends together and lifting out of the grooves. If there is a coating of enamel or dirt adhering to the outside of the joint, this must be removed as otherwise they may stick. Also, as the bearing assembly may be hard up against the ring laterally, a tap on the end of the joint fork, at the side being dealt with, will help to reduce end pressure on the ring.

With the ring removed, gentle tapping on the radius of the fork will then cause the needle-bearing assembly to emerge far enough to enable it to be pulled out by hand. This is best done from the bottom, with the bearing vertical, as it is easier to catch the needle rollers. The same operation is repeated on the opposite

bearing. This will leave the centre spider attached by its other two bearings, and with two exposed journal faces where the first two bearings work. The spider should be supported in soft faces to avoid damage to these surfaces, and the tapping process used on the other fork to remove its two races.

The spider with its four journals is now free, and the bearings completely dismantled. All parts can be washed in petrol and inspected. If there is any sign of pitting, corrosion or abrasive wear, it is essential to replace the parts; if not, they may be lubricated and assembled.

First, pack the bearings with an approved lubricant. This should be adequate not only to lubricate but also to keep the rollers positioned during assembly; the housings and spider arms should be liberally smeared. The spider should next be refitted into the yoke fork of the hub shaft. Position its gaskets at the bottom of

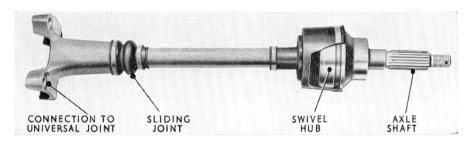

CONNECTION TO   SLIDING   SWIVEL   AXLE
UNIVERSAL JOINT   JOINT   HUB   SHAFT

FIG. 6.15. The B.M.C. front-wheel-drive axle shaft incorporates a sliding joint and a Birfield constant-velocity joint, which permits both steering and transmission motion (*lower right*). The shaft assembly is flexibly supported by a rubber-bushed universal joint (*lower left*). Periodic lubrication is not required by these joints.

165

the four journals, with a little shellac varnish or other jointing compound applied to the fork shoulders at this point to make a good seal. Tap the bearing assemblies into position with a copper drift, of a shade less in diameter than the yoke-hole. Repeat this operation on the two bearings for the axle shaft fork.

When all four races are firmly home, refit the snap rings, making sure they are located right down in their grooves. The joint may appear tight in its articulating movement, but a few taps with a mallet on the yoke centres will remedy this, as it is simply due to the races being a little too far

inwards. Finally, apply a little shellac to the area of the circlips, to discourage the entry of moisture.

It will be seen that renewal of the parts concerned will not compensate for wear in the bearing holes of the yoke forks. If these have worn oval or oversize, the complete yoke with its associated shaft should be replaced. Wear on the spider journals is taken care of, as the replacement set includes this component.

Jointed Half-shafts. The jointed half-shafts on independently-sprung cars may be dealt with as already detailed, if the joints are of Hardy Spicer type. Other

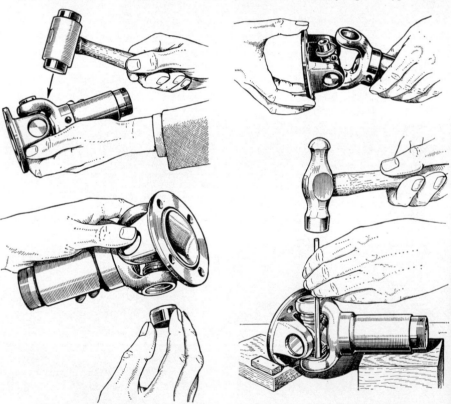

FIG. 6.16. Dismantling a universal joint. *Top left to bottom right:* (1) Tap the radius of each yoke lightly, when the bearing cup will begin to emerge. (2) Hold the joint upside down to extract the cup complete with rollers. (3) After both cups have been removed it will be possible to take off the sleeve yoke. (4) If the cups are very tight, an alternative method of removal is to support the sleeve yoke and joint on blocks and carefully tap out the cup from inside with a thin-edged punch, the blows being evenly applied.

types of joint—particularly when these incorporate rubber bushes—require special consideration and are not usually within the scope of the home mechanic. The complete coupling should be exchanged, when worn.

Whenever propeller shafts or drive shafts are removed, it is essential that flanges and couplings are re-assembled in the same relationship as originally. If necessary, paint-marking should be done to ensure this. Nuts and bolts must be pulled up very firmly, and when castellated nuts are used, locked by split-pins, the latter should be renewed and the legs bent back neatly and securely.

Self-locking nuts are being increasingly used, and the type incorporating a nylon insert can be used again so long as the insert is still effective. This is readily tested by noting that there must be appreciable resistance to movement when the nut is run on to its stud, as soon as the insert begins to "bite".

THE REAR AXLE

The established pressed-steel casing type of rear axle and differential unit (Fig. 6.17) has undergone design changes in recent years which make it less amenable to attention by the owner. However, along with such changes, modern axles give far less trouble than on earlier cars. It should be appreciated that within their relatively small dimensions, the crown wheel and pinion transmit enormous loads, since at times the full torque of the engine in the lowest gear at maximum crankshaft speed may be applied. Furthermore, the assembly has to cater for shock loads imposed by rough surfaces, hill re-starts and so on.

Routine Servicing. It follows from this that it is essential at all times to use the type of lubricant specified by the maker, and to maintain this at the correct level. Where periodic draining is called for, this must be done at the mileage laid down. The filler plug is frequently mounted in a position where it also serves as a level

indicator, but a few models have a separate plug or dipstick for the latter. In that case, the axle should never be filled above this point, otherwise oil is liable to leak from the axle shaft bearings into the wheel hubs and eventually on to the brake shoes.

Meshing of the crown wheel and pinion is nowadays generally done by shim selection within definite limits. Mechanically this is a perfectly adequate method, but occasionally one comes across an axle which is noisier than normal. If the adjustment is satisfactory, as evidenced by good running and absence of undue backlash, the situation must be accepted and above all no attempt made to quieten the axle by using thicker oil or non-standard ingredients.

Due to the high gear-tooth pressure set up, lubricants specified for the rear axle are usually of an extreme-pressure type, specially blended and containing all the additives necessary. Do not put other additives into the oil without first obtaining the car maker's opinion.

When checking the oil level, the car must be on a level surface. Tighten the plugs securely after refitting, and make sure that breather holes are clear, otherwise temperature rise may force oil past the oil seals.

The two general types of axle casing are the banjo and the split-flange, the difference being illustrated in Fig. 6.18. In the former, the differential unit is mounted on the front housing, which is secured to the casing by a ring of studs and nuts. After withdrawing the axle shafts, which are splined into the differential unit, the differential unit and final drive unit can be removed complete and rectified away from the car, or exchanged for a replacement assembly in case of trouble.

Rear Axle Adjustment. Meshing of the final drive may be adjusted either by shims or by screwed threads at the main bearings, and the method used must be ascertained before doing any work. On

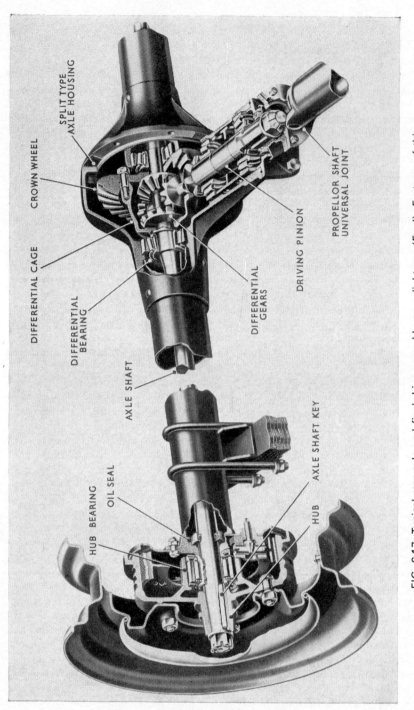

SPLIT TYPE
AXLE HOUSING

CROWN WHEEL

DIFFERENTIAL CAGE

DIFFERENTIAL
BEARING

AXLE SHAFT

DIFFERENTIAL
GEARS

DRIVING PINION

PROPELLOR SHAFT
UNIVERSAL JOINT

HUB BEARING

OIL SEAL

AXLE SHAFT KEY

HUB

FIG. 6.17. Typical rear axle and final drive assembly on a light car (Ford). Features of this particular design include a combined wheel hub and brake drum, a three-quarter floating axle shaft, a split-type axle casing, and a spiral-bevel final drive gear. The hub is secured to its axle shaft by means of a tapered key.

the whole, it is the best policy to make use of an exchange scheme, but for those with adequate facilities for undertaking such work, the main point to watch, after ascertaining that all parts are in good order, is that the gear and pinion teeth are contacting for maximum l ad capacity.

After adjustment, therefore, apply some lampblack to one set of teeth and examine the other wheel after rotating the pair. The marking should be transferred for the whole length of each tooth; intermittent marking indicates that full contact is not being obtained, which means overloading at some part of the tooth. (Note that this may not be the case where the gears are meshed to a specified pre-

load on assembly.) If renewal is required, both the crown wheel and pinion must be replaced as a matched set.

In the case of an axle having a circumferential flange in the casing, the whole axle must be removed and the casing split to gain access to the differential. Special gauges and tools are then necessary to set up the components when re-assembling, so this is very much a job for the service station.

Road Wheel Bearings. The method of mounting the road-wheel bearings depends on the type of axle (Fig. 6.19). In a fully-floating type, rarely seen nowadays, the axle shaft from the differential to the road wheel takes no load other than the driving torque; the wheel hub is fully supported on the outer tube of the axle casing, and a bolted flange on the axle-shaft end transmits power from the shaft to the hub.

The three-quarter floating type is found on many cars. In this case, the wheel hub is carried at its back end on the axle casing, but the front end is supported by the axle shaft,

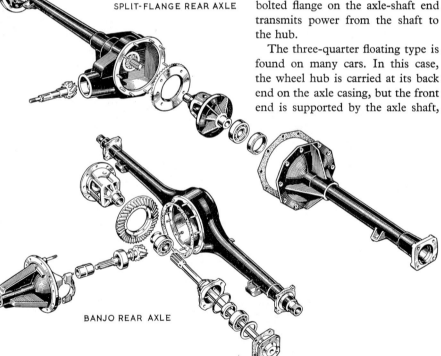

SPLIT-FLANGE REAR AXLE

BANJO REAR AXLE

FIG. 6.18. Examples of the two common types of rear-axle casing. The front housing of the banjo axle carries the differential unit, so that this and the half-shafts can be removed while the casing is in position on the car.

on which the hub is fixed. In the case of axle-shaft breakage the road wheel cannot leave the car, since it is restrained by the inner bearing. Some modern designs allow the axle shaft to take the complete load, both torsionally and in bending, as it runs in a bearing inside the axle casing and has the wheel hub firmly attached to its outer end.

The axle shafts are often splined at

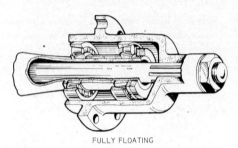

FULLY FLOATING

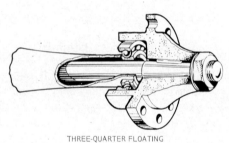

THREE-QUARTER FLOATING

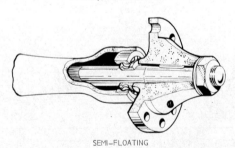

SEMI—FLOATING

FIG. 6.19. Forms of rear axle. In the fully floating type (now rare), the load is carried by the axle casing. In the three-quarter floating type, the outer bearing is between the hub and the casing, with the casing and axle shaft sharing the load. In the semi-floating type, the outer bearing is between the axle shaft and the casing, and the shaft carries the entire load.

their inner ends where they enter into the differential unit, their axial location being at the outer ends of the casing. This may take various forms depending on the design, but it will usually be found that the outer bearing assembly of the hub is enshrouded in a housing which is bolted to the casing. When this is unbolted the hub complete with axle shaft can be withdrawn.

In some cases access to the bearing can only be obtained after the hub has been drawn off the end of the shaft, and this will require the use of an extractor (Fig. 6.20). If none is available, a service station may oblige with a loan of one, or home manufacture may be possible. It must be emphasized that makeshift methods, such as levering or drifting, should not be resorted to.

A few old designs of axle shaft have the inner bevels of the differential forged integral with the shaft, so that the shaft cannot be withdrawn without completely dismantling the axle and differential cage. It is most important before considering the feasibility of amateur attention to find out the precise construction of the axle assembly. While a good degree of standardization is now the rule, many detail differences are to be found.

The hub bearings are often grease-packed, with housings designed for sufficient grease capacity to last for many thousands of miles; these do not require any attention until it is time to overhaul and inspect the complete assembly. At that time, the old grease is thoroughly washed out with petrol, and fresh grease inserted to the amount specified by the makers. It is most important not to over-fill the hub housings, as expansion with heat will cause the excess to be ejected through the oil seals. Apart from possible damage to the latter, the grease is liable to find its way on to the brake linings. For the same reason, hubs which are provided with lubrication nipples must

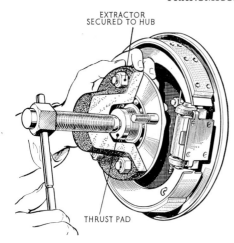

EXTRACTOR SECURED TO HUB

THRUST PAD

FIG. 6.20. This sectional view of an extractor tool shows how it is used to withdraw a rear hub from its axle shaft.

be dealt with sparingly, when using the grease gun.

In the case of cars with independent suspension, the hub housings and their shafts are completely self-contained The construction is usually quite simple, the two bearings being separated by a spacer and positioned by the shaft nut.

Rear Hub Troubles. In general, troubles with hub assemblies of any type are usually due to bearing wear and defective oil seals, the latter often resulting from the first. When oil or grease leakage occurs, therefore, seals must not be replaced before the bearing condition has been assessed. When handling ball and roller bearings it is essential at all times to maintain the most scrupulous cleanliness, and to use the correct equipment for removing and refitting.

Bearings which are very much worn or on the point of failing (with cracked balls or broken cages) will become noisy and exhibit undue free movement, to an extent which is likely to be felt in the steering. It is not very satisfactory to attempt to judge wear by rocking the wheel rims from side to side, since there

may be a small amount of side movement even when correctly adjusted, and this is of course magnified at the wheel rim. To ensure complete reliability, maintain the components in good condition, correctly lubricated and adjusted carefully in accordance with instructions—in cases where adjustment may be provided.

Oil seals are of a fairly standard type, often with metallic spring loading incorporated in the construction, the actual seal being effected by a ring of Neoprene or similar material. Seals are carefully selected both as to size and material for any particular location, but they will not function properly if the shaft journal, which runs in the seal, is worn undersize or scored. Where the journal takes the form of a renewable sleeve, wear is easily rectified, but otherwise the whole shaft must be either replaced or corrected by metal deposition. When replacing seals, it is essential to use a suitably-sized mandrel on which the seal can locate, so that it is squarely seated on its register.

DIFFERENTIAL GEARING

Trouble with the gearing inside the differential cage is most unlikely, since the bevel gear operation is intermittent, and at low relative speeds between the teeth. Access to the unit can only be obtained after dismantling the axle, but the construction is usually quite straightforward, comprising a split cage held together by through-bolts, which may in addition secure the crown wheel of the final drive to the differential. It is most essential that these bolts are evenly and thoroughly tightened.

Because the conventional form of differential gear depends for its balancing action on the reaction torque at each road wheel, it has certain shortcomings, notably in that when the reaction torque on one wheel is zero (as for example when the wheel spins in mud), the driving torque on the other (gripping) wheel is reduced

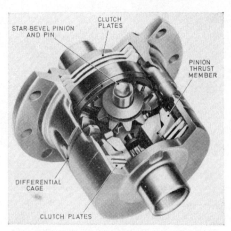

STAR BEVEL PINION AND PIN

CLUTCH PLATES

PINION THRUST MEMBER

DIFFERENTIAL CAGE

CLUTCH PLATES

FIG. 6.21. The Powr-Lok limited-slip differential fitted to high-performance cars embodies two plate clutches to transmit some torque regardless of differential effect.

to zero also, since the torques must balance. Thus, the gripping wheel will not turn.

The reason why it is sometimes possible to "rock" a car out of trouble by alternatively engaging forward and reverse gear, is that the spinning wheel in this case shows a momentary resistance to being speeded up (due to its inertia) as the clutch is engaged, and this resistance is transmitted to the gripping wheel in the form of a momentary driving torque. From this, it is evident that if the spinning wheel can be held in some way, without prejudicing the differential action, sufficient torque should be available on the other wheel to move the car.

Limited-slip Differential. Such a principle is used in the limited-slip differential, which is coming into increasing use on large and heavy cars, and those capable of very high speeds. In the latter case, such control is desirable to check runaway wheel-spin under fierce acceleration, thus ensuring that both driving wheels take a more nearly equal share of the load even when their tyre adhesion varies. Modern limited-slip differentials

are arranged to provide a partial lock between the axle shafts and the differential cage when spin is imminent, enabling power to be transmitted directly from the crown wheel, via the cage, to the shafts independently of the bevel gears inside the cage.

In the Powr-Lok differential (Fig. 6.21) a plate clutch is situated on each side between the axle-shaft bevels and the faces of the cage, while the pins carrying the differential star bevels have their ends located in V-tracks on the cage periphery. When a torque is applied to the crown wheel, it is transmitted via the cage to the pins in the normal way, but because of the method of pin location, there is an axial force applied which engages the plate clutches, thus tending to lock the cage to the half-shafts.

When the differential action is required, as when turning a corner, the differing speeds of the two half-shaft bevels causes the star-bevel pins to reposition in ·their V-tracks in the cage, freeing the clutches and allowing a normal gearing action of the bevels.

The Borg-Warner device is somewhat similar, but in this case cone clutches are formed behind the backs of the half-shaft bevels and the ends of the cage. The cage is split circumferentially, having a series of coil springs between the two halves which continually urge the cone clutches into light engagement. This is not sufficient to impede differential action when called for, and is augmented by the natural tendency for the bevel teeth to separate when the drive torque is applied, which applies further axial pressure to the cone clutches. Wheelspin on one side increases enormously the frictional retarding force in the cone clutch at that side, so that a corresponding torque increase is applied to the wheel which is not spinning.

Limited-slip differentials are up to now comparatively rare, and servicing will for some time be a job for specialists.

CHAPTER 7

STEERING GEAR AND SUSPENSION

To A CONSIDERABLE extent, the steering, wheels and tyres of a car are interdependent. Jointly and individually they influence the vehicle's road-holding, controllability and comfort. Even when the need for regular lubrication has been eliminated by modern design, therefore, it is advisable to carry out a thorough inspection of the steering and suspension at 6,000-mile intervals to detect and remedy faults such as damaged oil-retaining or dust-excluding gaiters, loose nuts or minor accidental damage, which might otherwise develop into more serious trouble.

It is also as well to have the geometry of the front suspension and steering gear checked every 6,000 miles by a garage which possesses modern precision servicing equipment, for faulty geometry will lead to excessive tyre wear and steering troubles. At the same time, the wheels and tyres should be checked on a dynamic balancing machine. Many modern cars are very sensitive to even a minor degree of

unbalance, especially in the front wheels and tyres—a small penalty to pay, perhaps, for their light, precise and responsive steering.

STEERING GEAR

Routine Servicing. On the majority of cars today, self-adjusting joints are used throughout the steering gear and front suspension, and rubber or plastics bushes, seatings and thrust washers have virtually eliminated the need for regular lubrication. But designs vary, and the instruction book for a particular model should be consulted for details (Fig. 7.1). Lubrication nipples may be provided at several points, or a blanking plug (Fig. 7.2) may be fitted, to be unscrewed at specified mileage intervals so that a lubrication nipple can be substituted and oil or grease injected. The arrangement of a steering gear with a divided track rod, an idler arm, and a

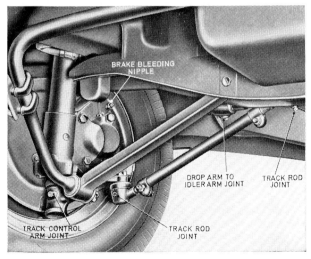

FIG. 7.1. Lubrication of the front suspension and steering may be required at the points indicated, but in many instances some or all of the joints are of the sealed type and do not need attention. The brake bleeding nipple should not be mistaken for a grease point.

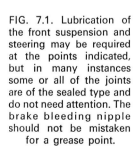

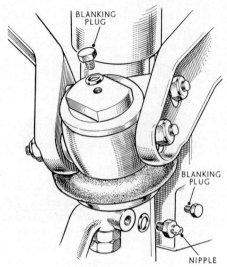

Fig. 7.2. On some cars blanking plugs are fitted to the suspension and steering lubrication points, and these must be removed to allow grease nipples to be screwed in. The nipples can be left in if desired.

conventional steering box illustrated in Fig. 7.3 is typical of modern practice for larger cars.

It is not possible to lay down hard-and-fast rules for servicing periods if such lubrication is required. For example, the

use of lithium-based multi-purpose grease may be specified at 3,000-mile intervals; but for molybdenum disulphide grease, the mileage may be 6,000. In other instances, lubrication may be needed only after 24,000-30,000 miles have been covered. The following notes on servicing apply generally to most cars on the road, and the owner will have little difficulty in adapting these to his own particular model.

Do not over-lubricate joints that are protected by rubber boots. If too much grease is pumped in, sufficient pressure may be generated to split the rubber. When disc brakes are fitted, particular care must be taken not to allow grease to reach the disc or the caliper. If the friction linings do become greasy, the only practical cure is to renew the brake pads.

Steering Gear. When a conventional steering box is fitted, its oil level should be inspected and topped-up if necessary with extreme-pressure gear oil at about 6,000-mile intervals. This is a wise precaution, especially on an older car where there is often a slight leak from the steering gearbox (past the rocker-shaft oil seal, for example), which may not be enough to justify dis-

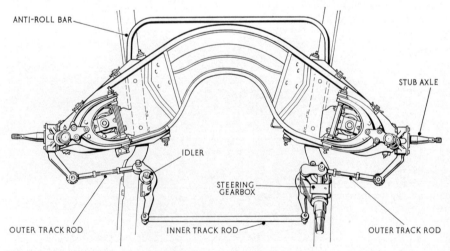

FIG. 7.3. Steering linkage layout. Alignment of the wheels is obtained by making adjustments to the two outer track rods, the lengths of which must always be kept equal.

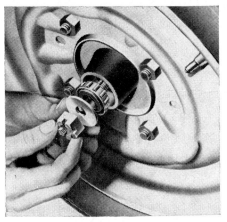

FIG. 7.4. Maintenance of front wheel bearings. (*Left*) After removing the hub nut, thrust washer and bearing race, the parts are cleaned and the hub half-filled with fresh grease. (*Right*) The hub nut must be tightened carefully to provide the correct degree of bearing play.

mantling the gearbox to renew the seal, but which will slowly deplete the oil supply.

In a rack-and-pinion design, the pinion housing is sealed at each end by a telescopic rubber gaiter. Provided that the gaiters are not damaged and that the clips are tight, oil leaks cannot occur, and topping-up is normally not required during the service life of the unit.

Front Wheel Bearings. Some instruction books recommend that the lubricant in the front-wheel hub bearings should be replenished or renewed occasionally. The mileage given for this item varies widely, examples being 6,000 and 30,000 miles. It is difficult to justify the lower figure since grease cannot escape from the hub unless the grease-retainer is faulty, trouble that will be revealed by the presence of lubricant in the brake drum or on the outside of the hub. But heat, mostly generated by the brakes in use, will cause the grease to deteriorate after a time, hence the recommendation made by some manufacturers that the hubs should be removed after about 12,000 miles, the old grease cleaned out from the bearings, and fresh lubricant packed in (Fig. 7.4).

The hubs should on no account be completely filled, and grease should not be packed into the hub cap. Otherwise excessive friction will be set up when the car is running, causing sufficient heat to melt the grease. It may be necessary to adjust the bearings after this. In any case, the bearings should be checked for slackness at about 12,000-mile intervals.

In some cases, no adjustment is provided and it is necessary only to tighten the hub nut fully after replacing the hub and to replace the split pin. Sometimes, a specified torque loading to apply a pre-load to the bearings is given, and in this case it is best to have the tightness of the hub retaining nuts checked by a service station that can apply a torque wrench as soon as possible after putting the car back on the road.

When the bearings are adjustable, tighten the hub nut up as far as it will go with a spanner of normal length until the bearings are properly seated, then slacken the nut back to align its nearest castellation with the split-pin hole in the stub axle, and secure with the split pin. After this, check that the wheel rotates freely but without perceptible shake in the bearings.

Some manufacturers specify a definite degree of end-float for the hub, usually

175

two or three thousandths of an inch. This is measured with a dial gauge and clamp, neither of which the ordinary owner is likely to possess, but if the bearings are adjusted so that all perceptible rocking movement is just eliminated, the result should be satisfactory. With disc brakes, excessive slackness in the bearings will cause judder or squeal, and may even transmit back to the brake pedal as vibration.

When disc brakes are fitted, it will be necessary to unbolt the caliper and slide it clear of the disc before the hub is taken off. Support the caliper on a box or sling it by a wire from a convenient point on the suspension, to avoid straining the flexible brake pipe.

When power steering gear is fitted, the level of the fluid in the reservoir should be checked at about 6,000-mile intervals (or more frequently if specified by the manufacturer). It should not be necessary to top-up the reservoir as the system is completely sealed; any leakage of fluid therefore calls for investigation. The hydraulic pressure in a power steering system is between 750-1,000 lb per sq in. and the hoses, unions and fluid seals in the pump and servo units must obviously be maintained in first-class condition.

PREVENTIVE MAINTENANCE

As has been indicated, the relatively service-free design of modern steering gear may result in regular inspection and preventive maintenance being neglected, so that small faults may not be detected before they develop into major troubles. At 6,000 mile intervals, therefore, jack up the front of the car and check the rubber boots and gaiters throughout the steering gear for any signs of oil leakage. If a gaiter is found to be torn or perished it should be renewed. There is a strong probability that grit or water will have entered the ball joint or bearing, and it is therefore best to renew the joint also.

With the front wheels raised clear of the ground, turn the steering from lock to lock and check for any binding or looseness.

Power Steering Maintenance. Carefully examine each of the components of a power steering gear when the engine is running, to detect any sign of fluid leakage (Fig. 7.5). Listen to the steering pump, which is usually mounted on the rear end of the dynamo, for any suspicious noises. Pumps usually have a very long service life, so it is reasonable to expect this unit to have a clean bill of health. The power-servo may be built into the steering gearbox or may take the form of an hydraulic ram connected between one of the steering rods and the car's under-frame. This seldom gives trouble, but if it does, the hoses may require renewal.

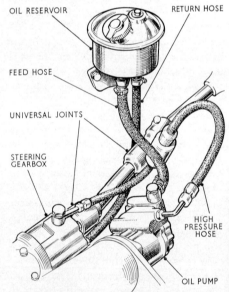

OIL RESERVOIR

RETURN HOSE

FEED HOSE

UNIVERSAL JOINTS

STEERING GEARBOX

HIGH PRESSURE HOSE

OIL PUMP

FIG. 7.5. Typical power-assisted steering. With the engine running and the steering set straight ahead, there is a continuous flow of oil through the steering unit supplied by the pump. When the steering wheel is turned, pressure is applied to a servo piston, supplementing the driver's effort. Maintenance includes checking the oil level in the reservoir and renewing its filter element (Austin).

When the front wheels have been lowered to the ground, turn the steering wheel slowly from lock to lock. If the amount of power assistance does not appear to be adequate, check the tension of the generator driving belt and replace it if it is worn or glazed. If the belt is not slipping, the most likely fault is the presence of air in the fluid, due to too low a level in the reservoir; but as has already been emphasized, the level can fall only if there has been external leakage at some point. Once this has been corrected, topping-up the reservoir and slowly turning the wheels from lock to lock to vent the system should restore full efficiency.

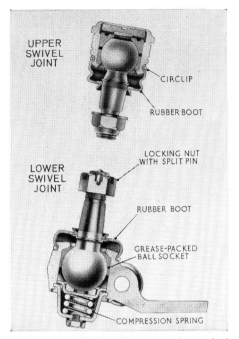

FIG. 7.6. A pair of sealed suspension swivel joints. These are greased for life and protected by rubber boots, while the lower socket incorporates a spring adjuster to take up wear automatically. Tie-rod joints are of similar construction, and may be either grease-packed or fitted with self-lubricating nylon bushes. Many steering joints are still fitted with grease nipples for regular lubrication.

STEERING OVERHAUL

Some years ago a practical owner could carry out a fairly thorough overhaul of the steering system without the need for many special tools, other than a suitable reamer to line-ream the king-pin bushes to the correct size when renewing bushes and king pins. Today, the situation has changed. The use of nylon or p.t.f.e. bearing surfaces in the swivel pins and in the steering joints has rendered it unnecessary to ream the parts to size after installation, but the need to protect these vulnerable surfaces from the slightest damage during installation usually calls for the use of special tools which are normally held only by the local agents for the car.

Replacement bushes are best removed or inserted in a press. Since it is advisable at the same time to check the various components of the front suspension for damage or distortion against detailed drawings, reconditioning is obviously a job for the expert.

This also applies, in most cases, to the ball joints in the steering linkage rods, which are often a very tight fit in the ends of the rods (Fig. 7.6). If the correct extractor is not available, it may be possible in an emergency to remove a joint by applying leverage with the tip of a tyre lever while the eye in the end of the rod is given a smart blow with a hammer. In normal circumstances it is best to have the job done with the correct equipment.

Modern steering gearboxes and rack-and-pinion gears are also seldom within the province of the home mechanic. Among the snags that are likely to be encountered are the need for special tools during dismantling and re-assembly and difficulty in measuring the correct pre-load on the bearings. A steering gearbox or a rack-and-pinion gear should never be dismantled, therefore, unless it is possible to refer to a workshop manual.

Many service stations, in fact, prefer to

177

take advantage of the service-replacement scheme, under which a reconditioned unit can be obtained in exchange for the worn assembly. This scheme is particularly useful when dealing with power steering gear, in view of the complexity of the units and the very fine tolerances to which they are assembled.

One further aspect which emphasizes the need for either a workshop manual or expert guidance is the fairly complex arrangement of the lighting, horn, head-lamp-flashing and direction-indicator switch mechanism, which is often incorporated in the upper end of the steering column or in its shroud. Unless the appropriate instructions are available (and, preferably, a wiring diagram), it is possible to do a certain amount of damage when attempting to remove the steering wheel and withdraw the steering column and gearbox assembly from the car. The actual work seldom presents much difficulty: it is the "know-how" which is important.

Steering gearboxes and rack-and-pinion gears, however, usually have a long life between overhauls. Adjustment of the

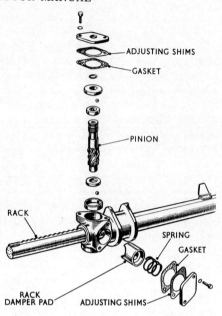

FIG. 7.8. Rack-and-pinion steering adjustments. Shims are provided under the rack housing cover to take up wear on the pinion shaft, and under the cover of the spring-loaded rack damper to obtain correct meshing of the rack and pinion.

mesh between the rocker-arm peg or follower and the cam in a steering gearbox, or between the pinion and the rack on a rack-and-pinion gear, is usually all that is required to take up normal wear.

Steering Gear Adjustment. Considering first the various types of steering gearbox in use today, when external adjustment is provided (and this is not always the case) it takes the form of a setscrew, locked by a nut, close to the oil filler plug in the cover plate of the gearbox (Fig. 7.7.). Adjustment must be carried out with both front wheels clear of the ground and set exactly in the straight-ahead position. Do not rely on the position of the steering wheel spokes but check that the front wheels are parallel with the rear wheels by stretching a string along the side of the car at hub height.

The reason for this precaution is that

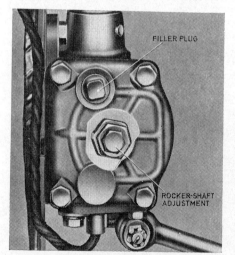

FIG. 7.7. The oil filler plug in the cover of a steering unit should not be confused with the rocker-shaft adjuster (if fitted), which is secured by a locknut.

the steering gear usually has a "tight spot" at the centre of the cam and a greater clearance between the cam and the peg or follower as the wheels approach each lock. Since most of the wear takes place over a small section of the cam around the straight-ahead position, it is thus possible to take up the excess clearance without causing the steering to bind as the wheels are turned towards full lock.

After slackening the locknut, screw in the adjuster until it makes contact with the rocker arm, check that there is a very slight tight spot as the wheels are slowly turned through the straight-ahead position, and check again after tightening the locknut.

On rack-and-pinion gears the adjustment is usually by means of shims between the rack housing and the cover or the screwed plug that retains the spring-loaded rack damping plunger (Fig. 7.8). Remove the cover or the plug, take off the shim pack and re-assemble the damper without the spring. Tighten the cover screws or the plug until a very slight drag is felt when turning the steering wheel. Measure the clearance between the cover or the flange of the plug and the housing with a feeler gauge. Select the correct number of shims

to fill the gap, remove the damper, refit the spring and re-assemble with the shims in position.

In some cases an adjusting screw and locknut may be provided instead of shims. Adjustment is then quite straightforward.

FRONT AND REAR SUSPENSION

As explained in Chapter 2, a variety of suspension arrangements is to be found on recent cars, but the "traditional" front coil-spring (Fig. 7.9) and rear leaf-spring (Fig. 7.10) systems illustrated remain perhaps the most typical.

As with the steering gear, the use of rubber, nylon or p.t.f.e. bushes has drastically reduced the number of lubrication points on modern suspension systems and in some cases the need for routine servicing has been eliminated. Where lubrication is required, a general-purpose or a molybdenum disulphide grease is usually specified, the latter allowing the period between services to be extended.

Routine Servicing. As in the case of the steering gear, a periodical check should be made on dust-excluding or grease-retaining rubber seals or gaiters and any which are damaged should be renewed (Fig. 7.11). This may not always be a

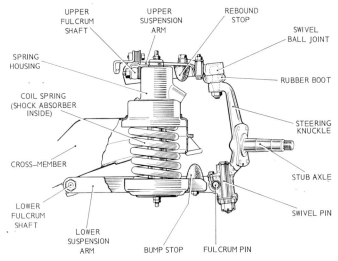

Fig. 7.9. Typical independent front suspension arrangement, showing most of the parts mentioned in the text. In this case the hub carrier swivels on a lower swivel pin (king pin) and an upper ball joint, but frequently a pair of ball joints is used. The upper end of the coil spring is housed in the cross-member and its lower end bears on the lower suspension arm.

UPPER FULCRUM SHAFT

UPPER SUSPENSION ARM

REBOUND STOP

SWIVEL BALL JOINT

SPRING HOUSING

RUBBER BOOT

COIL SPRING (SHOCK ABSORBER INSIDE)

STEERING KNUCKLE

CROSS—MEMBER

STUB AXLE

LOWER FULCRUM SHAFT

SWIVEL PIN

LOWER SUSPENSION ARM

BUMP STOP

FULCRUM PIN

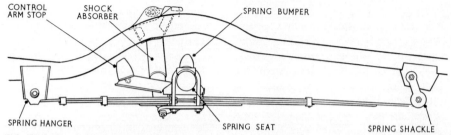

FIG. 7.10. Conventional leaf-spring rear suspension. The hanger and spring shackle are usually rubber-bushed and the tips of the spring leaves are fitted with anti-friction plastic buttons, when no maintenance is required. On older models the shackle may require greasing and the spring leaves may need occasional spraying with oil.

straightforward job and may entail partial dismantling of the suspension, but damaged or leaking seals must not be neglected if excessive wear of the bushes or ball joints is to be prevented.

When laminated leaf springs are fitted, it is important to check, from the instruction book or from the local agents, whether or not they should be lubricated. Modern springs usually have rubber or plastic interleaving, or wear-resistant pads at the tips of each leaf, which render lubrication unnecessary. Indeed, if rubber interleaving is used, the presence of oil or grease will cause rapid deterioration of the strips.

Furthermore, an advantage of a laminated spring from the designer's point of view is that it has self-damping properties and thus reduces the amount of work to be done by the shock absorber. If the spring is lubricated, most of this self-damping effect will be destroyed, the suspension will become much too flexible and in extreme cases one or more spring leaves may break.

While the general rule, therefore, is not to lubricate leaf springs, there are a few exceptions in which periodical brushing with engine oil or spraying with penetrating oil is specified; hence the need for checking this point. If the springs do require lubrication, be careful not to allow oil to reach the rubber bushes in the shackles, to avoid premature de-

FIG. 7.11. Rubber seals, boots and gaiters are widely used in modern suspension systems to protect joints and retain grease. These need regular examination, and should be kept free of oil which is harmful to rubber.

180

FIG. 7.12. Points to note in servicing a piston-type shock absorber, which has an operating lever connected by a rubber-bushed link to the rear axle.

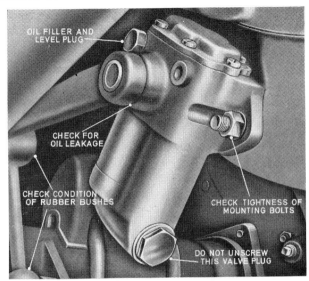

OIL FILLER AND LEVEL PLUG

CHECK FOR OIL LEAKAGE

CHECK CONDITION OF RUBBER BUSHES

CHECK TIGHTNESS OF MOUNTING BOLTS

DO NOT UNSCREW THIS VALVE PLUG

terioration of these important items, and keep it away from exposed brake discs and calipers.

Shock Absorbers. A routine job which appears in many older instruction books is inspection of the fluid level in the shock absorbers (or dampers) at intervals of about 6,000-15,000 miles. (Note that car manufacturers fitting the same type of damper vary widely in their recommendations.) They must be topped-up, if necessary, with the specified fluid. Modern shock absorbers seldom have any provision for fluid checks and even in the case of piston-type dampers, which have a filler screw in the upper part of the body, periodical topping-up is seldom specified nowadays (Fig. 7.12).

In any case, it is doubtful whether this service is either necessary or desirable. If a filler plug is removed there is always a risk of grit or dirt falling into the shock absorber during the topping-up process, unless the unit has been carefully cleaned beforehand. For this reason it often used to be specified that the dampers should be removed from the car in order to service them, a somewhat tedious job which probably entailed placing the car on a lift or jacking up the rear to a convenient height and securely supporting the axle or underframe on rigid stands.

There is one item that deserves checking, however. The rubber bushes in the shock absorber linkage or anchorages tend to become compressed in service and it is often possible to tighten the retaining nuts by a turn or two. This eliminates lost motion at these points, which might otherwise suggest that the shock absorbers were not fully effective in controlling small suspension movements.

A rough check on the effectiveness of the shock absorbers can be made by bouncing the front or rear of the car vigorously. If the movement is not checked almost immediately, the shock absorbers are probably due for renewal.

A more accurate test can be made by disconnecting the shock absorber link or the lower mounting eye (provided that this is not masked by a coil spring) and operating the shock absorber through a full stroke by hand. There should be an even resistance throughout the movement. If there is no resistance, or if it is erratic, the shock absorber is almost certainly faulty; but if it is provided with a filler plug, make a further check after topping it up with the correct fluid and operating it about a dozen times to expel any air.

Unfortunately, hand-testing of the shock absorbers is not conclusive, as the slow speed only partially operates the "bleed"

181

valve in the shock absorber. A large part of the resistance during normal running depends on the high-pressure or high-speed setting of the valve. Even a new shock absorber may therefore appear to be weak when operated by hand, and this should not necessarily be regarded as evidence that it is faulty.

Shock absorbers should be kept upright when off the car to prevent air entering the working chamber. If they are gripped in the vice, clamp them only by their mounting eyes or flanges, not by the body.

After about 20-30,000 miles in service, shock absorbers inevitably become less effective owing to internal wear. The only method of restoring satisfactory handling and road-holding is to fit either new or service-exchange units.

When a car has been performance-tuned, special shock absorbers are often a worthwhile investment. Although it may not be intended to enter for races or competitions, the greatly improved road-holding conferred by a rather stiffer suspension than standard is a useful safety factor. Adjustable shock absorbers are more expensive but enable suitable settings to be chosen for particular driving conditions. The keen driver, even if his car is not tuned, will appreciate the ability to select a moderately hard setting for fast driving or when a full load of luggage is being carried, and a softer setting for quiet driving in town or pottering along country roads.

Hydro-pneumatic Systems. What has been said so far applies chiefly to conventional spring suspension systems. When hydro-pneumatic suspension units are fitted, servicing should always be left to the agents for the particular car.

In the case of the B.M.C. Hydrolastic suspension, for example, special equipment is needed to pressurize the suspension units, if this should be rendered necessary either as the result of replacement of a damaged component or in order to re-adjust the height of the suspension. The pressurizing valves (Fig. 7.13) should never be tampered with; the pressure in the system will be reduced or lost if they are unscrewed.

SUSPENSION MAINTENANCE

In the maintenance of any suspension system, the essential jobs are regular checks for loose nuts and torn or perished oil seals, and to watch for fluid leakage in the case of Hydrolastic or self-levelling systems, and leakage from conventional shock absorbers.

Poor steering and general instability can often be traced to loose spring mountings, slack U-bolts or a broken spring which allows the rear axle to move under braking, accelerating or cornering stresses, thus imparting a disconcerting rear-wheel steering effect. A similar trouble can be caused by wear in the bushes of front or rear axle radius arms, when the axles are positioned in this manner.

It is a good plan to have the local agents for the car check the suspension height once a year to detect any abnormal settling of the springs or torsion bars. The workshop manual for the car will specify the correct heights, the methods of measurement and the weight which should be carried in the driving compartment during these tests.

When torsion bars are used, some form of adjustment is almost invariably provided at the fixed end of the bar. The position of the anchorage can thus be regulated in order to compensate for the "settling" which inevitably takes place during service. This job may be within the scope of an owner if the correct suspension height and the method of making the adjustment are ascertained from a workshop manual or from an agent for the car.

SUSPENSION OVERHAUL

From what has been said so far regarding steering linkage and suspension arrangements, it should be evident that the average owner will not usually be in a position to carry out a complete overhaul of the suspension system. Replacement of leaf springs may perhaps be within his scope, but coil springs and rubber-cone suspension units usually call for the use of special tools in order to compress the springs before the suspension units are dismantled. When the suspension units are pressurized, the work must obviously be left to an agent who has the necessary equipment for evacuating the system, refilling and pressurizing it.

When emergency methods must be used to dismantle and replace coil or leaf springs, some ingenuity will often make up for the lack of the correct equipment. A coil spring should preferably be released with a proper tool and keepers in position, as shown in Fig. 7.14. Where this is not possible, each spring should be compressed as far as possible by placing a jack under the lower suspension member. The coils should then be wired together before the jack is released, otherwise there is a risk of the spring suddenly expanding and causing

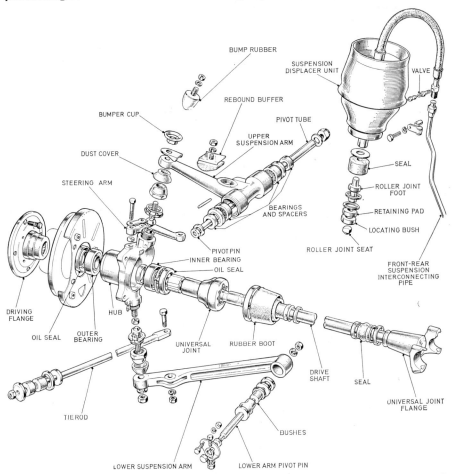

FIG. 7.13. B.M.C. Hydrolastic front suspension system, shown here dismantled. This example represents the suspension unit and drive shaft fitted to the 1100 range, but very similar layouts are used on other current B.M.C. front-wheel-drive models.

183

FIG. 7.14. Using a special tool to compress the coil spring of a front suspension, prior to dismantling (Hillman).

The anti-roll bar—an important feature of many modern suspension systems—is often overlooked. It may be fitted at the front or at the rear of the car. The bar is in effect a torsion spring and it restricts the tendency of the car to roll when cornering. It should be renewed, or at least checked, when the suspension is being overhauled. If an anti-roll bar is not fitted as standard, a suitable type may be available for amateur fitting from a motor accessory shop and will greatly improve the handling of the car.

The suspension bump rubbers should be renewed if they show signs of damage or excessive wear. In some cases they not only absorb the shock on full depression or rebound of the suspension but also act as auxiliary springs, stiffening the suspension as it approaches the limit of its travel.

An advantage of leaving suspension overhauls to a specialist is that he should have available the workshop manual diagrams which will enable him to check the components for accidental damage before attempting to recondition them. Vital steering-geometry angles, including castor angle, camber angle and swivel-pin inclination, are controlled either by the dimensions of the parts or by adjustment

damage or injury when a vital bolt in the suspension system is undone. It may also be extremely difficult to replace the springs if they are not compressed.

When dealing with leaf springs, worn shackle bolts and bushes can be renewed fairly easily if two jacks are used, one to carry the weight of the car and the other placed beneath the spring in order to compress or extend it until the shackles are an easy sliding fit in the bushes (Fig. 7.15). Unless this is done, it may be very difficult to remove or insert them. Unfortunately there are one or two examples of short-sighted design in which it is necessary to cut a hole in the chassis member or underframe before the shackle bolt can be tapped out.

A "tired" leaf spring, or one which has a broken leaf, can be re-tempered (or "set-up") by an expert, but it may be less trouble and little more expensive to fit a new replacement. Obviously, where semi-elliptic springs are used on both sides of an axle it is essential to renew them in pairs.

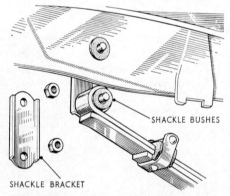

FIG. 7.15. Rear spring shackle bushes can be renewed when worn. After taking out the shackle pin, the worn bush will have to be forced out of position with a suitable tool, and the new bush pressed in by similar means.

during assembly. In some cases it is possible to correct these angles only by cold-bending the parts.

With modern body-chassis designs, too, the mounting points for the suspension units may be distorted as the result of a minor collision, and an efficient service station will check the complete under-frame for correct alignment, either by mounting the body in a jig or by taking measurements from specified points. The usual method is to project these points on to the floor beneath the car by means of a plumb bob and then to make a series of checks of the diagonals and of the measurements between the points.

With models on which the front and rear suspension units are carried on sub-frames, dismantling is considerably simplified, of course, by removing the complete assemblies from the car, but this calls for the use of good jacks and stands, or lifting tackle.

STEERING AND SUSPENSION FAULTS

As mentioned at the beginning of this chapter, the steering, suspension, wheels and tyres are closely related, and it is often hard to differentiate between the various components when diagnosing faults which affect the handling and road-holding of a car (Fig. 7.16). Systematic checks are the best answer to the problem.

Excessive Free Movement of the Steering Wheel. On some older models it was not unusual for free rotation of as much as 2 in., measured at the rim of the steering wheel, to exist even on a new car, but on most modern steering gears there should be a minimum of backlash when the wheels are in the straight-ahead position and the components are in good order. If there appears to be excessive play, the following tests should enable the worn components to be pinpointed.

Check the steering gearbox and steering relay mounting bolts for tightness. If the bolts have been loose for an appreciable mileage, the bolt holes may have worn oval and tightening may effect only a temporary cure. In that case it will probably be necessary to ream out the holes and fit oversize bolts.

Check the steering gearbox or rack-and-pinion unit for wear. Set the front wheels in the straight-ahead position. An assistant should hold the drop arm, or one of the tie rods when a rack-and-pinion gear is fitted, while an attempt is made to turn the steering wheel. Free movement in excess of an inch or so at the rim of the wheel indicates wear in the steering gearbox or rack-and-pinion unit. It may be possible to eliminate this by adjustment as described on page 179, but first check that the drop arm is not loose on the shaft.

Check the ball joints in the linkage by grasping the end of each rod firmly in turn and attempting to move the socket away from the ball. If the movement exceeds about $\frac{1}{10}$ in., or if the socket can be moved without exerting considerable force, the joint should be renewed.

Each front wheel should now be jacked up in turn so that the swivel pins and bushes (or ball swivel joints, as the case may be) can be checked for wear by grasping the tyre at top and bottom and attempting to rock the wheel in a vertical plane. This test will also reveal slackness in the hub bearings, indicated by movement of the hub in relation to the brake backplate (drum brakes) or of the disc in relation to the caliper (disc brakes).

Stiff Steering. A likely cause is, of course, lack of lubrication. When no lubrication nipples are provided, stiffness, or a squeak when the wheels are turned from lock to lock, can sometimes be cured by moving aside the rubber gaiters and injecting gear oil into the joints and bearings. Some earlier nylon steering joints suffered from this fault. If a rubber sealing boot or gaiter is found to be loose or torn, grit or dust will almost certainly have

185

entered the joint and a new joint should be fitted without delay.

If the rubber gaiters at each end of a rack-and-pinion gear appear to be in good condition, but oil has been leaking from the unit owing to a loose clip, disconnect the gaiter nearest to the pinion housing and inject about half a pint of oil to fill the unit. Do not force the oil in under pressure. Tighten the clip on the gaiter and swing the steering from lock to lock in order to distribute the oil. It should be possible to turn the steering wheel with one finger when both front wheels are raised clear of the ground.

Heavy Steering. Stiffness in the steering (see above) should not be confused with heavy steering at low speeds, or with "understeer", a tendency of the car to run wide on a bend, which results in considerable effort being required to hold it on the correct course. Heavy steering at low speeds and when parking may be due to under-inflated front tyres. This fault will also cause understeer, or will increase it if understeer is a normal feature of the car. Raising the front tyre pressures by about 3-5 lb per sq in. will often cure or minimize understeer. When power steering is fitted, check the points mentioned on page 177.

Steering Too Light. The converse of the fault just described is undue lightness of the steering or "oversteer", a tendency of the rear of the car to swing too wide when cornering, so that it is necessary to "unwind" the steering wheel to maintain the correct line. This may be caused by unduly low rear tyre pressures, and it is worth trying the effect of raising these pressures by 3-6 lb per sq in. Many front-wheel drive cars, however, are prone to oversteer if the throttle is closed while cornering, and in such cases it is not usually possible to eradicate the fault completely.

Steering Wander. This fault can be associated with excessive lightness, in which case raising the pressure in the rear tyres may cure it. If one front or rear tyre is running at a lower pressure than the other the car will be unstable and may pull to one side, especially when braking. Other causes of wander are looseness in the front or rear suspension mountings (defective rear suspension can cause "rear wheel" steering), incorrect steering geometry and possibly a badly buckled wheel. Wander at high speeds when the car is subjected to side winds may be an inherent design fault or may be due to the rear tyre pressures being too low.

Wheel Wobble and Vibration. The most likely cause of wheel wobble at high speeds, usually in the region of 60-70 m.p.h., is lack of balance of the front wheel and tyre assemblies (see Chapter 8). When the rear wheels and tyres are out of balance vibration usually occurs over a well-defined speed band, the trouble disappearing below and above the critical range of speed.

Wheel wobble at low speeds can be caused by gross unbalance of the front wheels and tyres, a distorted wheel, excessive wear in the steering joints, or weak shock absorbers. Before assuming that any of these faults is the sole cause of trouble, however, it would be as well to have the steering geometry checked with accurate equipment.

Wheel Tramp. This symptom is usually associated with a conventional rear axle when the car is accelerating hard in a low gear. The torque reaction lifts one wheel, power is momentarily lost as the wheel spins, the spring forces the tyre back on to the road and the other wheel lifts. A rhythmical tramping action is thus set up which causes a severe judder. This fault is peculiar to some models and is then difficult to cure. It is not experienced, of course, when the driving wheels are independently sprung. Check the rear springs and shock absorbers for weakness. Stiffer dampers may be needed if the engine

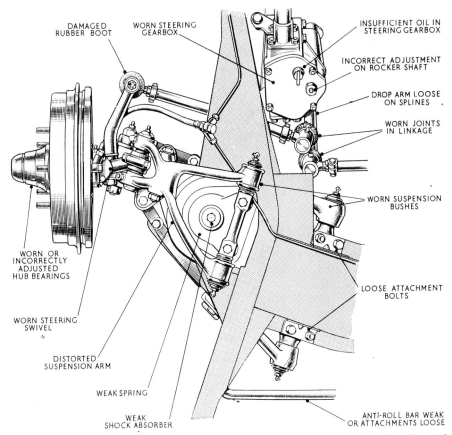

DAMAGED RUBBER BOOT

WORN STEERING GEARBOX

INSUFFICIENT OIL IN STEERING GEARBOX

INCORRECT ADJUSTMENT ON ROCKER SHAFT

DROP ARM LOOSE ON SPLINES

WORN JOINTS IN LINKAGE

WORN SUSPENSION BUSHES

LOOSE ATTACHMENT BOLTS

WORN OR INCORRECTLY ADJUSTED HUB BEARINGS

WORN STEERING SWIVEL

DISTORTED SUSPENSION ARM

WEAK SPRING

WEAK SHOCK ABSORBER

ANTI-ROLL BAR WEAK OR ATTACHMENTS LOOSE

FIG. 7.16. Possible front suspension and steering faults. A coil-spring suspension layout is illustrated, but many of these faults can also develop on torsion-bar, laminated-spring and rubber-spring systems.

has been tuned to develop extra power. Wheel tramp at high speeds is usually caused by unbalanced wheels and tyres or unequal tyre pressures, but again weak shock absorbers and road springs contribute to the trouble.

Abnormally Soft Suspension. The "ride" that may be expected from any particular model is, of course, largely a matter of the design of the suspension system. A softly-sprung car will obviously tend to roll more when cornering and pitch when braking and accelerating, than one which has a firm suspension designed for the more sporting driver. When an abnormal amount of roll is present, or the car pitches badly on a bumpy or corrugated road, the most likely culprits are the shock absorbers, or if these are in good condition, the road springs.

Harsh Suspension. As indicated above, the characteristics of the suspension depend on the design of the car. If the springing appears to be too harsh, points to check are: tyre pressures too high; dry or rusty leaf springs, on models where such springs require lubrication; seized spring shackles; non-standard shock absorbers; incorrect pressure in hydro-pneumatic suspension units; torsion bars incorrectly adjusted.

187

CHAPTER 8

ROAD WHEELS AND TYRES

A WHEEL, tyre and inner tube (where applicable) function as a single unit and are carefully designed to work together as a whole. During the design of each new car model they are carefully selected, or specially designed, to match with the vehicle's geometry, suspension system, manoeuvring characteristics and performance levels. A wrong choice of tyre can cause rapid tyre deterioration, increase fuel consumption, be uncomfortable to ride on and hazardous to drive with. If the vehicle is substantially modified, therefore, or its use appreciably changed, it is advisable to consult a tyre manufacturer or distributor, concerning the suitability of the existing tyres or their replacement.

In normal circumstances, to maintain a vehicle's efficiency, performance levels and maximum safety it is essential to observe a few rules concerning wheels and tyres.

CARE OF WHEELS

Two types of wheel are used on cars By far the most common is the *bolt detachable wheel*, which consists of a well base rim and a pressed centre disc. Until recently the two components were riveted together, but with the advent of modern production techniques they are more commonly spot welded. Repairs to bolt detachable wheels are not recommended and a damaged wheel should be replaced as soon as possible. Damage can be caused by accident, by overload, by driving up kerbs or into sharp stops, or by any behaviour leading to an excessive force on the wheel.

Overtightening of the fixing nuts can cause small cracks, extending from the fixing holes, which could continue to extend during service and become serious. On the other hand, loose fixing nuts can cause irregular wear of the fixing holes and produce irregular rotation of the wheel and uneven tyre wear, combined with disconcerting vibrations through to the steering.

It is advisable to tighten the nuts well but not excessively. Screw threads should be kept clean and the cone-shaped male end of each nut arranged inwards on to the wheel (bolt locating holes in the wheel are suitably recessed). Tightening should be by alternating pairs of diagonally opposing nuts.

When a wheel is to be changed, a useful tip is to loosen each nut a half-turn or so

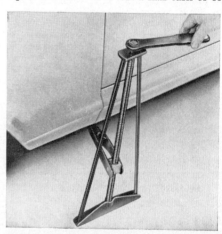

FIG. 8.1. Typical ratchet-operated screw jack in use. The jacking arm must enter the socket under the door sill fully and the jack be firmly seated, as upright as possible, before lifting is started. Put a board under the jack if it is to bear on soft or sandy soil.

before acking up and unscrewing the nuts fully (Fig. 8.1).

Centre Lock Wire Wheels. The second type of wheel is the centre lock wire wheel, commonly used on sports cars. Spoking patterns are generally determined by rim size, inset or outset dimensions, and the brake installation contour. In single-line spoking all spokes radiate from the hub shell to the tyre seat of the rim. In cross spoking they radiate from the nose or outer end of the hub shell to the well of the rim, and from the flanged or inner end of the shell to the tyre seat of the rim. The spokes do not follow a true radius but are either approaching tangential or actually tangential to the hub shell.

Damage to wire wheels can be made good by replacing the damaged parts and rebuilding, while simple eccentricity and out-of-truth can be remedied by re-tensioning the spokes. All such work is best entrusted to specialists. Again, damage can be caused by accident, by overload, by driving up kerbs or into sharp stops, or by any behaviour leading to an excessive force on the wheel.

The majority of wire wheels are fixed to the hub by a knock-on self-tightening nut which allows a speedy wheel change. The self-tightening is achieved by the use of left-hand threads for the offside wheels and right-hand threads for the nearside wheels. Splines inside the hub provide the necessary "key" action for transmitting driving and braking forces, and the splines and screw threads should be kept clean.

With both types of wheel, all parts should be kept free from rust, including the tyre bead surfaces of the rim. Oil or grease should not be used as a protection, particularly close to the tyre—they are both detrimental to rubber. Periodic inspection of rims and wheels is advisable. A cracked flange can seriously affect tyre performance, as well as constituting a safety hazard.

Out-of-truth produces irregular tyre wear and will also excite vibrations in steering. Wheels can be laterally and/or radially out-of-truth, which in both instances is noticeable by spinning the wheel, preferably on a trueing stand. High spots can be marked by holding a piece of chalk close to the rim when spinning. Seriously out-of-truth wheels should be replaced or, in the case of wire wheels, corrected by spoke adjustment. Wire wheels should be corrected to within 0·060 in., radial and lateral out-of-truth.

Wheel misalignment can cause rapid tyre tread wear, characterized by a feather-edge appearance, and should be remedied. Before adjusting reference should be made to the appropriate service manual, because a certain degree of misalignment in the static position is sometimes necessary to produce the correct alignment when the vehicle is on the move.

Wheel Balance. Balanced tyres and wheels are vitally important because out-of-balance can seriously affect steering control at certain speeds, more often in the high speed range. Out-of-balance can be caused by wheel damage or brake drum eccentricity, by uneven tread wear round the circumference, by cover or tube repairs, and by re-positioning a tyre on the wheel. Present-day tyres have an indication or location mark showing where it should be fitted, using the valve as the datum position.

There are two kinds of out-of-balance, "static" and "dynamic". The former can be detected by allowing the wheel to rotate freely on a centre; if it always comes to rest in the same position, then there is static out-of-balance. A wheel assembly which shows no static out-of-balance could still be dynamically out-of-balance. The weight distribution across the tyre or wheel could vary and yet be balanced about the axle. This produces an oscillation from side to side as the wheel rotates.

There are two types of balance testing equipment, one in which the tyre-wheel assembly is taken off the vehicle for testing on a precision balance machine and the other in which the balance tester is coupled to the wheel whilst it is still on the vehicle. These machines indicate, by an optical device, the size and position of the balance weights necessary to bring the assembly into correct static or dynamic balance.

It is always desirable to have the wheel balance checked when tyre wear is abnormal, when steering seems heavy or imprecise, after a kerb has been struck or a minor collision, and when new tyres are fitted.

Theoretically the whole of the wheel assembly should be in balance, as is the case when approved after testing on the vehicle. But doing so, however, lessens the chances of favourable interchangeability of wheels, as recommended by tyre manufacturers, without necessarily re-balancing on each occasion. Testing and correcting away from the vehicle is, therefore, generally preferred.

Lead balance weights are fitted with spring clips by which they can be securely attached to the rim flange (Fig. 8.2). Wheels larger than 16 in. in diameter with tubular flanges may be balanced by cementing a lead strip to the rim or, where this is impracticable, by cementing a balance adjustment rubber inside the crown of the tyre casing.

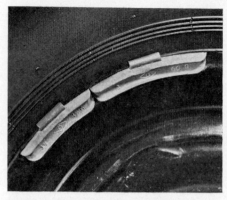

FIG. 8.2. Wheel balancing is carried out by attaching clip-on balance weights to the wheel rim, after checking on a dynamic wheel balancing machine.

CHOICE AND CARE OF TYRES

A driver's attitude towards driving largely governs the performance and life of his tyres. Fast cornering, fierce braking and rapid acceleration all wear down the tyre tread appreciably. (An extra 10 m.p.h. on cornering doubles the rate of wear during cornering.) Higher speeds than are catered for in the design of a particular tyre will produce excessive heat build-up, ultimately a deterioration of rubber compounds and lowering of adhesion between tyre cords and rubber, resulting in possible blow-out. On the maintenance side, mis-alignment of wheels, incorrect inflation pressures and bad fitting also influence the life and performance of a tyre.

All new and retreaded tyres should be run-in to condition the rubber and the cords for service. Fitted to a new vehicle, this coincides with running-in the vehicle itself and no additional period is necessary. For a replacement tyre, fitted to a car that does not require running-in, a maximum speed of 50 m.p.h. is recommended for the first 50 miles and a gradual increase to overall maximum speed during the next 50 miles. The tyre is then suitable for all speeds within its range.

A tyre casing that has been looked after is adequately suitable for retreading and will then give further generous service. Nevertheless, the tyre cords and primary adhesion areas between these cords and the rubber must be respected during their second life as a retreaded tyre. It is advisable, therefore, never to exceed 75 m.p.h. on a retreaded tyre. Retreaded tyres are sometimes referred to as remoulds, and must not be confused with recut or regrooved tyres. The latter are cheaper, but are definitely not to be recommended —they are dangerous on any vehicle (Fig. 8.3).

Tyre treads are designed to grip the road under a wide range of conditions, which may be changing every second of the journey. A wet road surface is a particular hazard for which tread patterns are essential, particularly those with circumferential grooves to channel away water and micro-thickness slots to finally wipe dry the road surface in contact with the tread. On a wet road a smooth tyre, or a tyre without an appropriately designed tread pattern, will aquaplane above certain speeds and become exceedingly dangerous, because of complete loss of steering control.

Special heavy tread patterns are recommended for mud, snow and slush; they are not suitable for speeds above 85 m.p.h. Normal inflation pressures, according to load, should be used, but an increase of 6 lb per sq in. is necessary for continuous driving at speeds between 75 and 85 m.p.h.

Steel studded tyres are recommended for ice and frozen snow. Fitting studs should be left to specially equipped service stations or to the tyre manufacturers.

It is good practice to periodically examine tyre treads for embedded stones, and remove these along with any other penetrating object. If a nail has penetrated the tread of a tubeless tyre and the tyre still retains pressure, make certain of having a repair kit near at hand, or alternatively a spare wheel, before extracting it. If

the nail has penetrated deeply enough removal will cause deflation.

Wipe the tyres clean of any oil or grease, using a rag moistened with petrol. Oil or grease ultimately swells the rubber if left in contact with it and will reduce its toughness and resistance to abrasion.

Radial Ply and Cross Ply Tyres. There are two distinct types of tyre made for modern cars and, although externally they may differ only slightly, it is important to be able to distinguish them (manufacturer's markings should be consulted). Their essential difference, which is not outwardly apparent, lies in the tyre cord arrangement. The cross ply tyre has its cords arranged in a criss-cross manner, whereas the radial ply tyre has the cords arranged radially, like spokes of a wheel, and also has a bracing layer of cords under the tread.

Both cross ply and radial ply tyres have certain advantages, dependent upon individual requirements and whether a particular vehicle has a suitably designed suspension system to accept the latter. It is very important, however, that they are not used as mixed sets in certain ways.

FIG. 8.3. This tyre has at some time been regrooved and reveals damaged tyre cords. It also shows the effects of excessive camber and misalignment.

FIG. 8.4. At normal working pressures a radial ply tyre (*left*) appears less inflated than a cross ply tyre (*right*) because of its different construction.

Thus, radial ply tyres should never be fitted on the front wheels only, even on front wheel drive cars, as this can produce unpleasant and often dangerous oversteer on cornering. Also, a radial ply tyre should never be fitted on the same axle as a cross ply tyre.

Certain radial ply tyres have steel breakers (bracing cord layers under the tread). If two of these are fitted with two all-textile radial ply tyres, then it is preferable to have the steel breaker tyres on the rear wheels.

If a spare wheel differs from an odd number of the remaining set, then even in an emergency it should only be used at moderate speeds, to return to the driver's home or to a garage. If it differs from two, then it can be paired and arranged so that the radial ply tyres are on the rear axle only.

When inflated correctly a radial ply tyre appears less inflated than a cross ply tyre, because its sidewalls are made deliberately more pliable and bulge appreciably more above where the tread rests on the road (Fig. 8.4). Always check inflation pressures with a gauge and not by appearance.

Fault Symptoms. It is advisable to examine tyres fairly frequently, watching for the following signs of trouble.

If the tread pattern is worn with sharp or feather edges towards one side, then the wheel is misaligned (Fig. 8.5).

If the tread shows heavy wear on one side only, there is a possibility of excessive wheel camber. On the other hand road camber has the same effect and is one reason for interchanging tyres regularly.

(*Left*) FIG. 8.5. This tyre shows the result of misalignment, with the ribs sharp and feather-edged towards one side. (*Centre*) FIG. 8.6. This shows the result of under-inflation, with heavy wear on the tread's outer edges. Over-inflation has the reverse effect, showing heavy wear in the tread centre.

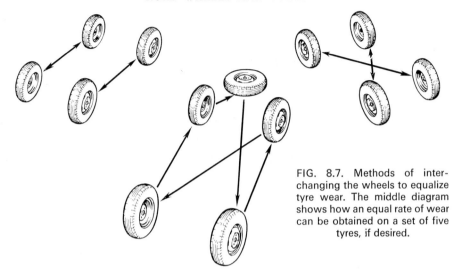

FIG. 8.7. Methods of inter-changing the wheels to equalize tyre wear. The middle diagram shows how an equal rate of wear can be obtained on a set of five tyres, if desired.

If the tread is worn appreciably more in the centre, then the tyre has possibly been running for a long period over-inflated, but if worn appreciably more on the edges, then the tyre might have been running under-inflated (Fig. 8.6).

If the tyre has one or more distinct worn patches around the circumference, braking has been too fierce on some occasion, or they may be due to the brake catching on a high spot during each wheel revolution, or to wheel out-of-truth.

When it is necessary to remove a tyre, always examine the inside for fractured cords due to impact damage. If present, they occur in lines along or across the cords of the inside ply, sometimes forming crosses. A tyre damaged in this way is usually irreparable. The tyre is weakened, although it may not fail completely until some time later, and constitutes a hazard. The magnitude of the hazard depends upon the extent of the damage. As a temporary measure, but only for a very short journey at a precautionary low speed, a reinforcing gaiter can be used. Gaiters are applied like tube repair patches, but adhere to the inside of the tyre over the damage and not the tube. When a gaiter is fitted to a tube-less tyre it is usually necessary to fit an inner tube.

Inflation Pressures. Check inflation pressures with a reliable gauge regularly, preferably once a week, and with the tyres cold—a warm tyre has a temporarily higher pressure. Check valve cores and caps from time to time. Always replace missing caps and screw these down finger tight only. Their main purpose is to keep fine grit from the valve seat. Any such grit on the rim of the valve will be blown into the valve during tyre inflation and possibly make the valve inoperative. The cap also acts as a secondary seal.

Interchanging. Unless the vehicle manufacturer recommends otherwise it is generally advisable to interchange tyres (with their wheels) every 3,000 miles. This helps to balance the particular type of wear associated with each position on the vehicle. When interchanging mixed tyres, radial ply tyres must never be put on the front wheels with cross ply tyres on the rear. A mixed set can only be changed from side to side, unless the spare wheel can be introduced with one of the pairs. For uniform sets, three ways of changing round are given in Fig. 8.7. After interchanging make sure that each tyre is at the correct pressure for its new position.

Checking Wheel Geometry. Specialized equipment is necessary for checking wheel geometry, with which tyre traders are usually equipped. All measurements should be checked with the vehicle's specification before making any adjustments. Through wear and tear and minor impacts the steering and suspension layout may be disturbed. Front wheel alignment, camber angle, castor angle and king pin inclination should therefore be checked at regular intervals. Misalignment can be caused by incorrectly adjusted toe-in and toe-out; worn wheel bearings or king pin bushes; bent suspension members, or members not properly aligned.

TYRE SERVICE

Tyre Fitting. Fitting a tyre is an easy operation to one experienced in the art and should be almost equally simple to a beginner, provided the correct procedure is taken (Fig. 8.8). Never use force enough to damage the tyre; if such force seems necessary then the procedure has not been correctly followed. The whole performance of a tyre depends upon correct fitting. Be careful not to distort or damage the beads.

To remove, first deflate the tyre and then place the wheel and tyre horizontally at a comfortable operating level, say on a low stand. If the two bead seats on the rim are unequal in width, make certain the narrow seat is uppermost (the narrow side of the rim uppermost). If they are equal in width, then it is more convenient to have the valve uppermost.

Lubricate the tips of two tyre levers with tyre bead lubricant or soap solution (not oil or grease) and gently use the levers to prise the top bead downwards away from the wheel rim. Work slowly round the rim, always keeping the levers moistened with lubricant. It sometimes helps to brush a little lubricant into the channel between the bead and the rim. If the bead is stub-

born do not try to force it at one spot only, but continue to work round the rim with slightly increasing leverage at each revolution.

When the bead is released press that side diametrically opposite to the valve position well down, so that the bead can freely enter into the well of the rim. With a tyre lever prise the bead on the valve side over the rim. To do this the opposite side of the bead must enter the well of the rim, and at this stage it may be necessary to assist this movement with the free hand. With the second tyre lever about 2 in. away from the first, prise another length of bead over the rim, whilst keeping the first lever in position. With the second tyre lever, gently work around the circumference of the tyre until the whole bead is prised over the rim. Always keep the tips of the levers lubricated and, if an inner tube is present, be careful not to trap it between the lever and the tyre bead or wheel rim.

Remove the inner tube if present. Turn the wheel over and release the second bead from the rim, using the same procedure as before. Turn the wheel over again and prise the second bead over the upper rim, again following the same procedure. Always remember not to try to force the bead over the rim unless the opposite side can move into the well.

Before fitting a tyre always make sure that the rim flanges and bead seats are clean and free of rust. If tubes are used, a new cover deserves a new tube. This is because tubes stretch in service and eventually take on a permanent set. When a stretched tube is fitted to a new cover, the tube may become creased and a costly tyre failure may result.

To fit a cover, first brush both rims of the wheel and the tyre beads with tyre bead lubricant or soap solution (not oil or grease). Place the wheel horizontally at a comfortable operating level, with the valve or valve hole uppermost. Then, as far as possible, slip the lower bead of the tyre

194

FIG. 8.8. Tyre removal and fitting. (a) Pressing the wire bead off its seating with two tyre levers. (b) Inserting the lever at the valve position. Press the bead into the well diametrically opposite the valve. (c) Levering off the bead, which is continued until the bead is clear of the rim. (d) Pulling the cover back over the flange. (e) Fitting is begun by placing the tyre eccentrically over the rim. The lower bead is pressed as much as possible into the well. (f) Levering the lower bead over the rim, this being continued until the bead is completely over the rim. (g) Levering the upper bead into position. Push the bead into the well diametrically opposite the valve.

195

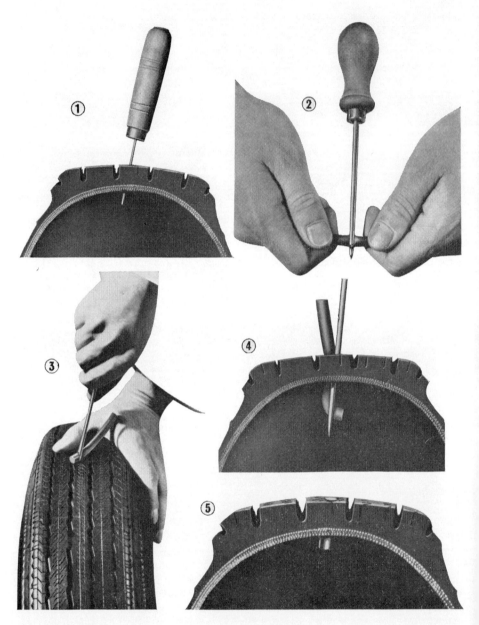

FIG. 8.9. Stages in repairing a puncture in a tubeless tyre. (1) A plugging tool supplied with the repair kit is used to check the direction of penetration through the tread. The hole is then well lubricated with rubber solution. (2) A rubber plug is rolled into the plugging tool and wetted with solution. (3) and (4) The doubled-up plug is pushed through the hole and the tool then withdrawn. (5) The plug is finally cut off flush with the tread surface.

over the upper rim, assisted by pressing as much of the bead as possible into the well of the rim. With a tyre lever, gently prise the remainder of the lower bead over the upper rim, always working slowly round the bead—do not endeavour to prise too much over the rim at once. Locate the tyre so that the location mark, if present, is adjacent to the valve hole, then press the lower bead close to the lower rim.

If an inner tube is required, place it inside the cover at this stage. Make certain that the correct tube has been selected. When fitting, the valve of the tube should be on the side pointing a little upwards to coincide with the valve hole in the rim. Once the valve is fitted inflate the tube a little, enough to remove the creases only; any real pressure will make fitting difficult or impossible.

Now press that part of the upper bead opposite the valve over the upper rim and into the well as far as possible. With levers gently prise the remainder of the bead over the rim. Again, remember to work slowly round the rim and prise only a small section at a time. Keep the tips of the levers lubricated and take care not to trap the inner tube, if present.

Inflation of Tubeless Tyres. When inflating a tubeless tyre first make certain that one bead is pressed completely home against the adjacent rim. This can be accomplished by leaning the wheel and tyre against a wall at approximately 60 deg. and then pressing the wheel centre so that the nearest bead obtains a firm hold on the rim seat. If the rim has one wider seat, press the adjacent bead on to that particular seat first; otherwise engage the valve side first. Quickly inflate the tyre and the opposite bead will seat itself against its adjacent rim seat (do not exceed 40 lb per sq in. air pressure or the tyre may be damaged). If unsuccessful use a tourniquet around the circumference of the tyre, to force the beads outwards, and then inflate.

A tourniquet is usually ineffective with radial ply tyres. Where there is still difficulty in obtaining a seal, use the following method.

Press the first bead on to its seat in the manner described above. Reverse the wheel, taking care not to dislodge the first bead. Lean the wheel at approximately 30 deg. to the wall. Whilst inflating press the wheel centre gently to seal against the second bead. Alternating hand pressure, rather than continuous pressure, and removing the valve may be found helpful.

If the tyre beads do not seat properly at the second attempt, then the wheel rim seat circumferences are suspect and should be checked. If necessary fit a new wheel.

Important. If using a fitting machine, lock the wheels down, stand clear of the tyre when inflating and do not lean over until the beads are properly seated.

Repairs to Tyres and Tubes. Inner tube injuries up to $\frac{1}{4}$ in. in extent can be repaired with specially prepared patches. Instructions are given with every repair kit. The general procedure is to clean and buff the surface around the hole; apply solution and allow to dry, then place the adhesive surface of the patch to the treated surface of the tube. Finish off by dusting with french chalk. More severe damage should be referred to a tyre repair specialist.

There is a variety of repair outfits for tubeless tyres available and careful instructions are given with every kit (Fig. 8.9). They usually involve a means of inserting a plug into the puncturing hole and at the same time fixing and sealing it with an adhesive. The plugging material is generally made from a rubber compound. The tyre is almost immediately ready for inflation and use, but the effectiveness of the repair must be improved as soon as possible by a cold patch repair on the inside of the cover, or by vulcanization. More severe damage should be referred to a tyre repair specialist. Do not use plug repairs for tyre shoulder or sidewall damage and never use more than one plug in one hole.

CHAPTER 9

BRAKING SYSTEM

IT IS the general practice to fit braking systems produced by specialist firms, and the majority of British cars employ either Girling or Lockheed brakes, though Rolls-Royce cars have their own system and a number of high-performance cars use the Dunlop disc brake system (now taken over by Girling Ltd.).

Features of all modern braking systems include powerful brake application in response to moderate or light pedal pressure and simplicity of adjustment, while routine servicing is reduced to a minimum. All-drum, all-disc and mixed drum-and-disc brake systems are currently employed, and on many cars the pressure of the driver's foot on the pedal is supplemented by a vacuum-operated servo unit, giving power-assisted braking.

General Servicing. All brakes, of whatever type, are subjected to wear every time the pedal is operated. Most of the wear occurs between the brake linings and the brake drums or disc plates, but the softer material of the linings is affected far more than the metal parts. Little wear takes place in the hydraulic operating system, but eventually its master cylinder and wheel cylinder mechanisms will be affected.

The usual indications of brake lining wear are excessive travel of the foot pedal before the brakes operate and a squealing noise as the car comes to rest. Wear in the hydraulic system is indicated by the fluid level in the reservoir gradually diminishing, by a "spongy" feeling in the pedal application, and by being able to press the pedal slowly to the floor after the brakes have been applied.

A certain amount of adjustment is available to take up wear on drum brake linings and this should be carried out, as described later, at regular intervals (every 6,000 miles). A general inspection of the braking system should be made every 12,000 miles with drum brakes, or every 6,000 miles with disc brakes. It is a simple matter to remove and examine the pads on disc brakes, but a proper inspection of a drum brake mechanism can only be made by removing the drum, which is not always easy.

Apart from the indications of wear already mentioned, some idea of the condition of the brakes can be obtained by making a road test.

Check for squealing when the brakes are applied hard, a tendency to pull to one side, skidding, and a "lumpy" pedal movement—a sign of ovality in the drums.

Brake manufacturers, though not all vehicle manufacturers in their handbooks, insist on the advisability of checking the level of fluid in the brake reservoir every 1,000 miles. At the same time a check should be made for leakages from the hydraulic system, particularly at the flexible hoses to each front wheel and the single rear hose, also the pipe unions.

BRAKE TESTING

The only accurate method of testing brakes on the road is to use a decelerometer or Tapley meter, which works on the pendulum principle—the more effective the brakes the more the pendulum swings; a meter then indicates the corresponding brake efficiency. With this instrument the efficiency can be measured when the

FIG. 9.1. A car's braking efficiency is best checked by the use of modern equipment such as this Hill Brake Tester. The car is driven while on the rollers and the electronic console can record its braking performance at speeds up to 90 m.p.h.

brakes are applied at any speed above 10 m.p.h.

As it is becoming increasingly difficult to carry out a road test on crowded roads, many garages today are equipped with a brake testing machine which has a set of rollers on which the car is driven while stationary. With this, the brake efficiency at each wheel is accurately measured by electronic means (Fig. 9.1).

Braking efficiency is measured as a percentage of gravity, as explained in Chapter 2, the braking force being converted into a percentage of the total weight of the vehicle and its normal load. In the annual compulsory test for older cars the minimum efficiencies required are 50 per cent for the foot brake and 25 per cent for the hand brake on four-wheel vehicles.

The only other practicable method of measuring braking efficiency is to check as carefully as possible the minimum distance in which the car can be brought to rest from a given speed by applying the foot pedal. The actual distance depends upon the type of road surface, condition of the tyres and whether these are correctly inflated, and whether conditions are wet or dry, while the driver's reaction time also affects matters considerably. However, the following table gives a rough guide to stopping distances.

Condition of brakes	Stopping distance from	
	30 m.p.h.	50 m.p.h.
Very good	32 ft.	92 ft.
Fair	50 ft.	140 ft.
Poor	100 ft.	280 ft.

If the brakes are being tested after maintenance has been carried out, it is essential to ensure that they are operating before taking the car on to the road. This can be done by jacking up the car, getting someone to depress the foot pedal and then ensuring that the wheels cannot be turned by hand. Care should be taken in making tests on the road, as uneven adjustment may cause the vehicle to slew to one side or other when the brakes are applied. The road chosen for testing must be level, with a good dry surface, and of course free from traffic.

The first application of the brakes should be made at comparatively slow speed (10-15 m.p.h.), and if braking is shown to be unsatisfactory then adjustments should be carried out before going on to making further tests at higher speeds. There should

BRAKING SYSTEM

Fault	Possible Causes
PEDAL TRAVEL EXCESSIVE (PEDAL REQUIRES PUMPING)	(a) Usually apparent when linings are worn or shoes need adjusting. If adjustment is at maximum, the shoes need relining. (b) Fluid in the master cylinder needs replenishing, in which case check for leakage from the hydraulic system. (c) Internal leak in master cylinder, usually after prolonged service, or rubber seals perished due to use of incorrect fluid.
PEDAL FEELS "SPONGY"	(a) Internal leak in master cylinder; sometimes shown by air bubbles rising inside fluid reservoir. (b) Slight leak in hydraulic system, usually at the pipe connections, flexible hoses or wheel cylinders. (c) Air present in hydraulic system which must be bled out. Unless this has occurred through parts of the system being disturbed, checks should be made to discover where the air is entering.
PEDAL FEELS SPRINGY	(a) Master cylinder loose on mounting bracket, or mounting weakened. (b) Shoe linings not yet bedded in.
BRAKES INEFFICIENT	(a) Grease or oil present on linings. Grease can get on to linings through over-lubrication of hubs or worn seals. Oil from the rear axle can in some cases reach the brake linings through a faulty seal. Worn seals in wheel cylinders will allow brake fluid to contaminate the linings. (b) Incorrect linings. Linings of different materials may have different coefficients of friction. (c) Shoe linings or disc pads worn down. Excessive wear will permit the shoe metal to contact the brake drum.

be no tendency towards slewing or skidding even in emergency-stop conditions.

Fault Tracing. Finding and remedying faults in the brake mechanical and hydraulic components are referred to later in this chapter, when maintenance and overhaul are discussed. The table on these pages should, however, prove a useful guide to the majority of faults that may occur on drum and disc systems.

If faulty braking is found to be due to linings having become contaminated by oil, grease or brake fluid, these cannot be satisfactorily cleaned as a rule. When a lining has been well saturated no amount of washing in petrol or heating to burn off the grease will cure the trouble, and the only answer is to exchange the linings or shoes. A small amount of contamination can, however, be washed off with petrol and the shiny lining surface roughened with emery cloth.

DRUM BRAKE MAINTENANCE

There are several types of both Girling and Lockheed drum brake systems fitted to British cars, with variations in brake sizes and details of the hydraulic components, but the following information is generally applicable to each make as indicated.

Apart from keeping fluid in the hydraulic reservoir topped up to within $\frac{1}{4}$ in. of the filler cap, the principal item of regular maintenance is checking the degree of wear on the shoe linings and adjusting the brakes to compensate for this wear. Note that in many cases the threaded adjusters mounted in the rear brake back plates have squared heads for which a special brake spanner is available. It is desirable to use this to prevent "rounding" of the corners on the adjusters, though an ordinary spanner will do the job.

FAULT-TRACING

Fault	Possible Causes
BRAKES DRAG	(a) Shoes too closely adjusted. (b) Shoe pull-off springs weak or broken, allowing shoes to make constant contact. (c) Hand brake linkage seized or over-adjusted. The hand brake is usually mechanically operated by rod or cable which is exposed to weather and can seize if lubrication is neglected. (d) Wheel cylinder piston seized, when the shoe will be held in contact with the drum. (e) Air vent in fluid reservoir filler cap blocked. This will tend to prevent return of fluid when pedal is released, thus maintaining shoe in contact with drum.
BRAKES REMAIN ON WHEN PEDAL IS RELEASED	(a) Shoes too closely adjusted. (b) Hand brake linkage seized or over-adjusted. (c) Rubber cups in master or wheel cylinders swollen, due to incorrect fluid or contamination by mineral oil.
UNBALANCED BRAKING	(a) Oil, grease or water on linings. (b) Distorted or worn drums caused by grit or exposed rivets on shoes. (c) Different grades of lining fitted to individual wheels. (d) Tyres unevenly inflated. Under-inflated tyres cause more drag. (e) Worn steering joints or loose brake back plate.
BRAKES GRAB OR JUDDER WHEN APPLIED	(a) Shoes require adjusting. (b) Brake drum worn or distorted. (c) Grease or oil on linings. (d) Shoe pull-off springs weak or broken.
BRAKES SQUEAL WHEN APPLIED	(a) Vibration in brake drum due to metal being too weak. (b) Incorrect type of lining material. (c) Water or dirt in drum. (d) Badly worn linings.

Brake Shoe Adjustment. The procedure for Girling front brakes is as follows. Jack up the car until the wheel to be adjusted is clear of the ground and clean off the dirt from the adjusters (Fig. 9.2). Most popular models have a two-leading-shoe arrangement at the front, when there are two adjusters on the back plate—one for each shoe. Certain models have two trailing shoes at the front.

The hexagon-headed adjuster must be rotated in a clockwise direction until the shoe locks on to the drum, and then turned back one click at a time until the wheel spins freely. The second adjuster is adjusted in the same manner, and the corresponding adjustments are then carried out on the opposite front wheel.

The car is then jacked up to allow adjustment of the rear brakes, which are normally of the leading-and-trailing type. Check that the hand brake is released before adjusting the single square-headed adjuster in the same way. Special care is needed in making the rear adjustments, as there is a certain amount of drag on the drums caused by the differential gears, which is apt to confuse the novice. If any adjuster can be fully tightened without locking the drum fully, this is a definite indication that the linings are badly worn or greasy and need replacement.

In the case of Lockheed systems, there are several different kinds of adjuster in use, but again the principle is to move the brake shoe closer to the drum when the clearance has been increased due to lining wear (Fig. 9.3).

In one type of Lockheed system adjustment is made by rotating a notched disc attached to the piston of the wheel cylinder, thereby lengthening or shortening the piston. Access to the adjuster is gained through a hole in the wheel and brake drum or else through an opening covered by a dust cap in the back plate.

After jacking up, the wheel is turned until the access hole comes into line with a notched disc. A screwdriver is inserted through the hole and used as a lever to rotate the disc until the shoe locks on the drum; then the disc must be slackened back (usually a matter of four notches) until the wheel will rotate without dragging. There are normally two adjusters on each front wheel and a single adjuster on each rear wheel.

Another popular Lockheed system employs "Micram" adjusters. Again, adjustment is made through a hole in the drum which must be aligned with the internal adjuster. Fit a screwdriver through the hole into the adjuster's slotted head, turn in a clockwise direction until the shoe locks on the drum, then turn back one notch to obtain the correct clearance. For closer adjustment, spin the wheel and apply the brakes hard. This positions the shoes correctly and further adjusment can be tried. Once more, two-leading-shoe brakes have two adjusters and the rear brake has one.

In the Lockheed system of leading-and-trailing rear brakes each wheel is fitted with a square-headed adjuster protruding from the back plate. The adjuster is turned clockwise to lock both shoes to the drum, then slackened one flat to obtain correct clearance with the wheel free to rotate.

Automatically Adjusted Brakes. Self-adjusting brakes are displacing the older type on many cars and these, apart from the hydraulic system, need no maintenance until the shoe linings have worn down to the usual minimum thickness. These brakes are supplied by both Girling and Lockheed, with several differences

FIG. 9.2. Girling brake adjustment. (*Upper*) At the front, each shoe has its own adjuster—note the use of the special brake spanner. (*Lower*) At the rear, a single adjuster serves both shoes.

FIG. 9.3. Various forms of Lockheed brake adjusters. (*Upper*) Old-type adjusters in the form of notched discs are rotated through a hole in the brake drum. (*Lower*) A cam adjuster that is reached from behind the back plate and a "Micram" version with screwdriver operation through a hole in the drum.

in design. The following notes on the Girling type show the general principle.

The front brakes are a conventional two-leading-shoe arrangement; in fact, they can be fitted with either manual or automatic adjusters. The automatic adjuster is a self-adjusting friction stop in which a post connected to the shoe web is located. The correct shoe clearance is established between the post and a location slot in the adjuster. When the brakes are applied, the adjuster clearance is taken up, after which any further travel results in the friction stop being rotated until the lining contacts the drum. When the brakes are released, the shoes can only retract the amount of clearance in the adjuster mechanism, and the adjuster remains in

this location until wear on the lining causes it to be repositioned.

On the rear brakes, automatic adjustment is effected by operating the hand brake lever and its associated linkage. Movement of the lever operates an arm which engages in a ratchet wheel, and this drives the adjuster screw on the wheel cylinder. When lining wear occurs, the additional movement on the hand brake lever results in rotation of the adjuster screw. Correct clearance is thus restored.

Hand Brake Adjustment. On drum brake systems, the hand brake acts on the rear wheel drums, a separate system of cables or rods being used to pull the shoes into contact with the drums. A common system embodies a single cable connected

FIG. 9.4. Self-adjusting brakes. On the Lockheed rear brake (*left*) movement of the sliding wheel cylinder causes a pawl to be traversed across a toothed adjuster wheel. If, owing to lining wear, the pawl traverses more than one tooth space, the wheel will rotate when the brakes are released, moving a shoe tappet outwards to take up the wear. Girling front brakes use a friction stop device (*below*), described in the text.

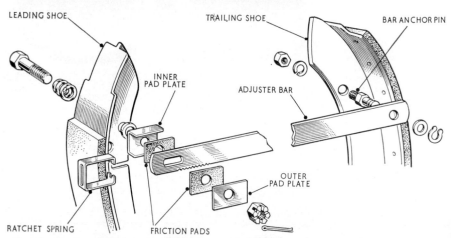

at one end to the control lever and at the other end to a rear-mounted equalising link; this device ensures equal pull on the short cables or rods which connect the equalising link with the two sets of brakes. Certain models have one cable for each wheel, connected directly between the control lever and the brakes.

It is also normal practice for each rear leading shoe to be moved directly by the hand brake lever, while the trailing shoe is simultaneously operated by a sliding movement of the wheel cylinder.

The hand brake is thus automatically adjusted when the rear shoes are adjusted, but in the course of time wear may occur in the system or the cables may stretch. This is shown if, after normal adjustment, the control lever requires more than five or six clicks of its ratchet to apply the hand brake firmly. Some form of adjustment to take up wear is usually provided at one or the other end of the cable, and this is generally a locknut or threaded clevis which permits the cable to be shortened (Fig. 9.5). The car must be jacked up and the cable adjusted until the shoes just begin to contact the drums, after which the adjuster is slackened just enough to allow free rotation of the wheel.

When this adjustment is required, all linkages should be checked for wear and worn parts or frayed cables replaced. The cable must move freely, since cable seizure leads to sticking brakes. Sometimes a lubricator is fitted which requires regular greasing, but on most recent models the cables are pre-lubricated and their conduits sealed to retain the grease. A stiff cable must be completely disconnected and worked free, lubricated with plenty of penetrating oil and then greased thoroughly with water-repellent, cold-resisting grease.

SHOE LINING REPLACEMENT

The rate of wear on the shoe lining material depends upon a number of factors, not least the driver's handling of the car, and although there have been steady improvements in the quality of linings, these have been offset to some extent by the increased tendency to wear imposed by modern traffic conditions, higher road speeds and the use of brake servo assistance. Even so, linings normally give good service for well over 12,000 miles.

Most car manufacturers recommend examining and cleaning the linings at least every 12,000 miles, and renewing them when they have worn to one-third of their original thickness (or when contaminated by grease, etc.). Both Girling and Lockheed supply exchange brake shoes fitted with new linings which have been finished to factory specifications, and it is far more satisfactory to exchange worn shoes for these than to attempt riveting new linings on to the original shoes.

It is important to replace brake shoes or linings with the correct type of lining material. There are many different kinds to suit the different operating conditions,

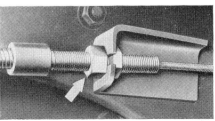

FIG. 9.5. The hand brake cable adjuster nut and locknut may be located by the control lever, at the rear end of the cable conduit, or at the equalising link, as shown in these Volkswagen and Ford examples.

but the two main types are moulded and woven. The moulded type is a compressed mixture of asbestos and may be either bonded or riveted on to the shoe metal. It often has a low coefficient of friction, reducing the risk of brake squeal, judder or grabbing; in this case higher operating pressure has to be used to obtain full braking efficiency. The woven type is usually riveted to the shoe and can be identified by the strands of asbestos woven into the texture. The linings on a car must be all of one type or the other, otherwise the varying coefficients of friction will lead to uneven braking.

The fitting of exchange shoes can easily be carried out by a service station or by the careful owner. Facilities to jack up and support the car are required, as it is preferable to have it completely off the ground, also the usual hand tools and some wheel bearing grease to repack the hub bearings.

Some general points should be borne in mind when doing this job. After the brake drums have been removed they should be examined for signs of wear, distortion and scoring of the surface. Accurate measurement of wear and distortion can only be made by special equipment, and professional advice should be sought if there is any suspicion of such trouble. It is possible to restore a scored or slightly worn drum by skimming on a special lathe, but the maximum permissible amount of metal that may be removed is 0·060 in., otherwise the drum will be seriously weakened. Badly worn or distorted drums must therefore be replaced.

All dirt and grease must be removed before removing any part of the brake assembly, and all internal hydraulic parts should be washed in methylated spirits or brake fluid. It is a wise precaution to replace the rubber boots on hydraulic parts by new ones whenever the brakes are over-hauled. Likewise, new pull-off springs should for preference be fitted with new linings. These are often colour-coded by car manufacturers and it is essential to obtain the correct type of replacement for each spring. In any case, a pull-off spring that shows signs of stretching or kinking should be replaced.

Fitting New Shoes. Having lifted the car and ensured that it is safely supported, start with the front brakes. It is often easier and in some cases necessary to take off the complete hub assembly when working on the brakes. Both adjusters should be slackened off fully before the hub complete with brake drum is removed. Then note the exact position of each component, and in particular the springs and their anchorages, to ensure correct re-assembly (Fig. 9.6).

The following instructions relate to most types of Girling brakes. First, remove the retaining clips from the shoes. Then prise one shoe free of the wheel cylinder abutment—a job that will be helped by the use of an adjustable spanner (Fig. 9.7). Both shoes and pull-off springs may now be removed, leaving the wheel cylinders on the back plate. Place a strong elastic band around each wheel cylinder to retain the pistons and prevent loss of brake fluid.

Clean down the back plate and remove all grease from the hub. Check the wheel cylinders for freedom of piston movement —when one piston is pressed in, the other should move slightly outwards. Each adjuster should turn easily, and given a drop of oil if at all stiff. If grease has found its way from the hub into the brake drum, a new hub grease seal should be fitted after tapping out the old seal with a hammer and drift.

Steady posts which may be either fixed or adjustable are to be found on all more recent systems behind the centre of each shoe web. Their function is to keep the shoes square with the drum. When a steady post requires adjustment, the locknut should be slackened and the posts un-screwed two turns.

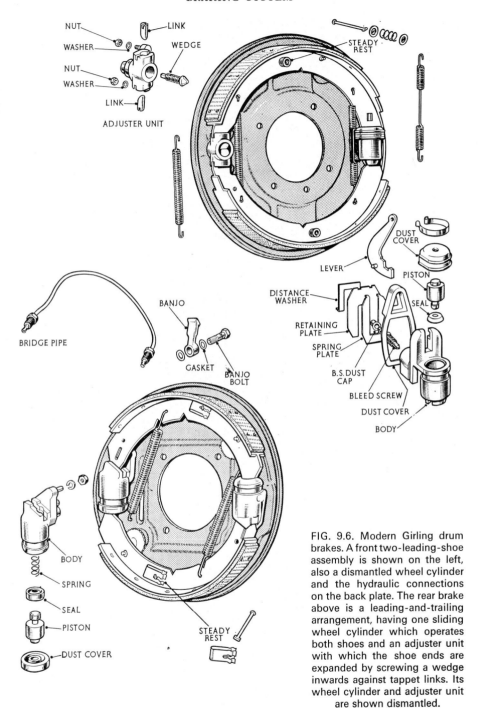

NUT

LINK

WASHER

WEDGE

NUT

WASHER

LINK

ADJUSTER UNIT

STEADY REST

DUST COVER

LEVER

PISTON

DISTANCE WASHER

BANJO

RETAINING PLATE

SEAL

BRIDGE PIPE

SPRING PLATE

GASKET

BANJO BOLT

B.S.DUST CAP

BLEED SCREW

DUST COVER

BODY

BODY

SPRING

SEAL

PISTON

DUST COVER

STEADY REST

FIG. 9.6. Modern Girling drum brakes. A front two-leading-shoe assembly is shown on the left, also a dismantled wheel cylinder and the hydraulic connections on the back plate. The rear brake above is a leading-and-trailing arrangement, having one sliding wheel cylinder which operates both shoes and an adjuster unit with which the shoe ends are expanded by screwing a wedge inwards against tappet links. Its wheel cylinder and adjuster unit are shown dismantled.

FIG. 9.7. Replacing Girling brake shoes. (*Top*) The back plate as it appears after the shoes and springs have been removed. Before fitting new shoes the back plate should be checked as indicated. (*Centre*) Using an adjustable spanner to prise a shoe away from its abutment. (*Bottom*) After fitting new shoes and springs, a final check should be made for correct operation

The new shoes and pull-off springs can now be prepared for fitting. On some cars the springs are connected between the shoes. In this case, fit the springs to the two shoes, ensuring that they will lie between the shoe webs and the back plate. Take care not to handle the linings more than necessary and keep them free of oil and grease. Place the shoes with springs attached against the back plate and position one shoe in its correct abutment, then ease the second shoe into position.

A slight variation is required where the current two-leading-shoe system is used, as in this case the springs are connected between the shoes and the back plate. Position the shoe so that the angled end of the web contacts the angled abutment slot in the wheel cylinder, and attach the spring to its hole in the back plate and to the hole adjacent to the cut-away portion of the shoe web. Lever the end of the web on to the wheel cylinder piston. If the brakes are self-adjusting, lift the shoe away from the back plate and rotate the hexagon-headed bolt to locate the pin in the adjuster slot. Fit the shoe hold-down spring and repeat this procedure with the second shoe and spring.

With all types, reset the steady post if required. Repack the hub with grease and then fit the hub and drum assembly. Remember that the adjusters will need resetting when the job is finished.

Work on Girling rear brakes is similar except that the shoes are engaged by the wheel cylinder and the shoe adjuster tappets. Also, pull-off springs of unequal length are used which must be the right way round. Most rear brake assemblies are exposed by removing the road wheel and taking out set screws that hold the brake drum in position. When the shoes and springs have been removed, check for free action of the plungers in the adjuster, the hydraulic piston in its cylinder, and the cylinder itself which slides on the back plate.

After final adjustment of all the shoes, the car should be road-tested. In about 250 miles of running the new linings will have bedded in and some further shoe adjustment may be needed.

The procedure for Lockheed exchange shoes is very much the same. After removing the drums and hubs the ends of the springs protruding through the shoes can be dislodged by striking them with a screwdriver. One new shoe is fitted with springs engaged, then the other shoe is attached to the springs and pulled out sufficiently to fit it into position. Take care not to damage the Micram adjusters when working on these brakes.

DISC BRAKE MAINTENANCE

Various designs of disc brakes are to be found on a wide range of cars: Girling and Lockheed on many family cars, and Dunlop on Jaguar, Aston Martin and other high-performance models. In all cases the principle is the same—a cast-iron disc which rotates with the road wheel is braked by the pressure of a pair of friction pads, hydraulically operated and enclosed in a caliper unit that straddles the disc. The design differences are mainly in the hydraulic actuating mechanism and construction of the caliper unit. Where the car is fitted with disc brakes at all four wheels, the rear units are provided with additional mechanism for hand brake operation.

Routine adjustment for wear is not required with disc brakes, because wear on the fricton linings of the pads is automatically taken up in the hydraulic system. For this reason the level of fluid in the brake reservoir may gradually fall as the thickness of the lining material diminishes. Where front disc and rear drum brakes are fitted, however, the rear brakes will require regular shoe adjustment as previously described (unless of the self-adjusting type). The hydraulic system, too, should be checked for fluid level and signs of leakage every 1,000 miles, irrespective of

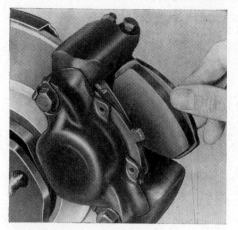

FIG. 9.8. Fitting a new friction pad in a Lock-heed disc brake. The pads in this type are retained by spring clips which can be removed after extracting two split pins.

the arrangement of disc or drum-and-disc brakes fitted.

Pad Replacement. The friction linings on the pads should be inspected for wear every 6,000 miles; this is best done by removing the road wheel concerned. When worn, the pads are easily removed and replacement pads fitted (Fig. 9.8).

Girling. The manufacturers of these brakes recommend replacing the pads when they have worn to a thickness of $\frac{1}{8}$ in. (3 mm). It is dangerous to use a car when the pads have worn down to $\frac{1}{16}$ in. thickness.

Three types of caliper have been introduced by this maker, involving slight differences in servicing. The two earlier types have pads which are retained by upper and lower plates. In some cases anti-rattle springs are fitted under these plates. The plate bolts must be loosened and the plates swung round to allow the pads to be withdrawn. The latest type has its pads secured by spring clips which can easily be removed to allow extraction of the pads.

When replacing worn pads, the car must first be jacked up and the road wheel removed. Then take out the old pads.

Before the new pads are inserted, the pistons must be pushed as far as possible into the cylinder bores, a job that may require quite heavy pressure. The new pads can then be fully inserted. If anti-squeak shims are fitted, make sure that these are located behind the brake pad and that the direction arrow on them faces the forward rotation of the disc. The retaining plates or spring clips can then be replaced and secured. This procedure applies to both front and rear brakes and after replacing all the pads it is only necessary to pump the foot pedal until solid resistance is felt, when the brakes will be adjusted for correct clearance.

A recent introduction is the Girling single-side swing caliper rear brake which incorporates the hand brake mechanism in the main assembly. A single pair of pads serves both foot and hand operation, and there is only one hydraulic operating cylinder. The caliper is mounted on a large hinge pin located inside the disc, and as wear develops the whole unit gradually moves round the pin. The outer pad is permanently attached to the caliper casting, the inner one slides under the action of either the hydraulic cylinder or the hand brake linkage; the design permits both pads to have equal braking effect.

On this type, replacement is not required until the pad linings have worn to a depth of $\frac{1}{16}$ in. The fixed outer pad is held in place by two bolts which, when removed, allow the pad to be withdrawn. The movable inner pad is bonded to a backing plate which slides along two other plates. These two smaller plates are unbolted to permit removal of the pad.

Lockheed. This range of disc brakes for light, medium and heavy duty are of similar design, and it is possible to check wear of the friction pads visually from the side of the caliper. The early-type pads were automatically adjusted by a fall-back device in each cylinder which retracts the piston and, while compensating for lining wear, maintains a constant clearance between pad and disc. This device is not used in the later type of unit where the pads are allowed to remain close to the disc when the brakes are off. Lockheed recommend replacing the pads on light and medium disc brakes when worn down to $\frac{1}{16}$ in. thickness, and on heavy-duty brakes when worn to $\frac{1}{8}$ in.

The procedure with heavy-duty brakes is as follows. Jack up the vehicle and remove the road wheels. The caliper unit must be removed, by taking out two set screws (carefully note the position of any spacing washers between the caliper and mounting bracket). Take care not to tug on the hydraulic hoses when removing the caliper. The pads are easily extracted by moving them to the centre of the caliper and sliding outwards.

Thoroughly clean the exposed end of the piston and all recesses in the unit, then push the piston back into the cylinder as far as possible. This will displace fluid which may cause the fluid in the reservoir to rise and overflow. Insert the new pads, check for free action, and carefully reposition the caliper.

The procedure is the same for light and medium brakes except that here it is unnecessary to remove the caliper unit. The pad assembly can easily be removed after taking out the retaining pins and spring. Replace any retaining springs that show signs of strain. The foot pedal should be pumped several times to obtain correct adjustment of the new pads and it may be necessary to top up the master cylinder.

Dunlop. Three versions of the Dunlop disc brake system have appeared, but the one most likely to be encountered is the Series III front brake used in conjunction with the Series IV rear brake. A feature of this system is a self-adjusting retraction device which ensures that whatever the wear on the pads, there is always a constant small clearance between the pad and the disc, when the brakes are off.

To replace the pads on the front brake it is only necessary to take off a retaining plate and then withdraw each pad by inserting a small hook into the hole in the lug of the securing plate. The piston, dust seal and backing plate must be cleaned thoroughly and the piston pushed back as far as possible. The new pads are then pushed into position; make sure that the small projection on the back plate slides in its location on the piston.

To replace the rear brake pads it is necessary to dismantle the pad carriers by disconnecting the adjuster bolt and pivot pins so that the old lining can be removed. Before fitting the new pads unscrew the adjuster bolt to allow for the extra lining thickness. As with the other systems, the final job is to pump the pedal several times to obtain correct adjustment.

A point to watch when servicing any disc brake is the condition of the disc plate, which has a critical effect upon braking efficiency. The disc must run true between its pads, the maximum permissible deviation being only a few thousandths of an inch. The surface, too, should be smooth. Scratches and light scoring which appear after a period of normal use are not detrimental, but a heavily scored disc will affect efficiency and increase the rate of pad wear. In either case it is desirable to have a new disc fitted, though it may be possible for an expert to regrind the old plate.

Disc Hand Brake Adjustment. The usual practice with the rear disc brake is to have a separate pair of small friction pads for hand brake operation, controlled by a cable system similar to that used with drum brake systems. With Girling brakes, adjustment for wear on the hand brake pads must be maintained so that there is not more than 0·003 in. (0·1 mm.) between each pad and the disc. If an operating lever and pull rod are employed, adjustment is made by tightening the adjusting nut on the pull rod. No other alteration to the hand brake cable or linkage should normally be made.

If there is excessive play in the hand brake cable or linkage, the pads should be tightened on to the disc by the adjusting nut, the hand brake cable adjusted, and the adjustment at the pull rod slackened to give correct clearance. If the clamping levers are operated directly by the hand brake cable then the cable must be adjusted to provide correct clearance at the pads. In both cases the hand brake must be fully off when the adjustment is made.

Except for the early models, the hand brake mechanism on Dunlop disc brakes is automatically adjusted by means of a ratchet and pawl. The system permits approximately 3 in. of free movement on the hand brake lever before the pads contact the disc. This increases as pad wear occurs until a maximum of 5 in. of free travel is present. At this stage the ratchet will adjust the nut by the equivalent of one tooth, so restoring the original 3 in. of free movement.

To fit new hand brake pads on the Girling brakes, first remove the adjuster nut on the pull rod (or remove the cable on cable-operated systems) and swing the two clamping levers outward, noting how the spring and washers should be replaced. Clean all parts and apply a little grease where necessary.

On one type the circular pads are then lifted out, the new pads inserted, and the clamping levers refitted. On another type it is necessary to remove Nyloc nuts in order to release the pads. Disconnect the hand brake rod from the operating lever and take the adjuster nut off the tie rod. The operating lever will swing down, making both Nyloc nuts accessible. Unscrew the nuts and remove the pads. Fit new pads and secure with the new Nyloc nuts which are supplied. In all cases, final adjustment must be made to ensure correct clearance.

As already mentioned, the Girling single-side swing caliper rear brake employs one pair of self-adjusting pads to serve both foot and hand brake operation. Its hand brake mechanism consists of a shaft and cam. When the actuating lever is moved, the shaft turns and the cam works on the same rocking lever as is operated by the hydraulic piston. No form of adjustment is normally required.

THE HYDRAULIC SYSTEM

General servicing is confined to inspecting the level of fluid in the system's reservoir and topping up with fresh fluid when required, as previously explained. In practice, topping up should rarely be required, and any sudden drop in the fluid level must be regarded as a danger signal that fluid is being lost either through leakage in the pipelines or because of faulty seals in the operating cylinders.

Brake manufacturers recommend renewing the whole of the fluid in the system every 18 months. This is because the fluid tends to absorb moisture from the atmosphere, thereby reducing the temperature at which the fluid will boil. This could affect braking when the car is used under arduous conditions as in mountainous country. The operation involves draining off the fluid through the bleed valves, refilling the system and finally bleeding off all air present, as described later. It is important never to put mineral oils, petrol, alcohol, etc., into a hydraulic system, and to ensure that the filler cap is absolutely clean before removing it for inspection.

The correct types of fluid to be used in both brake and clutch hydraulic systems are Castrol Girling Crimson brake fluid for all Girling systems and Lockheed Super Heavy Duty brake fluid for all Lockheed systems.

Bleeding the System. This operation is carried out when it is required to drain the hydraulic system or extract air that has entered the fluid, due to leakage or neglect of the fluid level in the reservoir. If frequent bleeding is required this usually indicates that rubber cups in the cylinders are worn and need renewing. The job is easily carried out by a garage, but the owner can do it himself if he has an assistant to help him.

Equipment required is a supply of the correct type of brake fluid, a foot or so of rubber tubing that will fit over the bleed valve nipples on the brake back plates, a glass jar and a spanner to fit the bleed valves (usually $\frac{7}{16}$ in. AF). All parts must be cleaned before handling and scrupulous cleanliness observed throughout the job. Start by ensuring that the fluid reservoir is fully topped up. Bleeding should start at the rear offside wheel if the car has drum brakes, but at the front offside wheel if it has front discs. Front brake adjusters should be slackened and rear adjusters locked hard on.

Put enough clean brake fluid into the glass jar to allow one end of the rubber tubing to be submerged and attach the other end of the tubing to the bleed nipple (Fig. 9.9). Unscrew the bleed valve half a turn, which will enable fluid to pass down into the jar. Your assistant, sitting in the driver's seat, must now pump the foot pedal to force fluid out through the valve.

With Lockheed systems the pedal must be depressed slowly and allowed to return quickly. With Girling centre-valve (aluminium body) master cylinders the pedal should be depressed fully, given three short strokes, then allowed to return quickly to its stop. With Girling compression-barrel (cast-iron body) master cylinders, the piston should be depressed slowly and allowed to return slowly, pausing a few seconds before repeating the action.

As fluid is pumped into the jar the air present will show up as bubbles. The fluid in the reservoir will quickly go down and must be frequently topped up. As soon as air bubbles cease to appear, stop pumping and close the bleed valve. Repeat this

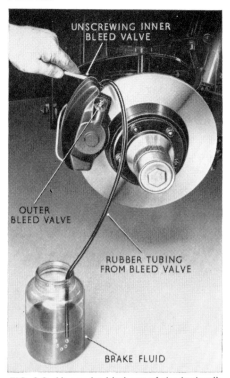

FIG. 9.9. Air can be bled out of the hydraulic system by pumping the brake pedal after unscrewing the bleed valve on a wheel cylinder. The same method is used for both disc and drum brake systems.

operation at the next nearest wheel and then at the others. Finally, top up the fluid once more, adjust all brakes for correct clearance and check the pedal action.

A simple one-man bleed valve is on the market which can be fitted in place of the normal bleed nipple. This has a one-way valve and when slackened half a turn permits bleeding by simply pumping the pedal. It does not, however, indicate when all trace of air has been expelled from the system.

Even though the system may give no trouble, manufacturers recommend renewing all seals, rubber cups and flexible hoses every 40,000 miles or every three years, whichever occurs first. Kits of these parts are obtainable from brake agents and motor

213

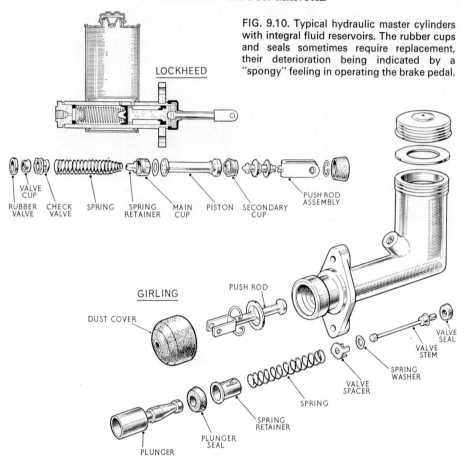

FIG. 9.10. Typical hydraulic master cylinders with integral fluid reservoirs. The rubber cups and seals sometimes require replacement, their deterioration being indicated by a "spongy" feeling in operating the brake pedal.

LOCKHEED

VALVE CUP
RUBBER VALVE   CHECK VALVE   SPRING   SPRING RETAINER   MAIN CUP   PISTON   SECONDARY CUP   PUSH ROD ASSEMBLY

GIRLING

PUSH ROD

DUST COVER

VALVE SEAL
VALVE STEM
SPRING WASHER
VALVE SPACER
SPRING
SPRING RETAINER
PLUNGER SEAL
PLUNGER

factors. The amateur mechanic is advised to leave overhaul of the hydraulic system to a service station, but the following notes may be useful.

Wheel Cylinders. A possible fault with these is dragging of the brakes caused by seizure of the piston. This can be checked by observing the operation of the brakes while someone slowly presses down the brake pedal; with a two-leading-shoe arrangement, one shoe must be held in position with a screwdriver while this is done. In this event the cylinder must be dismantled and cleaned (Fig. 9.6). If the piston is too tight to move by gentle tapping, the internal parts are damaged

through dirt or corrosion and a new cylinder assembly should be fitted.

For normal maintenance on Girling systems, it is not necessary to remove the front cylinders from the back plate. The fluid must be drained through the bleed nipple, the dust cover removed, and all internal parts cleaned with Girling Cleaning Fluid or brake fluid. Unless the cylinder bore or piston have developed scoring or ridges, new rubber seals can be fitted after being moistened in brake fluid. Overhaul of the rear wheel cylinders is similar except that these have to be removed after disconnecting the hand brake linkage and pipe connection.

FIG. 9.11. Lock-
heed disc brake,
showing the con-
struction of the
hydraulic parts.
Split-type caliper
units should not be
separated by the
amateur, the re-
placement of seals
or other internal
servicing being a
job for the specialist.

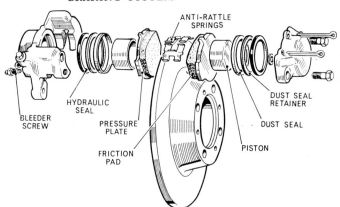

ANTI-RATTLE
SPRINGS

HYDRAULIC
SEAL

BLEEDER
SCREW

PRESSURE
PLATE

FRICTION
PAD

DUST SEAL
RETAINER

DUST SEAL

PISTON

Master Cylinders. There are differences in operation between the Girling and Lockheed types, but the basic principle is the same (Fig. 6.10). Depressing the foot pedal moves a push rod which in turn moves a piston in the cylinder and so displaces the fluid. On some cars the fluid reservoir is integral with the unit, on others it is separate with a pipe connection.

Overhaul entails draining off the fluid and removing the master cylinder from the car. On the Girling unit, pull back the rubber dust cover and remove the circlip underneath, allowing the push rod and dished washer to be removed. The piston assembly can then be taken out and examined. Again, if either the piston or cylinder bore surfaces are scored or ridged a new master cylinder should be obtained. If the rubber seals on the plunger are loose and appear oversize, the cause is probably contamination by mineral oil in the fluid. When a hydraulic system has been affected by mineral oil, all seals and flexible hoses should be changed and the whole system flushed out with clean brake fluid.

Disc Brake Wheel Cylinders. At long intervals the rubber rings or seals should be changed for new ones. On a typical installation, the procedure is first to drain fluid from the system through the bleed valve on the caliper, then to remove the road wheel. Detach the hose from the chassis connection, remove the bolts securing the caliper unit to the axle and lift off the caliper complete with hose. The lining pads are then removed and the pistons blown out of their bores with an air line. The seals are exchanged, all parts cleaned in special cleaning fluid, and the bores and pistons checked for signs of abrasion or corrosion before re-assembly of parts (Fig. 9.11).

Tandem Master Cylinder. A few high-performance cars (Jaguar, Aston Martin) employ a "split" braking system based on the Lockheed tandem master cylinder. In effect, this is two master cylinders combined in one unit and supplied from a fluid reservoir divided into two compartments. One cylinder actuates the front brakes and the other works on the rear brakes. Thus, if one system should fail, the other still functions. At the same time, by making the rear brake piston dependent upon the pressure built up by the front brake piston, equal hydraulic pressure is obtained at all four wheels (Fig. 9.12).

No special maintenance is required by this system, but the brake shoes should be adjusted regularly so that there is always $\frac{1}{2}$ in. of free travel at the brake pedal pad, and the fluid level must not be neglected.

Associated with safer braking is the development of anti-wheel-lock devices, already fitted to a few models. At present these are used solely to control rear wheel

215

locking. The simplest device is a pressure limiting valve (used, for example, on the B.M.C. Mini and 1100 models) which sets a limit to the fluid pressure applied to the rear brakes. More advanced is the "g sensitive" skid control valve fitted to cars including the B.M.C. 1800 models.

Pressure Limiting Valve. This Lockheed device is inserted in the pipeline that serves the rear brakes, in order to limit the braking effort developed at the rear wheels and thus prevent the wheels locking under heavy braking conditions. The valve body houses a spring-loaded plunger which controls the passage of fluid to the rear brakes.

Under light and moderate braking conditions, fluid passes through ports in the plunger to the brakes, but as the fluid pressure increases the plunger compresses the spring and shuts off the fluid supply. Any further increase in pressure will now be applied only to the front brakes. When the foot pedal is released, the spring returns the plunger and fluid is able to return from the rear brake cylinders to the master cylinder.

The regulating valve needs no attention other than renewal of the rubber seals when the system is overhauled. If the rear brakes lock prematurely, however, it would be advisable to have the regulating valve checked by an expert.

Skid Control Valve. This is an inertia type valve, made by both Girling and Lockheed, which ensures that the correct front-rear brake balance is maintained at all vehicle decelerations and loading conditions, by providing a progressive change in rear brake output dependent upon weight transfer from front to rear under severe braking conditions. The unit contains a steel ball which travels up a ramp under the influence of severe deceleration

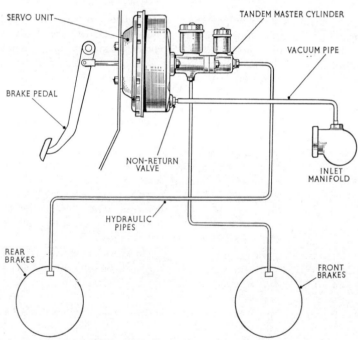

FIG. 9.12. Details of a divided-line braking system with vacuum-servo assistance. Front and rear brakes are controlled by separate hydraulic circuits, with two compression chambers in the master cylinder supplied from individual fluid reservoirs.

and shuts off the normal fluid supply to the rear brakes. The supply of fluid is then metered through a spring-loaded valve which controls the pressure applied to the rear brakes so as to achieve the optimum braking ratio. No maintenance is normally required by this unit.

VACUUM SERVO UNITS

Vacuum-operated servo units that provide additional braking power are becoming popular on cars of all types. They are almost essential on heavier models with disc brakes, because the disc brake does not possess the self-energizing effect of two-leading-shoe drum brakes, and higher operating pressures are therefore required between the linings and the discs. Unless some form of assistance is available in this case, heavy pedal pressure is needed to apply the brakes.

Various types of Girling vacuum unit have been fitted as original equipment with Girling braking systems, while Lockheed units have been used with both Lockheed and Dunlop systems. Servo units are also supplied by both manufacturers for fitting to any existing type of hydraulic system. Servo assistance can be provided in any of the following ways.

First, a mechanical servo unit can be coupled by means of a pull rod to the brake pedal, helping to draw the pedal downward as soon as it begins to be depressed (Fig. 9.13). This type is entirely independent of the hydraulic system. Secondly, there is the direct-acting vacuum-hydraulic servo, which is interposed between the pedal and the master cylinder and supplements the force acting on the piston in the master cylinder (Fig. 9.14). Thirdly, there is the indirect-acting vacuum-hydraulic servo, which is interposed between the master cylinder and the wheel cylinders and supplements the compression of the fluid in the pipelines (Fig. 9.15).

The direct-acting type is often combined with the master cylinder to form a single unit. Servo units such as the Girling Powerstop, for fitting to an existing non-servo system, are usually of the indirect-acting type.

The operation of the vacuum unit itself is similar in all three cases, the vacuum present in the engine's induction system being utilized to move either a diaphragm or a piston in a cylinder. The earlier servos were of the atmosphere-suspended type, in which air at atmospheric pressure is normally present on both sides of the diaphragm; vacuum is admitted to one

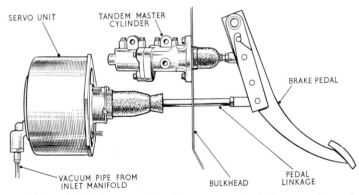

SERVO UNIT   TANDEM MASTER CYLINDER

BRAKE PEDAL

VACUUM PIPE FROM INLET MANIFOLD   BULKHEAD   PEDAL LINKAGE

FIG. 9.13. Suitable mainly for larger and heavier cars, a mechanical servo unit may be installed to supplement the driver's foot pressure on the brake pedal. This is a typical installation for a divided-line system, with a tandem master cylinder to supply the front and rear brakes through separate hydraulic systems.

217

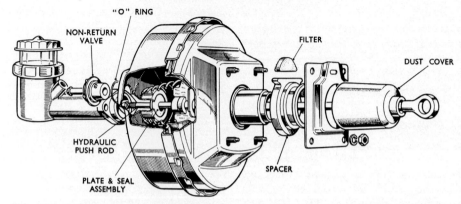

FIG. 9 14. A Girling direct-acting vacuum servo unit. This applies pressure to the piston in the hydraulic master cylinder, with which it forms an integral assembly. The only servicing required is renewing the air filter every 20,000 miles.

side of the diaphragm when the brakes are applied.

This type has been largely superseded by the vacuum-suspended type, where in normal running there is vacuum present on both sides of the diaphragm; air at atmospheric pressure is admitted to one side when the brakes are applied. A more rapid response is obtained with vacuum-suspended units, but it will be seen that both types depend for their operation on the creation of an air pressure difference across the diaphragm or piston.

In practice, filtered air at atmospheric pressure is admitted to the vacuum unit through a reaction valve controlled by movement of the brake pedal. Vacuum is obtained through a pipe connecting with the engine inlet manifold, a non-return valve being incorporated. On some cars a vacuum reservoir may also be fitted, consisting of a sealed tank which stores vacuum and permits operation when the engine has stalled; this is not usually required with vacuum-suspended units.

Installation. It is not difficult to fit a vacuum servo unit to an existing braking system, and the kit supplied includes all fitting instructions and parts required (Fig. 9.15). Normally the unit is bolted to the engine bulkhead, but it can be installed anywhere convenient. For preference, however, it should be vertical if possible and below the fluid level in the brake reservoir. It should also be at least 6 in. away from the exhaust pipe, otherwise a heat shield should be fitted between them.

The hydraulic pipe from the master cylinder must be disconnected and a new pipe fitted connecting with the servo unit. An additional pipe connection is required between the servo and the existing supply line to the wheel cylinders. These pipes should be kept as short as possible, without sharp bends. The inlet manifold must be drilled and tapped to take the vacuum pipe connection, unless it has a blanking plug which can be removed. The vacuum pipe should rise from the manifold and bend over it to prevent the entry of petrol into the servo unit.

Servicing. The only maintenance necessary for Girling servo units is to replace the air filter element every 20,000 miles, or each time relined brake shoes are fitted. Where a rubber cover is fitted, this should be inspected and replaced if it shows signs of deterioration. Hydraulic seals should be renewed whenever other seals in the brake system are changed.

Lockheed servo units are fitted with an

air filter in a metal casing. This should be removed for cleaning every 10,000 miles or after six months. The filter merely requires washing in methylated spirits and blowing through with compressed air.

At the same time the piston in the servo should be lubricated with 20 c.c. of Shell "Tellus" 33 or similar oil. The atmosphere-suspended type is lubricated through slots in the end cover, while the engine is running and the brake pedal is operated repeatedly. With the suspended-vacuum type, first pump the brake a few times, with the engine stopped, then pull the short length of connecting hose clear of the pipe junction and inject lubricant into the pipe elbow on the end cover.

Servo Faults. Troubles in a vacuum servo system are rare, and if the brakes fail to function normally the brake mechanism and hydraulic system should always be checked before deciding that the servo unit must be faulty.

The likeliest cause of trouble is a leakage at some point, allowing air into the system or loss of vacuum. Lack of vacuum may be indicated by the brake pedal feeling hard when operated. Air leakage into the vacuum system may be shown by lack of assistance on heavy braking, by the servo operating only when the engine is running, or by poor idling of the engine. One other trouble that may occur is excessive friction between the vacuum piston and its cylinder (on Lockheed units, due to lack of lubrication); this can cause the brakes to grab, snatch or hang on.

Remember that a vacuum unit, like the main hydraulic system, can be affected by using the wrong type of brake fluid.

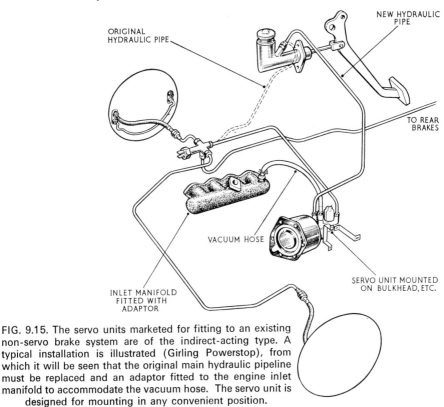

FIG. 9.15. The servo units marketed for fitting to an existing non-servo brake system are of the indirect-acting type. A typical installation is illustrated (Girling Powerstop), from which it will be seen that the original main hydraulic pipeline must be replaced and an adaptor fitted to the engine inlet manifold to accommodate the vacuum hose. The servo unit is designed for mounting in any convenient position.

219

CHAPTER 10

ELECTRICAL SYSTEM AND INSTRUMENTS

THE electrical equipment—battery, generator, starter motor, lighting and accessories —will operate for long periods without trouble if routine maintenance is systematically carried out. All the above items, and also mechanical and electrical instruments, are dealt with in this chapter, but not the ignition system which is considered in Chapter 4.

Safety Precautions. Certain precautions must be taken in working on the car's electrical system, to prevent possible damage. When possible, the live terminal of the battery should be disconnected—an accidental short circuit could ruin components, or even burn through cables and start a fire in the car. As an alternative, it may be sufficient to isolate the section of the circuit concerned by removing a fuse.

It is very undesirable to close the generator cutout contacts manually. If the generator is at rest it will act as a motor and try to crank the engine when the contacts touch, possibly burning out the armature winding, wiring or control unit.

When a battery is gassing freely, while charging or just after charge, a spark can easily ignite the highly explosive mixture of hydrogen and oxygen being liberated. Similarly, care must be taken not to cause a spark when working in the vicinity of the fuel tank, pump or carburettor, because of the danger of igniting petrol.

GENERAL TESTING

A voltmeter, ammeter and ohmmeter are useful instruments for locating faults in a circuit, but much good work can be done with a home-made test lamp, consisting of a 12-volt car bulb in a suitable holder fitted with wander leads terminating in crocodile clips. The two common types of faults are known as open circuits (i.e. a broken circuit) and short circuits, where the current takes a shorter path to complete the circuit. The latter may result in there being no resistance to limit the amount of current flowing, so that a fuse blows or else the wiring overheats and burns the insulation.

Open Circuit Testing. In this case the test lamp is connected in parallel with the faulty circuit, an example being given in Fig. 10.1. Start at the battery with one test lamp lead connected to chassis and touch the other lead to terminal A. If the lamp does not light, the battery is flat or the terminal loose or corroded. If it lights, move the test lead to points B, C, D and so on until the faulty section is found.

Short Circuit Testing. In this case the test lamp is connected in series with the faulty circuit, as shown in Fig. 10.2. The simplest way is to disconnect one lead from the battery and connect the lamp between the battery terminal and the disconnected cable. For this kind of test it is best to use a bulb of 24 or 36 watts, to avoid giving a false indication where a number of lamps are connected in parallel in the circuit.

If there is a short circuit on lamp A then current will flow through the test lamp and other components until it reaches A, where it by-passes the faulty lamp filament which normally limits the amount of current flow. The test lamp will therefore glow with full brilliance; the other lamps will not light. Correcting the fault will cause the other lamps to light, while the test lamp will glow with reduced brilliance.

Wiring Harnesses. The car's complete "loom" of wiring (Fig. 10.3) is usually made as several complete sections which are connected by various methods such as screwed terminals or multiple plugs and sockets (Fig. 10.4). The harness connectors on most modern cars take the form of flat "Lucar" clips which slide on to spade terminals on the various components.

The individual harness may start at the facia main controls with a dozen or more wires, but proceeding round the vehicle "tails" are dropped off to connect up to the various components until the last connection is made, say, to a rear lamp. The return circuit from each component is nearly always made through the vehicle main chassis.

When harnesses are installed they should be firmly held by spring clips or the metal tabs welded to the body section. If the clip is too tight it is possible for the plastic cable to be cut or conductors brought into contact due to the softening effect of engine heat on plastics, when obscure faults could occur.

Do not pull harness or lamp cables tight round the edges of any metal because of the risk of the insulation chafing through. Do push right home the circular bullet type of harness connector, as a short circuit can be caused through the nipple being left proud and contacting earthed metalwork.

On wiring diagrams a reference is always given to the colour coding used for identifying individual cables (Fig. 10.5). The colours used on recent cars are indicated in the table on page 224; wiring on older vehicles may employ a different colour code. Solid colours are used for the wiring up to a switch, then from the switch to the component that it controls a coloured tracer is added.

Repairing Harnesses. It is important to use cables of adequate carrying capacity when fitting new components or replacing broken wires and the table on page 224 also shows the usual cable sizes and current ratings.

It is often possible to make a satisfactory

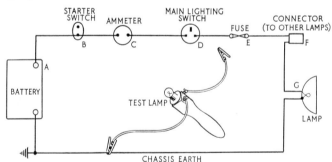

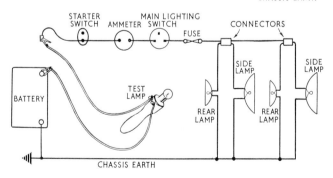

(*Upper*) FIG. 10.1. Simple circuit of one lamp and points at which a test can be made for a break in the connections. Testing is explained in the text. (*Lower*) FIG. 10.2. Short-circuit fault location in a typical lighting circuit, using a test lamp.

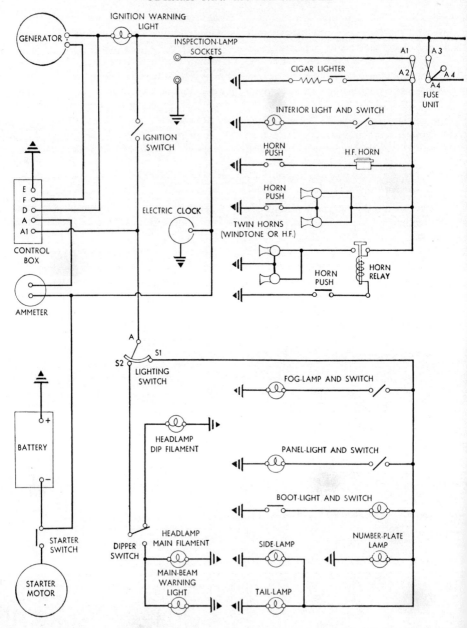

FIG. 10.3. This basic wiring diagram shows that the car's electrical system can be regarded as a series of simple circuits supplied with current from the battery, the return connection in nearly all cases being made by earthing the component to chassis or bodywork.

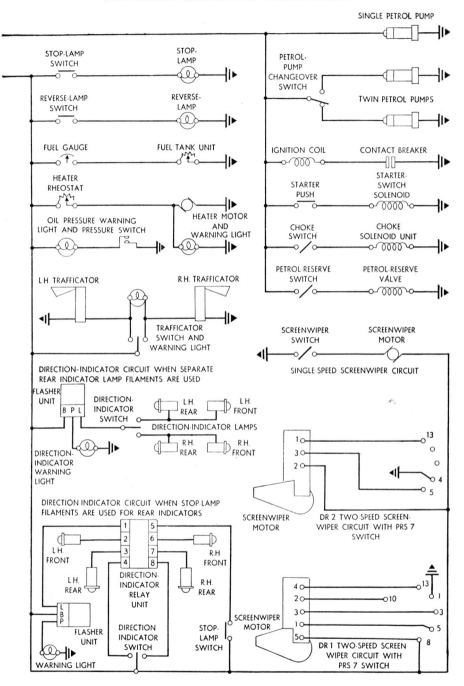

SINGLE PETROL PUMP

STOP-LAMP SWITCH

STOP-LAMP

PETROL-PUMP CHANGEOVER SWITCH

TWIN PETROL PUMPS

REVERSE-LAMP SWITCH

REVERSE-LAMP

FUEL GAUGE

FUEL TANK UNIT

IGNITION COIL

CONTACT BREAKER

HEATER RHEOSTAT

STARTER PUSH

STARTER-SWITCH SOLENOID

OIL PRESSURE WARNING LIGHT AND PRESSURE SWITCH

HEATER MOTOR AND WARNING LIGHT

CHOKE SWITCH

CHOKE SOLENOID UNIT

L.H. TRAFFICATOR

R.H. TRAFFICATOR

PETROL-RESERVE SWITCH

PETROL-RESERVE VALVE

TRAFFICATOR SWITCH AND WARNING LIGHT

SCREENWIPER SWITCH

SCREENWIPER MOTOR

DIRECTION-INDICATOR CIRCUIT WHEN SEPARATE REAR INDICATOR LAMP FILAMENTS ARE USED

SINGLE-SPEED SCREENWIPER CIRCUIT

FLASHER UNIT

B P L

DIRECTION-INDICATOR SWITCH

L.H. REAR

L.H. FRONT

DIRECTION-INDICATOR LAMPS

R.H. REAR

R.H. FRONT

DIRECTION-INDICATOR WARNING LIGHT

13

1
3
2

4
5

DIRECTION INDICATOR CIRCUIT WHEN STOP-LAMP FILAMENTS ARE USED FOR REAR INDICATORS

SCREENWIPER MOTOR

DR 2 TWO-SPEED SCREEN-WIPER CIRCUIT WITH PRS 7 SWITCH

1   5
2   6
3   7
4   8

L.H. FRONT

R.H. FRONT

L.H. REAR

DIRECTION-INDICATOR RELAY UNIT

R.H. REAR

13
1

L B P

4
2
3
1
5

10
3
5
8

FLASHER UNIT

DIRECTION INDICATOR SWITCH

STOP-LAMP SWITCH

SCREENWIPER MOTOR

DR 1 TWO-SPEED SCREEN WIPER CIRCUIT WITH PRS 7 SWITCH

WARNING LIGHT

WIRING COLOUR CODE, SIZES AND CURRENT RATINGS

Cable Colours	Cable Size	Current Rating (amps.)	Circuits
Brown	44/·012	27·5	Battery and generator circuits.
Yellow	14/·010	6	Overdrive circuits.
White	28/·012	17·5	Ignition circuit and accessories protected by
	14/·010	6	ignition switch but unfused (petrol pump etc.).
Green, or	14/·010	6	Auxiliary circuits fed through ignition switch and
Light green			fuse 4 or A4.
Purple	14/·010	6	Auxiliary circuits fed through fuse 2 or A2.
Blue	28/·012	17·5	Headlamp circuits fed from terminal S2 or H on
	14/·010	6	lighting switch.*
Red	14/·010	6	Lighting circuits including side, tail, fog and panel
			lamps.
Black	Various	Various	Earth return circuits.

*Colour blue to dipper switch, then blue/white for main beam and blue/red for dipped beam.

repair to a broken harness wire by stripping back the harness covering and then stripping the wire insulation for about an inch, soldering on a new length of wire with either resin-cored solder or solder and a non-acid flux, then taping up the joint and finally taping the harness covering. If this cannot be done with satisfactory results, it is always better to have the entire harness section replaced.

PROTECTIVE DEVICES

Some older cars are not equipped with fuses, but the majority of recent models have

at least two, while some cars (notably Vauxhall) also have a thermostatic interrupter for protecting the lighting system. The fuse ratings are given in the vehicle instruction book, and it should be noted that the rating quoted refers to the fusing current, not the safe carrying current of the fuse. Thus, a fuse marked 25 amperes may soon blow if it carries that amount of current. Common fuse ratings on British cars are 25 and 35 amperes for lighting and auxiliaries, 5 amperes for direction indicators, 2 and 5 amperes for radios.

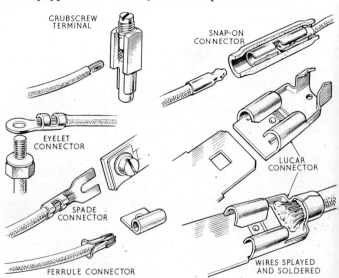

FIG. 10.4. Wiring terminals and connectors for various electrical components. The "Lucar" system is now standardised on British cars. This uses a spring-loaded connector which slides over a blade-type terminal; the bottom right illustration shows how a Lucar wiring joint is made.

CRUBSCREW TERMINAL

SNAP-ON CONNECTOR

EYELET CONNECTOR

LUCAR CONNECTOR

SPADE CONNECTOR

FERRULE CONNECTOR

WIRES SPLAYED AND SOLDERED

224

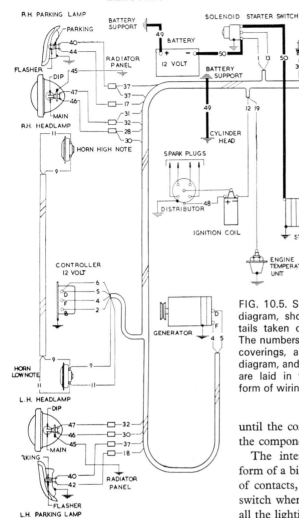

FIG. 10.5. Section of a Vauxhall car wiring diagram, showing the actual harness, with tails taken off to the various components. The numbers refer to the colours of the cable coverings, a key being provided with the diagram, and the direction in which the wires are laid in the harness is indicated. This form of wiring diagram is much easier to read than some others.

until the connection is finally broken and the component put out of action.

The interrupter mentioned takes the form of a bimetal strip operating on a pair of contacts, often located on the lighting switch where the strip and contacts carry all the lighting load and the live accessory load. If a short circuit occurs, the extra load causes the bimetal strip to break circuit momentarily, preventing overheating of the wiring insulation. This will be shown by the lights flashing on and off, but allowing the car to reach a service station where the trouble can be remedied.

Polarity. It is general practice to complete the circuit for each electrical component by connecting it to some part of the car's metallic structure, when the bodywork acts as an "earth return". Either the positive side of the circuit can

The two accessory circuits are usually fuse-protected. One fuse protects components controlled by the ignition switch (warning lamps, car heater, wiper motor, direction indicators and sometimes the horn); the other protects the roof lamp, radio, clock, cigarette lighter and sometimes the horn. The rear lamps and panel lamps are sometimes fused separately. The fuses may be located in a fuse box under the bonnet, or in a bayonet fitting in the wiring itself, usually under the facia. Uncovered fuses tend to corrode in time,

be connected in this way, when the battery positive terminal will be connected to the bodywork, or the negative side. Most British cars, but not American or Continental vehicles, have for many years employed a positive earth system. Mainly because of the introduction of transistor devices, however, there is now a trend towards negative earth return systems. Whichever system is used, it is important to connect batteries and other components with the correct polarity.

THE BATTERY

The primary purpose of the battery is to supply the heavy current required by the starter motor for starting the engine, but it also supplies the lamps, radio etc. when the engine is not running. When the engine is running, current is being drawn from the battery to feed the ignition system and electrical accessories, but at the same time it is being recharged by the generator, which is automatically connected to the battery when the engine has reached a certain speed.

A 12-volt battery consists of six separate cells connected in series, each cell giving 2 volts. Each cell contains positive and negative plates interspaced with separators, and liquid electrolyte consisting of dilute sulphuric acid. When a discharged battery is being recharged, hydrogen is given off at the negative plate and oxygen at the positive plate. The lead-oxide paste in the positive plate changes to lead peroxide, the paste in the negative plate changes to spongy lead, and lead sulphate from the plates combines with the electrolyte to restore its original specific gravity. A reverse chemical action takes place when the battery is discharging, hydrogen being formed at the positive plate and oxygen at the negative plate. Lead sulphate then re-enters the plates, thus diluting the electrolyte and lowering its specific gravity. The active material of both plates is converted to lead sulphate.

If the battery is left in a partially discharged condition too long the lead sulphate thus formed may change into a hard crystalline state which reduces the active material and impedes the chemical action just described. Heavy sulphation is difficult to get rid of by recharging and it is therefore important to maintain a battery in a fully charged condition at all times.

Battery Maintenance. The most important regular service is to top up the electrolyte in each cell with distilled water, every 1,000 miles or once a month, whichever is sooner. This is necessary because the chemical reactions due to normal operation produce heat which evaporates the water content of the electrolyte. Tap water should not be used for topping up because any salts or other impurities it may contain will be retained in the battery and shorten its life by their cumulative effect.

The correct level of the electrolyte is just above the plates. A proper battery filler is useful to prevent spillage (Fig. 10.6). Do not add acid, nor anti-freeze to prevent the battery freezing in cold weather. The battery is best protected against freezing by maintaining it in a fully charged condition, when the electrolyte will not freeze.

Apart from this attention, the battery top must be kept clean and dry, and the metal posts and connectors should be coated with either petroleum jelly or a proprietary anti-corrosive grease. (Ordinary grease may soften the cell top sealing compound.) Corrosion of the battery crate and surrounding parts is caused by overfilling the cells, and can be cleaned off with a solution of washing soda or ammonia in hot water. Leave the parts to soak until the corrosion has cleared, then clean off and dry well, taking care that the solution does not enter the cells.

Installing a New Battery. It is important to follow the instructions issued with the battery, as these vary with

FIG. 10.6. Points
to note in servicing
a battery. The use
of a battery filler in
topping up the cells
avoids over-filling,
which may lead to
corrosion as acid
escapes through the
plug vents.

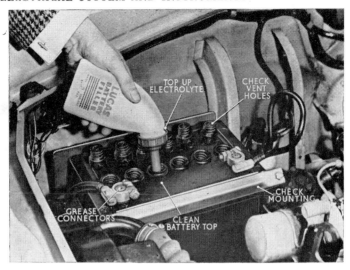

different types. Most owners will have the initial charging carried out by a service station, but the following notes may be useful to others.

Two-stage filling is normally employed for uncharged batteries or those having wet-wood separators. Half-fill each cell with electrolyte of the stated specific gravity, allow to stand for 6-12 hours until the battery cools, then fill with the same electrolyte to the tops of the plates. Allow to stand for a further 2 hours, then put on charge at a rate of 1/15th of the battery's capacity at the 10-hour rate. Charge for 80 hours or until the voltage readings and temperature-corrected specific gravity readings show no increase over five successive hourly readings. Check the specific gravity at the end of charge.

One-stage filling is employed for dry-charged batteries. The battery must be filled to the tops of its plates with electrolyte of the stated specific gravity. It will then be 90 per cent charged and may be put into service immediately. If time is available, however, a four-hour charge at 1/10th of the battery's capacity at the 10-hour rate will prove very beneficial.

The life of a battery depends mainly on the conditions of usage and its main-tenance. Battery life is reduced especially by the shedding of paste from the plates, brought about by repeated cycles of charging and discharging, and by corrosion of the plate grids, caused by frequent over-charging. Long life is best ensured by attending to the maintenance already described and ensuring that the battery is not over-charged or left in a discharged state for long periods.

The most common cause of a battery being discharged is not the use of the starter, but the steady drain over long periods when the car is parked with lights on and possibly the radio or other acces-sories in operation. In these conditions it will help to prolong battery life if a small parking lamp is used instead of the full set of parking lamps, as described later.

Battery Testing. The simplest test for a battery is to switch on all lights and see if the headlamps dim after a few seconds, in which case the battery is low. A more severe test is to operate the starter with the lights switched on. If the starter is sluggish and the lights dim then the battery is low, but starter and terminal faults can influence these rough tests, so standardized tests have been evolved which are applied directly to the battery. A

227

hydrometer test, showing the battery's state of charge, is easily carried out by the motorist. Service stations employ a high-rate discharge test, which tests the battery under load with a special tester, and a capacity test which indicates the battery's general condition.

Hydrometer Test. The specific gravity of a lead-acid battery increases with its state of charge up to a maximum, and may be measured with a hydrometer which can be bought cheaply (Fig. 10.7). To use, insert the end of the rubber tube into a cell, squeeze the bulb and slowly release so that electrolyte drawn from the cell floats the marked float freely. The specific gravity is then read off the scale where it emerges from the electrolyte, while holding the hydrometer at eye level. If the electrolyte is seen to be discoloured, this indicates shedding of paste from the plates. At a temperature of 60 deg. F., readings are as follows.

Hydrometer Reading	Battery Condition
1·280	Fully charged
1·240	Three-quarter charged
1·200	Half charged
1·160	Quarter charged
1·120	Discharged

To these figures 0·002 specific gravity should be added for every 5 deg. F. above 60 deg., or subtracted for every 5 deg. F. below. Each cell should be tested in the same way and the readings should be uniform—any large variation is an indication of a faulty cell.

Battery Charging. With a car in frequent use, the charging system should be capable of maintaining the battery in a fully charged condition. During the winter months, and especially where the car is used only for short journeys, it may be necessary to charge the battery occasionally from an external source. There is a wide range of battery chargers available

for this purpose (they are further discussed in Chapter 15). The cheaper ones known as trickle chargers supply a current of 1 ampere, and may be used for long periods without risk of over-charging, although they require 40-50 hours to recharge a flat battery. More expensive types supplying 2 or 3 amperes are more useful in maintaining a battery in peak condition as the larger current helps to keep down sulphation of the plates.

The engine should never be run while the battery of an a.c. system is being charged from an external source while on the car. This would result in a high voltage on the generator field coils and the system would be damaged through overloading. As there is no cutout fitted, it is safest to disconnect the battery before using a fast charger.

A battery should not be stored in a discharged condition as the plates will quickly sulphate. It should be fully charged before storing, and freshening charges given whenever the specific gravity of the electrolyte falls below 1·230, or alternatively every 30 days.

Battery Faults. A discharged battery may take the blame for a charging circuit fault or starter circuit faults, and should therefore be given one of the tests just outlined to determine whether it is in fact at fault. Apart from the inevitable deterioration resulting from long service, the following are the more common battery faults.

Rapid loss of electrolyte. This can be caused by over-charging, sulphation of plates, or the battery being fitted in position exposed to excessive engine heat. Loss from a single cell is usually due to a crack in the casing, which is best located by tapping the casing very gently with a rubber hammer to produce vibration and open the crack.

Internal short circuit. This results from conducting material lodging between negative and positive plates, or from faulty separators that allow the plates to touch, resulting in a constant internal discharge of current. If the battery is otherwise in good condition, it is possible to fit a new cell group with separators to the faulty cell.

Open circuit. This can be caused by a broken cell bridge to which the plates are welded, or by a loose cell connector, the effect being to make the whole battery dead. Sometimes the fault is intermittent, making location more difficult.

Sulphated plates. If badly sulphated it will be difficult to charge the battery even from an external source at a rate higher than a few amperes, while the cells affected will become much hotter than normal. If sulphation is not too severe it may be removed by giving the battery a slow charge for a period two or three times the normal. Otherwise the only remedy is to replate the battery. Symptoms of sulphation are a low specific gravity, high temperature and voltage on charge, reduced capacity and low output. This trouble

results from using a battery for long periods in an under-charged state, or leaving it idle while discharged.

Reversed polarity. A less common fault, caused by one cell becoming discharged before the remainder, when the discharge current from the other cells charges the faulty one in the reverse direction and results in the overall battery voltage being reduced. The remedy is to give a long charge from an external source, when the cell will revert to its normal polarity.

Mechanical faults. These include loose terminal posts, which require the fitting of a new cell top, and cracks in the cell tops or casing, which can be repaired using a proprietary battery sealing compound.

Generally, it is more economical to scrap a battery with an internal fault than attempt to have it repaired, especially where the unit has already been in use some time. This applies also to restoring batteries which are failing through old age, despite the claims of so-called battery reconditioning additives which have appeared on the market from time to time.

A point to bear in mind is that a battery suffering from sulphation or an internal fault causing it to have a charging voltage greater than 16 cannot be recharged on the car because the generator output is controlled at either 15 or 16 volts. In this case an external charger with a higher voltage output will be required.

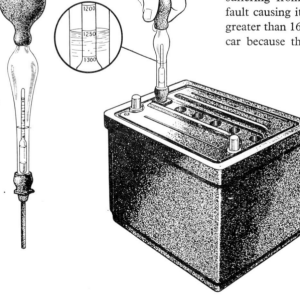

FIG. 10.7. Testing a battery's specific gravity with a hydrometer. The reading is taken on the graduated stem of the float, while it is floating freely in the electrolyte. Thus, a reading of 1.250 s.g. is shown here.

CHARGING CIRCUIT

Current to maintain the battery charge is supplied by a d.c. generator, or *dynamo*; or in the case of many recent models by an a.c. generator (*alternator*). The d.c. charging circuit also includes a regulator and a cutout, both being housed in a control unit on the engine bulkhead.

The generator is usually a two-pole, two-brush, shunt-wound machine, fitted with a cooling fan so that maximum output .may be used without overheating. This type of machine has two field coils, wound to give north and south poles, the field being connected in shunt or parallel with the rotating armature so that only a small percentage of the armature current passes through the field coils to energize them. One of the two current-collecting brushes is connected to earth, the other to the output terminal.

As the armature is rotated, its windings cut through a magnetic field which exists between the field coils. Current is then induced in the armature windings which is collected by the carbon brushes from the copper segments of the commutator, at which the windings terminate. The electrical output of the generator will depend on both its speed of rotation and its field strength, and in order to control the output over a wide range of engine speed and compensate for external loads and varying battery condition, the field strength is automatically adjusted by some form of regulator.

Regulator. The open-circuit voltage of a fully charged 12-volt battery is 12·6 volts; this increases on charge to approximately 15·6 volts. If the generator is regulated to give a constant output of 16 volts at all speeds the result will be a very small charging current when the battery is fully charged, but a large current when the battery is discharged. This desirable state of affairs is brought about by the use of the *compensated voltage control* system, as

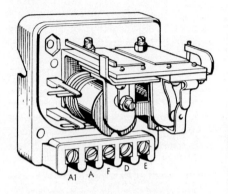

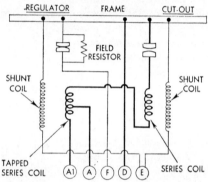

FIG. 10.8. A Lucas control unit consisting of a cutout and a compensated voltage regulator. The adjustment of these two regulators should be left to expert attention.

found on most older cars (Fig. 10.8).

With the development of higher-output generators to meet increasing electrical loads, however, the c.v.c. system gives less effective control of the maximum output. The solution is to provide two regulators with their contacts connected in series in the generator field circuit, one regulator being shunt wound and responsive only to voltage, and the other series wound and responsive only to current. This *current-voltage control* system is employed on many modern cars (Fig. 10.9).

Built into the same control unit though separate from the voltage regulator is the cutout. This is a switch connected between the generator and the battery and operated electromagnetically. Its function

230

is to automatically connect the generator with the battery when the former's output voltage is sufficient to charge the battery, and to disconnect it when the generator is not running or when its voltage is below that of the battery. Otherwise, the battery would discharge itself through the generator windings and damage the machine. The cutout does *not* switch off the charging current to the battery when it becomes fully charged, the charging rate being controlled entirely by the regulator.

Charging System Maintenance. Apart from the generator, no adjustment or routine servicing is required by the charging circuit components. The control unit is sealed by the manufacturer and should not be tampered with. A burnt-out regulator is usually caused by incorrect rewiring or a fault in the generator field circuit, so it is advisable to locate the cause of the trouble before fitting a new unit.

Usually, the first sign of failure of the charging system is given by the ignition warning lamp failing to go out or the battery becoming discharged.

The main faults that arise in the system are as follows. *Generator:* driving belt broken or slipping on the pulleys; worn armature bearings; worn or dirty brushes or commutator; broken, loose or shorted connections in the armature circuit; shorted or open-circuit field coils; wrong or broken wiring connections. *Control unit:* incorrect wiring; faulty earthing; dirty or worn contacts on regulator or cutout; incorrect air gaps on regulator or cutout; incorrect voltage setting on regulator; incorrect cut-in voltage setting or drop-off voltage setting on cutout.

A quick check of the system may be made by removing the wire from the "A" terminal of the control unit and connecting an ammeter between the wire and terminal. With the engine running at charging speed, the charging current should be shown on the ammeter as follows.

Battery S.G.	Charging Rate
1·270	5 A or lower
1·250 or lower	8-12 A
1·200 or lower	15 A or higher

Finally, switch on all the lamps. With the engine running at about 3,000 r.p.m. the ammeter should read between 0-4 amperes on the "charge" side.

Servicing of the control unit should always be entrusted to a competent auto-electrician. Modern regulators seldom need adjustment, but after being in use for 30,000 miles their contacts may need cleaning and the voltage-current settings checking.

Ignition Warning Lamp. This is also connected into the charging system, and gives an indication of whether the generator is charging or not. If the light fails to go out when the generator is running above idling speed, it indicates that the battery is not being charged. The fault may lie in the charging system, but the most common

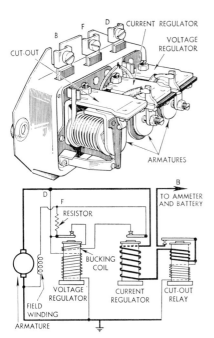

FIG. 10.9. In this later type of Lucas control unit two regulators are used to give current-voltage control, combined with a cutout.

cause is loss or slipping of the generator driving belt. If the light remains on with a dim glow, this indicates that the cutout contacts require cleaning or adjusting, or there is a high resistance in the ignition switch, in the connections, or in the appropriate fuse.

GENERATOR SERVICING AND OVERHAUL

At intervals of 6,000 miles, the rear bearing of a d.c. generator requires lubrication. Inject a few drops of engine oil into the hole marked "oil" on the end cover, or on older models unscrew the lubricator cap and apply high-melting-point grease to the felt pad. At the same time, check the tension and condition of the generator driving belt (see Chapter 4). If the bottom of the generator pulley is shiny, this means that either the pulley or the belt is worn, and the belt is slipping under load. The belt should grip the sides of the pulley and not touch the bottom.

At intervals of 12,000 miles, repeat the service just mentioned, and check for excessive sparking at the generator brushes by looking through the rear end-plate slots while the engine is running at about 3,000 r.p.m. If sparking is excessive, the brushes will need checking for wear or sticking in their holders and the commutator must be cleaned with a cloth moistened in petrol.

At intervals of 24,000 miles, an additional check on brush wear should be made. This is quite simple in the case of old-type generators fitted with a removable inspection band, but modern machines must be dismantled for the purpose (Fig. 10.10). The brushes fitted to Lucas generators have an average life of 50,000-60,000 miles, except in the case of the smaller machines fitted to cars such as the B.M.C. Mini, where brush life is of the order of 25,000 to 30,000 miles.

Generator Overhaul. This is best left to an automobile electrician although the

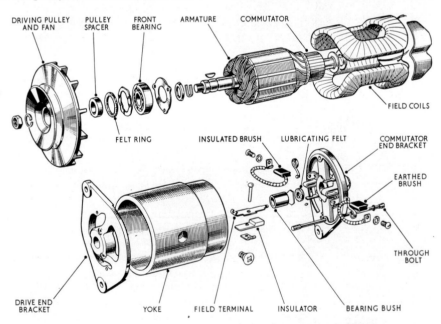

FIG. 10.10. Parts of a typical D.C. generator (dynamo), with the armature and field coils shown above and the carcase and brush gear below.

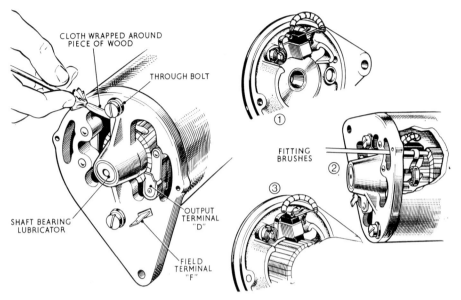

FIG. 10.11. Servicing a generator. (*Left*) Oil is injected into the oil hole for the rear bearing. The condition of the commutator can be inspected through the holes in the end bracket, and cleaning undertaken by using a cloth moistened in petrol and wrapped over a stick. (*Right*) When new brushes are fitted, each brush is inserted in its holder and held up off its seating by wedging with the spring (1). The machine is assembled, and then the brushes released by unhooking the springs (2). Finally, the brushes are bedded down to the commutator with the springs hooked over them (3).

home mechanic can replace worn brushes and clean the commutator as required. Modern generators are dismantled by removing the two long through-bolts, then withdrawing the armature from the carcase complete with front end-plate and pulley. The rear end-plate complete with brush gear can then be removed, after disconnecting the field coil connection.

The commutator can be cleaned with a petrol-moistened cloth or, if it is slightly pitted, polished with a strip of fine-grade glasspaper—*not* emery cloth (Fig. 10.11). If the brushes are half-worn, these should be replaced by new brushes, which are preformed to the correct curvature and do not require bedding. Old brushes should always be re-assembled in their original positions, to preserve correct bedding.

Before refitting the generator to the car it should be given a motoring test for satisfactory operation. Connect it to a battery of equivalent voltage, with the positive lead to the carcase and the negative lead to the "D" terminal (positive earth system).

Bridge terminals "F" and "D" with a jumper lead. The armature should now revolve in a similar way to an electric motor. After running for a few seconds, disconnect the jumper lead from the "F" terminal, when the generator should run at a higher speed. This test shows that the armature and field circuits are operating correctly.

In the case of a generator with negative earth, the battery connecting leads must be reversed, otherwise the generator field will be polarized in the wrong direction and a reversed charge will be given. To polarize correctly the field circuit when the generator is correctly wired and

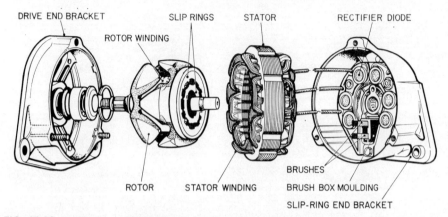

DRIVE END BRACKET   SLIP RINGS   STATOR   RECTIFIER DIODE

ROTOR WINDING

BRUSHES

ROTOR   STATOR WINDING   BRUSH BOX MOULDING

SLIP-RING END BRACKET

FIG. 10.12. Parts of an alternator. Six rectifier diodes fitted in the end bracket convert the alternating current to direct current for charging the battery. Cooling is by a fan (not shown) assembled with the drive pulley.

fitted on the vehicle, it is only necessary to remove the field wire from the control unit "F" terminal and touch it on the control unit "A" or "B" terminal for about one second, then refit the field wire. This polarization is required whenever a negative-earth generator is fitted to a positive-earth vehicle, or vice versa.

A.C. Generators. As the electrical loading of modern cars has increased, the design of d.c. generators capable of the additional output has presented increasingly severe problems in regard to size, weight and commutation at high speeds. This has resulted in the introduction of the a.c. generator or alternator, which can supply twice the current of a d.c. machine of similar size. It can also produce a useful output at engine idling speed and will operate at high running speeds (Fig. 10.12).

In an a.c. generator the equivalent of the dynamo's armature winding is the output winding. This is stationary, so that no commutator or brushes are required. The field winding is on the rotor and fed through slip rings which give long service without wear. No current-limiting device is needed to control the output, this being effected automatically by the machine's reactance; nor is a cutout required, as this function is performed by the rectifier which converts the a.c. output into direct current.

Although no current controller is necessary, a transistorized voltage controller is used to regulate the output to suit the electrical load and the battery's state of charge.

Servicing the A.C. Generator. As the machine runs at a higher speed than a dynamo, the rotor shaft is carried on a ball race at the front end and on needle-roller bearings at the rear. Both sets of bearings are grease-packed and need no further lubrication between major overhauls. The only routine attention is to check the tension and condition of the driving belt every 3,000 miles, in the same way as a dynamo belt.

At intervals of 24,000 miles, the slip rings and brushes may be examined for wear. These are accessible by removing the brush box moulding which carries the field terminals, and which is retained by two screws. Brushes should be replaced when worn down to half length (about $\frac{1}{4}$ in.) and slip rings cleaned with a cloth, or with fine-grade glasspaper if slightly pitted. Also, the silicon diodes should be cleaned if covered with dust or oil.

234

Any other servicing or repair work should be entrusted to a competent auto-electrician, as specialized equipment is required. Faults may arise in the machine, the driving belt, the electromagnetic relay which energizes the field coils when the ignition is switched on, or the voltage regulator.

When working on an a.c. system, it is important to ensure that the battery or regulator leads are not reversed. Similarly, when a battery is to be fitted one should check whether the car has positive or negative earthing. Wrong connections will result in the rectifier diodes being burnt out.

STARTER CIRCUIT

An electric starter motor is similar in construction to a dynamo, with a cylindrical magnet frame, field coils, rotating armature with a commutator, and two pairs of brushes (Fig. 10.13). It operates in a reverse manner, however. When current is supplied to the armature windings, mag-

netism is induced in the field which causes rotation of the armature. The windings are formed of heavy copper strip to handle the heavy current drawn, and a special type of brush is used. The motor is coupled to a ring gear on the rim of the engine flywheel by drive gear carried on an extension of the armature shaft.

The motor may be controlled by a switch built on to the machine and operated by a wire cable from the facia, or by an electric solenoid switch remotely operated.

The drive gear is usually of the inertia-engaged type, of which there are several versions (Fig. 10.14). As the armature begins to rotate, the drive gear pinion also rotates, but more slowly because of its inertia. It is carried along a screwed sleeve and engages with the flywheel ring gear. Since the flywheel resists the turning force, the pinion is screwed further along the sleeve until it compresses a spring or rubber unit which cushions the shock of engagement. When the engine begins to

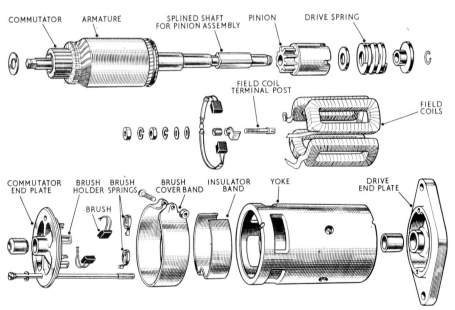

FIG. 10.13. Parts of a typical starter motor, showing the armature and drive gear, the brushes and field coils, and the carcase. Brushes are accessible through the slots in the yoke.

run, the flywheel starts to drive the pinion faster than the armature shaft, so the pinion is screwed back out of engagement.

More expensive cars are sometimes fitted with a pre-engaged drive gear, which is more positive in action and reduces wear. The pinion is moved into engagement by a forked lever, operated manually or by a solenoid, before the switch contacts close. An over-running clutch is provided to allow the pinion to slip on the armature shaft after the engine has fired.

Starter Maintenance. The only attention normally required is to apply a little oil occasionally to the squared end of the armature shaft, which has a small metal cover. The need for lubrication at this point is shown by a groaning noise emitted when the starter switch is released, after the engine has fired.

When a solenoid switch is used, this is fitted in the engine compartment, or sometimes on the starter motor itself. It contains the main switch contacts, which are operated electromagnetically by a current supplied through the driver's control switch, and its use avoids the need for lengthy heavy cables on which there could be appreciable voltage drop between the battery and starter. In the event of failure, the solenoid switch can be operated manually by pressing on the rubber cup at one end (except in the case of cars having automatic transmission, where this practice could be dangerous). Faulty or burnt-out solenoid units are not repairable and must be replaced by a new switch.

Starter Faults. The procedure for freeing a starter that is jammed in gear is described in Chapter 3. This may occur through wear on the flywheel ring gear or pinion, when the worn parts should be replaced. If the starter does not turn the engine fast enough to fire, the cause is usually a faulty battery, but other possibilities are a fault in the motor or solenoid switch, or loose or corroded starter lead connections. If the motor rotates normally but does not turn the engine the pinion is probably jammed on the screwed sleeve and the parts should be examined and cleaned.

Starter Overhaul. The brushgear and commutator on the motor should be inspected at intervals upwards of 20,000 miles, after removing the motor from the car. After cleaning the motor and checking for play on the armature shaft bearings, the inspection band on the motor carcase

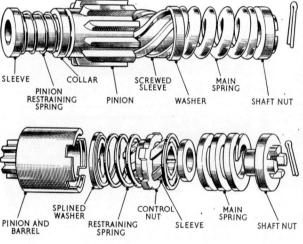

SLEEVE   COLLAR   SCREWED   MAIN
                    SLEEVE   SPRING
   PINION
   RESTRAINING   PINION   WASHER   SHAFT NUT
   SPRING

SPLINED   CONTROL   MAIN
WASHER   NUT   SPRING
PINION AND   RESTRAINING   SLEEVE   SHAFT NUT
BARREL   SPRING

FIG. 10.14. (*Upper*) Lucas S-type starter drive. The screwed sleeve on which the pinion runs is splined internally and fits over splines on the armature shaft. When the drive is engaged, the sleeve moves along the shaft against the main spring to cushion the shock. The pinion-restraining spring prevents the pinion being vibrated into contact with the flywheel while the engine is running. (*Lower*) The Lucas SB-type drive is similar but the pinion is carried on a barrel. This allows a smaller pinion with fewer teeth, and therefore a higher gear ratio.

FIG. 10.15. Typical bulb-type headlamp assembly. The backshell must be pulled out of the light unit in order to gain access to the bulb. The rubber dust excluder prevents the entry of dust and water.

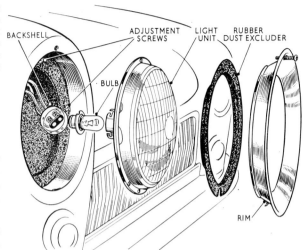

should be slid along to reveal the holes that give access to the brushes. No attention is needed if there is no more than 0·010 in. end play on the armature shaft, and the brushes appear in good condition.

If the brushes are worn down to half their length, new brushes should be fitted. The motor is dismantled by removing the two through bolts and then withdrawing the armature complete with front end-plate and drive gear. The rear end-plate complete with brushgear is then withdrawn. The commutator may be cleaned with fine-grade glasspaper and a cloth moistened in petrol.

On older machines, the pigtails of the new brushes can easily be soldered on to the flat copper strips at the ends of the field coils. On later models where the field coils are of aluminium alloy strip, it is best to leave about ½ in. of the original pigtail connected to the field coil, and to solder the new pigtail on to this. The joint should then be taped up.

To dismantle the drive gear, grip the squared end of the armature shaft in a vice and release the securing nut. The gear should be cleaned and lightly oiled before re-assembly, with the pinion able to move freely on its thread and the main spring lightly compressed.

LIGHTING CIRCUIT

Modern lighting systems give very little trouble and the bulbs used are long-lasting. It is important always to replace a bulb by one of the correct type and wattage, details of which are always given in the car instruction book.

Headlamps. These may be of either the bulb or sealed-beam type. With the former there is a light unit consisting of a reflector shell and front glass, sealed to prevent the entry of dust and moisture, and fitted with a pre-focused bulb (Fig. 10.15). The sealed beam unit is of glass and gas filled, with built-in filaments instead of a bulb. Although robust, the sealed beam unit must be replaced by a complete new unit if it becomes faulty (Fig. 10.16). The twin-filament bulb used for headlamps is normally rated at 40/50 watts, the brighter filament being used for the main headlamp beam.

With a four-headlamp system the outer (or in appropriate cases upper) lamps are fitted with twin-filament bulbs rated at 50/37½ watts, and the inner or lower lamps have single-filament 37½ watt bulbs. All four lamps are in use on main beam, giving a total of 150 watts, while the inner or lower lamps only are used for dipped beam, with a total of 100 watts.

For Continental touring, British cars must have their headlamps converted to

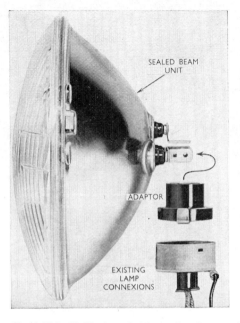

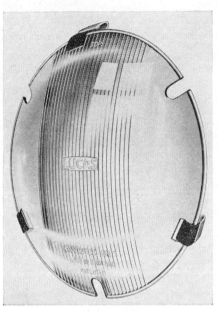

(Left) FIG. 10.16. A sealed-beam headlamp, with an adaptor which allows this type of lamp to be fitted to cars with bulb-type headlamps. *(Right)* FIG. 10.17. For Continental motoring, a pair of lens converters can be fitted, which change the headlights to an amber colour and switch the beams from left to right (Lucas).

dip to the right instead of to the left, and for this purpose special pre-focus bulbs can be obtained, or plastic lens converters that fit over the front glass of each lamp (Fig. 10.17).

Headlamp Alignment. Although neither kind of headlamp system needs focusing, the headlamps must be correctly aligned so that the main beams point straight ahead, parallel with each other and with the road surface. It is possible for the alignment to vary over a period, for various reasons, and at least once a year the setting of the headlamps should be checked. A service station has precision beam-setting equipment with which very accurate alignment can be obtained.

If it is necessary to align the lamps without such equipment, a reasonably accurate setting can be obtained with care (Fig. 10.18). The tyres should be inflated to their correct pressures, and the car loaded normally. If this is not possible the headlights should be aimed one degree below the horizontal, which is represented by a drop of 5 in. below horizontal on a wall at a distance of 25 ft. The car should stand squarely facing the wall and on level ground, and marks made on the wall to correspond with the headlamp beam centres. (Some instruction books contain the required dimensions.)

Each headlamp is checked separately, the other lamp being covered up during this operation. There are normally three adjustment screws in the inner headlamp unit rim, the top screw giving vertical adjustment and the two screws at the side giving horizontal adjustment. The screws should be carefully adjusted until the centre of the headlight bright spot is centred on the wall mark. After making adjustments, ensure that both beams dip and switch to the left when on dipped

238

beam. Fog and spot lamps may be aligned in a similar manner.

Side and Rear Lamps. Many cars have a twin-filament side lamp rated at 6/21 watts, the brighter filament being used as a flashing direction indicator. This arrangement is not permitted on cars made after September 1965, when a separate flasher lamp is required under the Lighting Regulations. Modern cars therefore use a single-filament 6-watt bulb for the side lamp.

At the rear, it is common to use a twin-filament bulb of 6/21 watts for each combined rear/stop lamp, the brighter filament being used for the stop light. The bulbs are usually accessible from inside the boot. A 6-watt bulb or bulbs is also used for the number-plate lamp. The stop lamps are controlled by a pressure-operated switch fitted to the brake hydraulic system.

DIRECTION INDICATORS

British regulations now require all flasher lamps to be of amber colour and optically separate from other lamps, while the frequency must be between 60 and 120 flashes per minute. The direction indicator system comprises four flasher lamps controlled by a switch, a flasher unit, and a warning lamp on the instrument panel or built into the control switch. Whether of single or double filament type, the flasher lamps must be rated at 21 watts, otherwise the warning lamp will not operate correctly.

The flasher unit is sealed and non-adjustable. Essentially it consists of a pair of contacts controlled by a moving armature, and a piece of wire which heats and expands when current flows through it (Fig. 10.19). The contacts are normally open, and when the flashers are switched on current flows through the actuating wire and a ballast resistor which prevents illumination of the lamps. The expanding wire allows the spring-bladed armature to close the contacts. Current now short-circuits the actuating wire and ballast resistor, passing through the contacts and armature to illuminate the lamps and

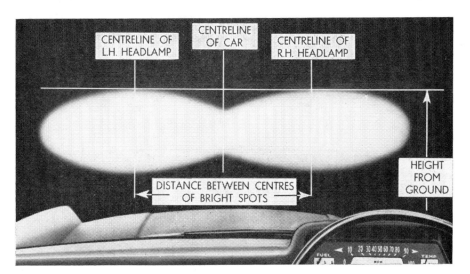

FIG. 10.18. To check headlamp alignment, position the car about 25 ft. away from a wall or vertical surface, and on level ground. On main beam, the centres of the bright spots should be at the same height as the lamp centres and spaced the same distance apart. For accuracy, suitable alignment marks should first be made on the wall.

239

warning lamp. The short-circuited actuating wire cools and contracts, until it pulls open the armature and parts the contacts. The cycle of operations then starts again.

An advantage of the system is that if one of the indicator lamps fails, current flow in the flasher unit will be reduced and the armature will fail to close the contacts for the warning lamp. The latter will therefore not operate, thus attracting the driver's attention. If the warning lamp fails because its own 2·2-watt bulb has burnt out, the indicator lamps will be found to continue working normally.

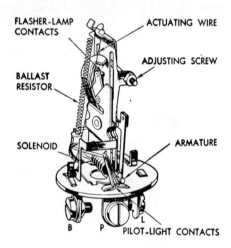

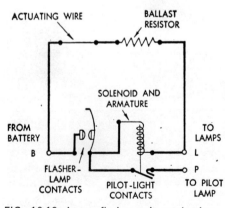

FIG. 10.19. Lucas flasher unit mechanism, with its internal connections. Operation of the device is explained in the text.

Faults may arise through wiring trouble, which can be traced with the aid of the car's wiring diagram, or through failure of the flasher unit or lamp bulbs, when new parts must be fitted. To check whether the fault lies in the flasher unit and not externally, bridge the three terminals on the base of the unit and switch on the ignition. The appropriate indicator lamps and the warning lamp should now show a continuous light when the control switch is operated to either left or right.

The flasher unit for a normal four-lamp system is rated at 42 watts. A heavy-duty unit or special switching system is required for six-lamp systems used when towing a caravan or trailer.

Two-level Signalling. Many modern cars are designed to have rear flashers and stop lamps of normal brightness during the daytime, but reduced brightness at night. This is arranged by mounting a small relay unit in the boot, connected to the lamp circuits concerned. When the driving lamps are switched on at night, current is fed to the relay unit, energizing a relay which brings current-limiting resistors into the rear flasher and stop lamp circuits. To avoid upsetting the operation of the flasher unit, an additional resistor is connected in parallel with it, consuming the balance of current necessary to maintain normal functioning (Fig. 10.20).

While it is possible to convert a car to two-level signalling by fitting this simple relay unit, it should be noted that the rear lamp lenses must also be replaced by special high-intensity lenses; otherwise the night-time light intensity may be reduced to a level which is inadequate for signalling.

Lighting Faults. These are usually due to a burnt-out bulb, a discharged battery, a fuse blown, or a bad connection. More rarely, a control switch may fail. Testing can be carried out as outlined at the beginning of this chapter.

A flickering lamp is likely to be caused

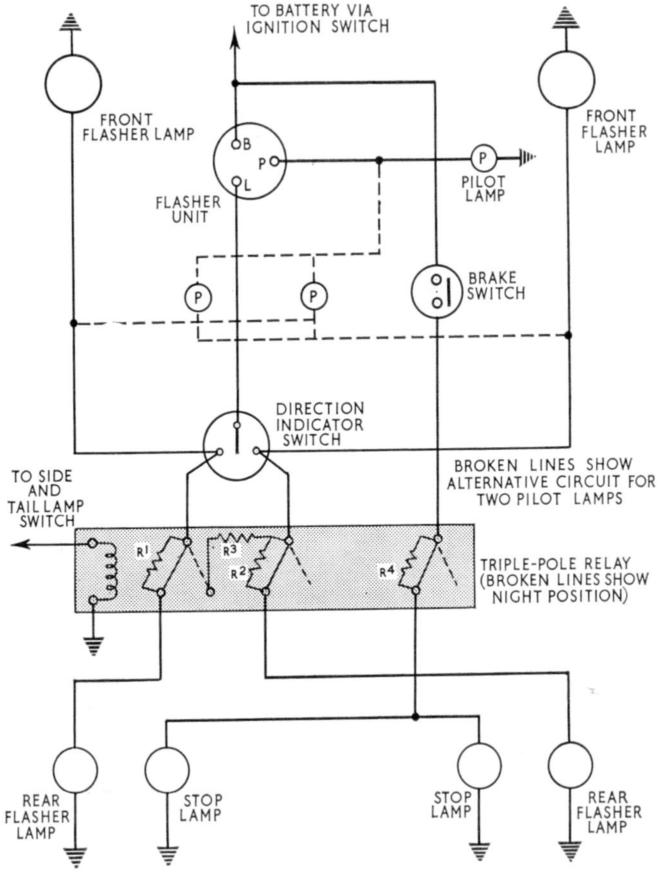

FIG. 10.20. Wiring dia-
gram of the normal
flasher indicator circuit
and stop-lamp circuit,
shown modified for
two-level signalling. A
relay unit is fitted
(shaded), which
reduces the brightness
of the rear flasher and
stop lamps when the
side lamps are on.

by a loose connection,
or sometimes a faulty
bulb, while on some
cars a faulty thermo-
static interrupter will
cause flickering of
the headlamps. In-
adequate illumina-
tion may be due to a
high-resistance con-
nection, limiting the
current, to bulbs
ageing, or to a dirty
reflector, apart from
being due to a dis-
charged battery, of
course. If bulbs burn
out frequently, there
may be a fault in the charging circuit.

AUXILIARY LAMPS

There is a wide range of auxiliary lamps
which can readily be fitted by the motorist,
including fog lamps, long-range or spot
lamps, reversing lamps, parking lamps,
boot or under-bonnet lamps, map-reading
lamps and warning lamps.

Fog and Spot Lamps. These are
available both with bulbs and with sealed-
beam light units. The usual bulb type has
a single-filament bulb of 48 watts. Another
type uses tungsten/iodine vapour bulbs,
which are smaller than ordinary bulbs yet
give far more light. They are claimed to
have a long life (up to 350 hours) and to

eliminate blackening of the bulb. With
ordinary bulbs, a transverse filament is
required for a fog lamp, and a spiral
filament for a spot lamp.

These lamps must be fitted so that their
light centres are between 2 ft. and 3½ ft.
above ground level; if lower than 2 ft.
they may only be used in conditions of fog
or falling snow. Furthermore, they must
be aligned so as not to cause dazzle to a
person at a distance greater than 25 ft.
away from the car, whose eye level is
3½ ft. or more above ground.

The earth terminal on the lamp must be
connected to a suitable earthing point on
the car. A wire from the live terminal is
taken to the control switch, and this in turn

241

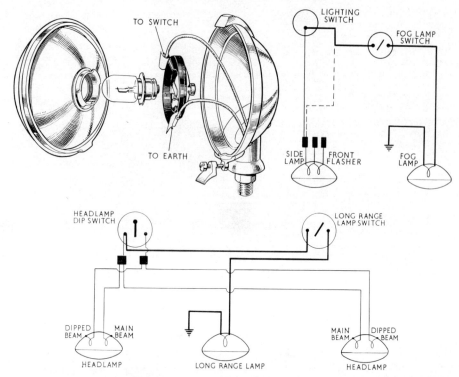

FIG. 10.21. Installing auxiliary lamps. (*Upper*) A typical fog lamp and wiring circuit. The supply can be taken from either the lighting switch or a side-lamp connector. (*Lower*) Wiring circuit for a spot or long-range lamp which ensures that the light is cut off whenever the headlamps are switched to dipped beam.

is connected to the A3 or A4 terminal of the control unit or fuse box. The lamp will then be fuse-protected and energized only when the ignition is switched on. On some cars a "tail" is left in the harness for this purpose. Alternatively, the feed can be from a side lamp circuit, so that the auxiliary lamps are inoperative until the side lamps are switched on, while there is less chance of overloading the ignition switch (Fig. 10.21).

Wiring must be of 14/·010 cable, protected by rubber grommets where it passes through holes in metalwork, and with good connections. It is best to follow the route of a main harness cable and use the same clips to secure the extra wiring.

Reversing Lamps. These are fitted in a similar manner, but in this case there must be a warning device to show the driver when the lamps are in operation, unless the switch operates automatically when reverse gear is engaged. Otherwise, to comply with the law a separate switch should be fitted incorporating a warning lamp. If the lamps are fed from fuse terminal A4 they can be used both by night and day, and cannot be left on inadvertently when the ignition is switched off.

Parking Lamps. These are permitted for all-night parking in most towns, and are useful in that they save draining the battery. It is handy to use a clip-on type wired to a two-pin plug which fits a socket. The socket is mounted on the facia and wired to the fuse box A2 terminal and to earth. If there is no A2 terminal the wiring can be connected to A1 terminal and a cartridge-type fuse incorporated in the lead (parking lamp leads are easily trapped in doors and windows and should always be fused). Another scheme is to fit a double-pole switch which will operate the offside lamps for parking and cut off the nearside lamps and also the ignition—thereby providing anti-theft protection (Fig. 10.22).

AUXILIARIES AND ACCESSORIES

Electrically operated auxiliary components include horns, windscreen wipers, petrol pumps and gauges, while some cars have electrical hood-raising gear, window gear, electrically heated windows etc. The car heater employs an electric blower (see Chapter 9). Accessories are of many kinds and include lamps, radios, screen washers (see Chapter 9), instruments, kettles, anti-theft devices and clocks.

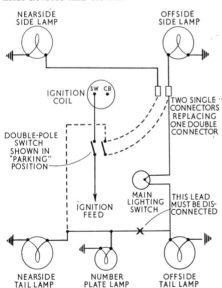

NEARSIDE SIDE LAMP OFFSIDE SIDE LAMP

IGNITION COIL (SW CB)

DOUBLE-POLE SWITCH SHOWN IN "PARKING" POSITION

TWO SINGLE CONNECTORS REPLACING ONE DOUBLE CONNECTOR

IGNITION FEED   MAIN LIGHTING SWITCH   THIS LEAD MUST BE DISCONNECTED

NEARSIDE TAIL LAMP   NUMBER PLATE LAMP   OFFSIDE TAIL LAMP

FIG. 10.22. A useful modification for parking at night. When the auxiliary double-pole switch is closed, the electrical system works normally. When it is open, the offside parking lamps only operate, and the ignition supply is cut as a precaution against theft.

A full complement of such equipment represents a heavy electrical load on the battery and wiring system, and correct installation is therefore important.

Horns. There are two types, the high-frequency horn and the windtone instrument. The actuating mechanism is similar in both types, with an electromagnet, moving armature, contacts and diaphragm operating in a similar manner to an electric bell. Pressing the horn push causes current to flow through the electromagnet, which is energized and attracts the armature until the contacts open, releasing the armature. The contacts then close and allow the diaphragm to vibrate at a sound frequency.

When a pair of horns is fitted, with high and low notes, a relay is used if the total current drawn is over 12 amperes. This minimizes voltage drop and protects the horn switch contacts and spring. It is operated by a light current from the horn push, and supplies a heavy current to the adjacent horns (Fig. 10.23).

No maintenance is required by a horn except to check the security of its mounting and connections occasionally. If the horn fails to operate the fault will probably lie in the wiring, and a check should be made on this with a voltmeter before assuming that the horn is at fault.

First, with the engine stopped and all lamps switched on, check the battery voltage which should not be less than 11 volts. Then connect the voltmeter across the two horn terminals and press the horn push. If the reading is more than $\frac{1}{2}$ volt below the battery voltage, connect the voltmeter between the battery terminal and the horn supply terminal. On pressing the push, the voltmeter should read less than $\frac{1}{2}$ volt. If higher, check the feed wiring connections.

If this does not reveal the trouble, connect the voltmeter between the battery earth terminal and the horn terminal, when full battery voltage should be shown. On pressing the push, the reading should be

243

0-½ volt; if higher, the earth connections should be checked. If these are satisfactory, the horn unit is faulty.

Some horns have an adjuster screw fitted on the mechanism or the back of the casing, which provides a degree of adjustment on the contacts after long service. The method is to release the screw until the horn just fails to operate, then to screw down the adjustment nearly half a turn. Any other attention should be left to an auto-electrician.

Windscreen Wipers. Most cars have a pair of wipers driven by a single electric motor, though there are still some with vacuum-operated wipers (see Chapter 9). The motor unit is mounted in the engine compartment and the drive taken to the wiper arm wheel-boxes through a flexible cable in a conduit (Fig. 10.24). A limit switch incorporated in the drive mechanism ensures self-parking of the blades, and some motors are fitted with a thermostatic cutout which prevents overloading when the screen is covered with snow or ice. The only maintenance needed is to apply a few drops of oil occasionally to the wiper spindles, and to replace the wiper blades when these become worn and tend to smear the screen. At intervals of 30,000 miles the motor should be dismantled and overhauled. The brushes should be replaced if worn down to half their length and the commutator cleaned with fine-grade glasspaper, while the motor gearing should be repacked with white oxide water-repellent grease.

If the wipers fail to operate, the fault is usually to be found in the wiring, or the A4 fuse may be blown. Sluggish operation may be due to binding or stiffness of the blade mechanism or excessive pressure of the blades on the screen. Erratic operation may be the result of free play in the mechanism or loose mounting of the motor or wheel-boxes. A faulty motor is best exchanged for a reconditioned unit.

Fitting Accessories. Never connect electrical accessories directly across the battery, nor to the ignition coil terminals. The correct method of wiring depends upon the accessory's function, but the object should be to spread the additional load over as many circuits as possible. The three circuits mainly used for accessories are as follows.

Group 1. Battery circuit, for components

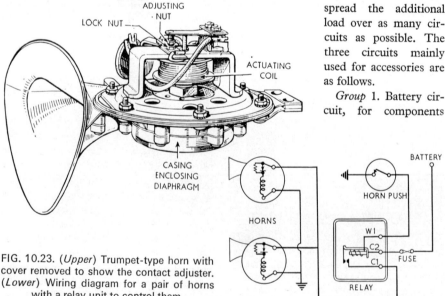

FIG. 10.23. (*Upper*) Trumpet-type horn with cover removed to show the contact adjuster. (*Lower*) Wiring diagram for a pair of horns with a relay unit to control them.

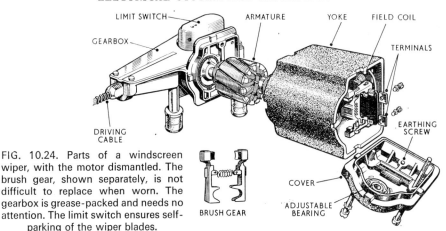

FIG. 10.24. Parts of a windscreen wiper, with the motor dismantled. The brush gear, shown separately, is not difficult to replace when worn. The gearbox is grease-packed and needs no attention. The limit switch ensures self-parking of the wiper blades.

which may be required when the car is stationary—radio, parking lamp, interior lamps, clock, cigarette lighter etc.

Group 2. Lighting circuit, for components required only when the side lamps are on—fog lamps, spot lamps, etc.

Group 3. Ignition circuit, for components required only when the ignition is switched on—wipers, horn relay, direction indicators, heater blower, warning lamps, gauges etc.

The lighting switch in Group 2 and the ignition switch in Group 3 act as master switches that over-ride all accessory switches in their circuits.

The terminals for connecting accessories are to be found on the control unit and fuse boxes (some control units incorporate

the fuses). Their use is shown in the table below. Note that terminals may be marked A1, A2 etc., or simply 1, 2 etc.

Clocks. To avoid being switched off, a clock should be fed from terminal A2 or else fuse No. 3. As the current drawn is very small, sound connections and good earthing are essential.

Anti-theft Devices. There is a wide variety of devices on the market designed to make a vehicle and its contents secure against theft. Apart from mechanical devices such as hocked bars to clamp the steering wheel and padlocked chains, there are several kinds of electrical devices (Fig. 10.25).

A popular home-made device consists simply of a switch, located in a secret

ACCESSORY TERMINALS

A and B	Connected direct to the battery via starter switch. Unfused.
A1	Connected to the battery, supplies current to main lighting switch. Unfused.
A2	Connected to terminal A1 through a fuse. Use for wiring accessories in Group 1. If this terminal is not provided, use A1 and incorporate a line fuse in the wiring.
A3	Energized from the ignition switch. Unfused.
A4	Energized from terminal A3 through a fuse. Use for wiring accessories in Group 3. If this terminal is not provided, use A3 and incorporate a line fuse in the wiring.
E	Earth connection. May be used for earthing any com onent.
F	Generator field circuit. May not be used for any other purpose.
D	Generator armature circuit. May not be used for any other purpose.
Lighting switch	Use terminals S or T on the switch for wiring accessories in Group 2. If inaccessible, use a side or tail lamp connector.
Ignition switch	Some Ford, Vauxhall and other cars have an accessory position on this for wiring radio, cigarette lighter etc.

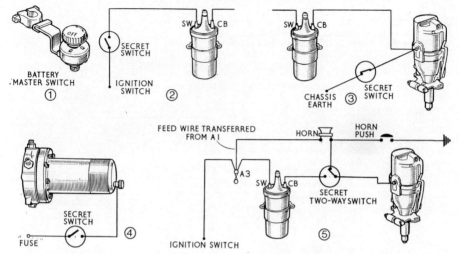

FIG. 10.25. Simple beat-the-thief devices. (1) A Lucas battery master switch disconnects the entire electrical system and is useful when the car is laid up for a period. (2) and (3) A switch can be fitted in a hidden position which will either cut the ignition supply or short-circuit the contact breaker and so prevent the engine being started. (4) If the car has an electric fuel pump, a switch can be inserted in its lead. When open, the engine will start normally but will run out of fuel within a short distance. (5) A more elaborate modification. With the hidden switch closed, turning on the ignition will simultaneously cut the ignition supply and operate the horn.

position, which breaks the battery feed to the ignition coil SW terminal so that the ignition circuit is rendered inoperative. This is easy to fit, but it is necessary to use a good-quality switch and heavy-current cable for the connections as otherwise high resistance may be present in the circuit which will hinder cold starting. A drawback is that it is only necessary to connect a temporary jumper lead between the battery and coil to get the car started.

A variation of this idea which is sometimes more convenient is to fit the switch so as to short-circuit the contact breaker when it is "on." Another method is to use a two-way switch which sounds the horn when the ignition switch is turned on, as well as cutting the ignition feed.

There are a number of commercial devices which employ switches and relays in various forms to cut the coil feed, earth the contact breaker, and sound the horn, and it is also possible to fit switches on

doors, boot lid and bonnet that will operate the alarm system.

CAR RADIOS

The majority of present-day cars have provision for installing a radio set. In many cases the car manufacturer specifies a particular model, but there is a wide range of sets that can be fitted to any car. In general, the installation of a radio should be left to a specialist fitter, although some of the cheaper transistor sets are quite easy to fit oneself.

Most older car radios are of the all-valve type, and consume 3 to 4 amperes of current using a vibrator power unit. Another type utilizes both valves and transistors, which reduces the current drain. Most modern sets are of the all-transistor variety, where the current drain is less than one ampere. All these types are capable of giving good reception.

Many people, however, carry an ordinary transistor portable in the car. These rarely prove satisfactory, since their built-in aerials have directional properties and cause fading, while they are sensitive to ignition interference. Better results are often obtained by fitting a clip-on car aerial with a lead which plugs into a socket on the set.

A point to watch when installing a radio is the polarity of the car chassis (earth). The radio earth must be of corresponding polarity—transistors in particular can be ruined by a "wrong way" current flow. Many car radios therefore have a plug or switching device which permits installation

with either positive or negative earth, as required.

A spare lead may be provided in the car's wiring harness for use as a radio power supply lead, otherwise the set should be connected to terminal A2 (if this is not fitted, use terminal A1). Most sets are supplied with a fuse, and any replacement fuse should always be of the correct rating, to avoid the risk of damage to the car wiring as well as the set itself.

The loudspeaker may be mounted under the facia, in a side panel or at the rear, and some sets will feed two speakers (Fig. 10.26). Leads and plugs are supplied with

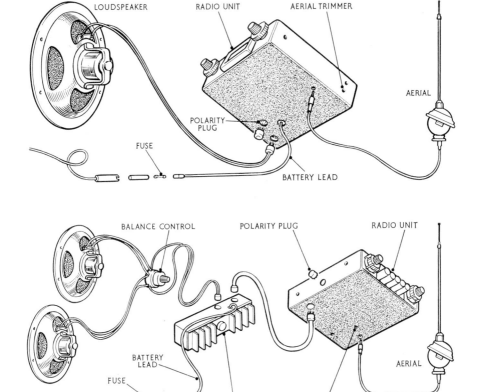

FIG. 10.26. Car radio installations. (*Upper*) A single-speaker layout suitable for a small car. (*Lower*) A more elaborate installation for the larger car, with two speakers and an additional amplifier. A special plug is provided on each set to adjust for either positive or negative earthing, and a trimmer screw for matching the aerial (Radiomobile).

247

CAR RADIO INTERFERENCE

Type of Interference	Source of Interference	Remedy
Interference when engine and all accessories are switched off.	Outside the car, such as from other vehicles.	None.
Regular clicking, varying with engine speed.	Ignition system.	(a) Fit capacitor between coil SW terminal and an earth point. (b) Fit resistors in leads at sparking plugs, or replace plug leads by ignition suppressor cables.
Continuous whine, varying with engine speed, after cutout has cut in.	Generator.	Fit capacitor between generator D terminal and generator earth.
Continuous crackling which ceases periodically.	Control unit.	Fit special Lucas filter in control unit circuit.
General interference when an accessory is switched on.	Wiper motor, clock, blower motor, electric fuel pump, etc.	Fit capacitor between the accessory's supply terminal and an earth point.
Intermittent general interference at all engine speeds.	Loose wire or poor connection in main wiring or aerial circuit.	Check all wiring. Aerial lead screening must be properly earthed.

the radio kit and must be properly fitted, while the speaker should be securely mounted so as to avoid vibration.

Correct installation of the aerial is especially important, as a poor aerial system is frequently the cause of interference or weak reception. Several types of aerial are on the market, including wing-mounted, rear-mounted and roof aerials. There are also remote-controlled aerials operated by a cable drive or an electric motor. When a retractable type is fitted, ensure that the retracted aerial will not foul the wheel underneath whichever way the steering is turned.

Good connections from the aerial to the set are important for satisfactory reception. Use only the proper leads and plugs and ensure that the metal braiding inside the cable is well earthed. Many radios are provided with a trimmer capacitor which permits the aerial to be correctly matched to the set. The set is tuned to a weak signal at about 250 metres, keeping the aerial fully extended, and the set-screw trimmer control is rotated until maximum volume is obtained.

Rear-mounted aerials are supplied with a special lead and a plug incorporating a capacitor to reduce losses caused by the length of the lead; do not use odd lengths of lead or coaxial cable for connecting such aerials.

Interference Suppression. The principal trouble with these sets is poor reception due to interference. There are two aspects of this matter. In the first place, the car's ignition system can radiate high-frequency waves which interfere with nearby domestic radio and television sets, and Government regulations require all cars to be fitted with equipment to suppress such radiation.

In many cases, Lucas distributors are fitted with an H.T. contact in the distributor cap which consists of a special resistive carbon brush. This acts as an efficient interference suppressor without in any way harming the efficiency of the sparking plugs. Other ignition systems employ special resistive cables for the sparking plug leads which have the same effect.

In the second place, the ignition and electrical components on the car can

FIG. 10.27. Modern self-contained instrument box with a speedometer, total mileage recorder, temperature gauge and fuel gauge (Vauxhall). The lower view, with the facia removed, shows the cylinder of the "advancing line" type speed indicator.

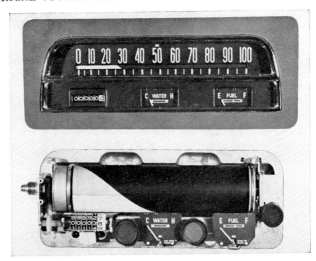

radiate interference which is picked up by the car's own radio. A proper car radio (not a transistor portable) has a fully screened casing and a filter circuit in the power input to reduce such interference, but additional suppressors may be found necessary. The table shows how to suppress troublesome components.

The capacitors (condensers) used as suppressors are normally rated at 1 microfarad; they should be fitted as close to the interfering component as possible, and the wiring kept short. For suppressing sparking plugs, special resistors are supplied by Lucas, though fitting a 1 mfd. capacitor between the coil SW terminal and earth is usually sufficient to eliminate ignition interference.

The bonding of component casings to earth by means of thick, flexible metal braiding often improves matters considerably. It should be appreciated that the metal bodywork of a car, especially the bonnet, helps to "bottle up" interference, and it is often difficult to remedy such trouble on cars with glass-fibre bodywork which do not possess this advantage.

GAUGES AND INSTRUMENTS

The driver's indicating instruments include both mechanical and electrical devices. Some instruments are to be found only on higher-priced cars, but there is a variety of accessory instruments that can be installed by the motorist.

In older cars the instruments were often mounted and wired individually on the instrument panel, but modern practice is to install them in one or two instrument boxes fronted by a surround or facia (Fig. 10.27). Each box contains in addition warning lamps and one or more illuminating lamps. A considerable mass of wiring may have to be connected through the back of the more complex instrument box, and wiring is greatly simplified by the use of a printed-circuit back plate (Fig. 10.28). The printed circuit technique is also used as a variable resistance for dimming panel lamps.

It is often difficult to gain access to the wiring or instrument fixings. In some models it is possible to reach up into a space between the instrument boxes and the bulkhead, in others the back of the instrument panel can be reached from the engine compartment, while certain cars have an instrument panel hinged at the bottom which can be opened to expose the back.

Removal of the surround or finisher may expose the fixing screws of the instrument assembly, allowing individual instruments to be taken out. Instruments may also be installed from the front and fixed by studs and nuts; installed from the rear and fixed in the same way; or installed from the front and fixed by screws through lugs on the instrument box on to a back plate.

Warning Lamps. These use miniature bulbs of either the M.E.S. (screwed base) or M.C.C. (bayonet) type, rated at 2·2 or 6 watts, and fitted in insulated holders which are sprung into position. Care should be taken not to tug on the wires when removing the holders.

Warning lamps in general use are for *ignition warning*, connected between the generator and ignition switch; *oil pressure warning*, connected to a pressure-operated switch in the engine crankcase; *main beam warning*, connected to the headlamp dip switch; and *flasher warning*, connected to the flasher unit.

Speedometer. The usual type is mechanical, operated through a flexible drive cable from the rear of the gearbox. The instrument also incorporates gearing to work the total-mileage and trip-setting indicators. The speedometer rarely fails, but trouble may arise because of a worn drive gear in the gearbox, a broken inner drive cable, wear on the inner cable, or clogging of the instrument head with grease due to over-lubrication of the cable. Wavering of the needle may be caused by a bend or kink in the inner cable, lack of lubrication on the inner cable, or mal-adjustment of the cable and its collar at the

instrument end of the drive. The top end of the drive cable can be undone and the inner cable pulled out of position quite easily. When rolled over on a clean flat board it should show no signs of bending. After cleaning, the lower third only of the cable should be smeared with a soft grease and it can then be refitted.

Fuel Gauge. Two types of electrical gauge system are in use. In the older type, there is a float arm in the fuel tank which moves a slider arm over a resistor according to the level of the fuel, and thus controls the flow of current to the gauge mounted on the facia. The gauge has a terminal marked T connected to the tank and a terminal marked B connected to the ignition switch, and is of the moving-iron variety (Fig. 10.29).

In the later type, a similar tank unit is employed, also a gauge. In addition, the instrument assembly contains a heating coil round a bimetal strip, the free end of which is linked to the gauge needle. Movement of the needle is controlled by expansion of the strip, which in turn depends upon the flow of current from the tank unit. The system incorporates a voltage stabilizer mounted on the rear of the instruments, intended to avert movement of the needle due to fluctuation of battery voltage. This type can be identified by the slow movement of the needle on switching on or off.

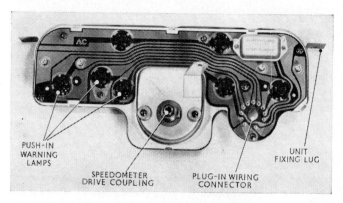

FIG. 10.28. Back of a self-contained instrument box employing a printed circuit for the connections to gauges and warning lamps (Ford). The bulb holders bayonet into position, the bulb connection being made automatically when the holder is correctly located.

PUSH-IN WARNING LAMPS

SPEEDOMETER DRIVE COUPLING

PLUG-IN WIRING CONNECTOR

UNIT FIXING LUG

FIG. 10.29. Fuel gauge circuits. (*Upper*) A popular type comprising a tank unit and a moving-coil gauge connected by a single wire. (*Lower*) Pair of gauges with a bimetallic-strip voltage controller which ensures more accurate readings without "needle-swinging."

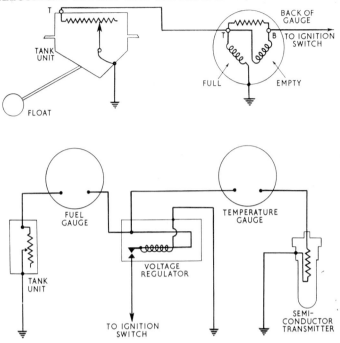

The most common faults in either type are wiring troubles. With the older type, a "below empty" reading indicates no current reaching the gauge, a burnt-out instrument, or a jammed needle. A permanent "empty" reading, when the tank is partly full, indicates a short circuit to earth on the wire between the tank unit and instrument or at the tank unit. An "above full" reading indicates an open circuit (break) in the wire between the tank unit and instrument, or a faulty tank unit. Faulty units are best replaced by new ones.

With the later type, since there are three units connected in series there should be some voltage drop across each, and this permits a simple test with a voltmeter. There should be full battery voltage at the "feed-in" terminal on the voltage stabilizer, something less at the junction of this unit and the gauge unit, and still less at the junction of the gauge unit and the tank unit. If the tank unit is faulty there will be full battery voltage at both sides of the voltage stabilizer and both sides of the

gauge unit, and also at the tank unit terminal.

Water Temperature Gauge. Two types are in use. The mechanical type utilizes a liquid which vaporizes at a certain temperature and is contained in a small bulb fixed in the engine cylinder head, block, thermostat housing or water pump. The bulb is connected to the Bourdon-type pressure gauge on the facia by a capillary tube. As the liquid vaporizes due to engine heat the pressure in the tube increases and this controls the gauge reading. This type has to be serviced as a complete unit. Failure to operate is usually caused by a break in the capillary tube, which must not contain sharp bends or kinks and should have two or three turns between the engine and bulkhead to absorb vibration (Fig. 10.30).

The electrical type comprises an engine unit which takes the form of a resistor whose value varies with engine temperature, and a moving-iron meter on the facia. The meter reading is controlled by current

251

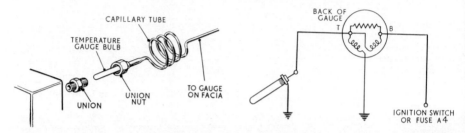

FIG. 10.30. Water temperature gauges. (*Left*) The capillary tube type operates the gauge as a result of the increasing vapour pressure of a fluid when heated. It cannot be dismantled, so a hole must be made in the bulkhead large enough to accept the bulb unit. The bulb may be mounted in a tapping on the cylinder block, in the radiator header tank, or in the top radiator hose. (*Right*) The electrical type has a similar bulb unit, and both this and the gauge must be well earthed.

passing through the engine unit. Where a fuel gauge with voltage stabilizer is fitted, the water temperature gauge is likewise stabilized.

A useful check for an electrical temperature gauge is to substitute a 12-volt 2·2-watt bulb for the engine unit when, if the meter is serviceable, an approximate "hot" reading will be obtained. A check should be made on the water thermostat before condemning a temperature gauge as faulty, in case the thermostat valve is not closing fully and preventing the attainment of full water temperature.

Oil Pressure Gauge. Here again, both mechanical and electrical types are in use. The former takes the form of a Bourdon

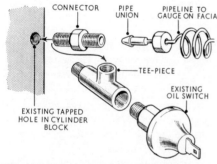

FIG. 10.31. An oil pressure gauge can be connected into the cylinder block in place of the switch unit for an existing oil-pressure lamp. Alternatively, the use of a tee-piece allows both the gauge and the lamp to function.

pressure gauge on the facia connected by a pipe to the oil feed line for the engine bearings; it reads the actual oil pressure. This gauge works on the principle that a curved tube will tend to straighten under pressure, the free end of its tube being linked to the gauge needle.

The electrical type uses a flexible-diaphragm switch connected to the oil feed line and a warning lamp instead of a meter. At normal oil pressure the switch contacts are open and no current reaches the warning lamp, but if pressure falls below about 10 lb. per sq. in. the switch operates the lamp. This type therefore shows only that the engine has something above the minimum oil pressure. The usual fault is failure of the switch contacts to close, so that the lamp does not light.

Many motorists prefer a pressure gauge in place of the warning lamp, and it is quite easy to make the adaptation. The pressure gauge is supplied with a kit which includes all necessary parts. A union can be screwed into place instead of the switch unit, and a small-bore pipe connected to the gauge, or alternatively the warning lamp can be retained by fitting a tee-piece in place of the union, with the pressure-gauge pipe connected to one end and the switch unit to the other (Fig. 10.31).

Ammeter. Some makers fit an ammeter of the centre zero type, reading charge on one side and discharge on the other, to their cars, and it gives much useful information. It is normally connected in the battery circuit between the battery terminal of the starter switch and terminal A on the control unit, so as to read the total load on the electrical system (Fig. 10.32).

The generator output can be calculated approximately by watching the deflection of the needle. If there is a discharge of, say, 10 amperes with lamps on and engine stopped, and the needle advances to show a charge of 10 amperes when the engine is running above idling speed, then the generator output is 20 amperes.

An ammeter is easy to fit by disconnecting the wire on terminal A and connecting this to one side of the meter, with another lead connecting the other side of the meter with the terminal. If the ammeter is then found to read wrong way round, the connections are simply reversed. Any additional cable should be size 44/·012 or larger, and joints must be sound and tight.

Engine Speed Indicator. Also known as a tachometer, this instrument indicates crankshaft speed and is often fitted to high-performance cars. Three types are in use.

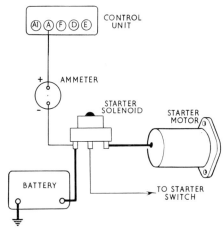

FIG. 10.32. An ammeter can be wired into the main supply lead from the battery as shown. Sound connections are essential as the whole electrical load is carried by this lead.

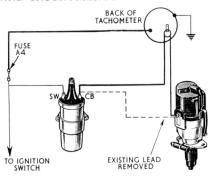

FIG. 10.33. Wiring diagram for an engine speed indicator (rev. counter or tachometer) of the popular electronic impulse type.

The mechanical type is similar to a speedometer and is driven through a flexible cable from the distributor drive shaft, camshaft or generator. Faults with this type are the same as for speedometers and should be dealt with in the same way.

The electrical type consists of a small alternator driven by the engine camshaft and connected to a meter on the instrument panel. The alternator is self-exciting and is not connected to any other part of the electrical system. Faults in this should be left to a competent auto-electrician.

The electronic impulse type is connected to the electrical system via the ignition coil. Electrical impulses are triggered off by the contact breaker and coil primary winding, suitably amplified and fed into the meter on the facia. This type of tachometer is much less expensive than the others and several models are available for easy installation in any type of car (Fig. 10.33).

Properly installed, an electronic tachometer should give little trouble. In the event of a failure, it should be remembered that since the triggering current is in series with the battery feed to the ignition coil, if the engine will run this circuit must be in order. If there is a current feed (usually from fuse terminal A4) and the meter is well earthed, failure to operate must be due to a fault inside the instrument.

CHAPTER 11

BODYWORK AND FITMENTS

REGULAR care of your car's bodywork throughout its life will be amply repaid. Not only is there greater pleasure to be derived from driving a car that is clean, well-kept and free of noises and rattles, but the car will fetch a higher price when the time comes to resell it. It is worth bearing in mind when considering the purchase of a used car that while worn or faulty mechanical parts can usually be replaced quite easily, bodywork damage may prove expensive to repair. Points to watch in the general care of bodywork are illustrated in Fig. 11.1.

CLEANING AND POLISHING

The basis of effective body care is undoubtedly the routine wash-down, followed when necessary by polishing, and accompanied by cleaning out the interior, boot and engine compartment. Whether once a week or once a month, the car should be washed regularly both summer and winter. Never apply any kind of polish to a dirty car; always wash and dry it first. Road grit is a harsh abrasive and polishing will cause it to be ground into the paint finish, resulting in a mass of scratches.

Since dirt is abrasive, it is asking for trouble to wipe or scrub it off with a wet cloth or sponge. The best idea is to float it off the surface by soaking the car with a good flow of water. Sometimes one can only slosh water from buckets over the body and then sponge over lightly, but if possible use a hose with a copious flow but little pressure, and play this on the car for five minutes or so.

In present-day traffic conditions, cars tend to pick up a good deal of greasy film and oil spots which resist plain water. A

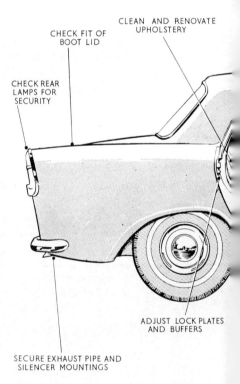

CHECK FIT OF BOOT LID

CLEAN AND RENOVATE UPHOLSTERY

CHECK REAR LAMPS FOR SECURITY

ADJUST LOCK PLATES AND BUFFERS

SECURE EXHAUST PIPE AND SILENCER MOUNTINGS

FIG. 11.1. General maintenance of bodywork and interior. Cleaning, lubrication and security checks should be carried out systematically as part of a regular maintenance routine. Servicing of the items mentioned here will not occur with the same frequency, but adopting a simple check system should enable all the points to receive regular attention.

car shampoo is therefore recommended, and an effective method is to use a hose-brush which accommodates a detergent dispenser in its handle (Fig. 11.2). A mild household detergent may be used to remove grime deposits, but some of these cleaners attack certain kinds of paintwork and p.v.c. upholstery.

Start by hosing the bottom of the body and work upwards, keeping all the surfaces well wetted. Try to avoid getting water into window surrounds, the door, bonnet and boot lid openings, joints between panels, and the radiator. Only after the car has had a thorough soaking should you wash off with the sponge or hose-brush. With this, begin at the roof and work downwards, wiping along the length of the

car and washing out the sponge frequently.

The wheels and tyres should not be neglected, and an old sponge may be kept for cleaning off the accretions of oily dirt on the wheels. It also pays to wash off as much mud as possible from the underside, especially the wings. When large clods of mud are allowed to remain underneath, they retain water thrown up from a wet road and can start large rust areas.

After shampooing, rinse the body with plenty of clean water, then leather-off. Synthetic leathers are cheap, but there is nothing as satisfactory as a large wash leather of genuine chamois.

Some smearing may be left on the windows after leathering, but this is easily removed with a clean cloth moistened in

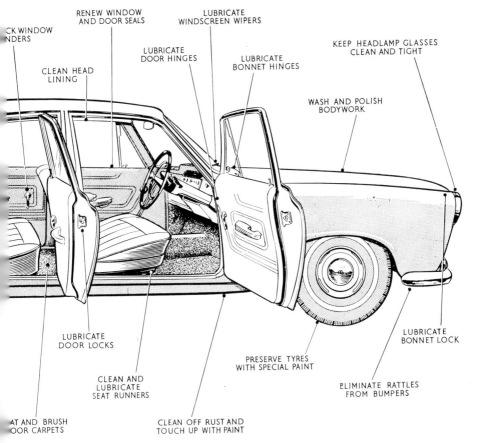

RENEW WINDOW
AND DOOR SEALS

CK WINDOW
NDERS

LUBRICATE
WINDSCREEN WIPERS

KEEP HEADLAMP GLASSES
CLEAN AND TIGHT

LUBRICATE
DOOR HINGES

LUBRICATE
BONNET HINGES

CLEAN HEAD
LINING

WASH AND POLISH
BODYWORK

LUBRICATE
DOOR LOCKS

LUBRICATE
BONNET LOCK

PRESERVE TYRES
WITH SPECIAL PAINT

CLEAN AND
LUBRICATE
SEAT RUNNERS

ELIMINATE RATTLES
FROM BUMPERS

AT AND BRUSH
OOR CARPETS

CLEAN OFF RUST AND
TOUCH UP WITH PAINT

methylated spirits. Use this also for cleaning the blades of the wipers, which tend to pick up oil film from a dirty screen and cause subsequent smearing.

Polishing. The objects of applying a polish, apart from raising the gloss, are to protect the paint from weathering and to make subsequent cleaning easier. The requirements of finishes vary in regard to protection. Many older cars, and some hand-finished luxury models, are finished in cellulose paints. These relatively soft finishes need frequent cleaning and polishing if they are to give long service.

A large number of modern cars are finished in synthetic enamels, which are harder and more durable, but still require polishing to give protection. Acrylic paint finishes have now been introduced by certain makers, and these are claimed never to need any kind of polish. Nevertheless, many owners consider an occasional wax-polish treatment to be beneficial in its "caulking" of panel joints and nooks and crannies where corrosion may get a hold.

Almost any of the wide range of car polishes on the market today can be used with confidence, as those older kinds that tended to strip the paint films have largely disappeared. Liquid emulsion polishes often contain silicones which form a water-resistant film on the surface, and these give a high gloss with minimum time and effort. More popular, probably, are the wax polishes in liquid or solid form, which give a deep, durable gloss that forms a water-proof film and withstands several washings.

Any of these polishes can be used on synthetic enamel and acrylic paint finishes. On a cellulose finish, a wax polish is to be preferred. The liquid type is very satisfactory, but the hard solid waxes are perhaps best in the long run, although they entail a fair amount of work in application. A wash-down followed by all-over treatment with solid wax two or three times a year is all that the average car really needs in the way of polishing.

The technique is as follows. Avoiding conditions where the car is exposed to either hot sunshine or damp, foggy weather, first wash and dry off, taking care to remove all traffic film and grease. Use a soft pad to apply the wax to main surfaces and an old toothbrush to work it into joints and crevices, and complete one panel at a time. Polish off the wax with a large clean cloth that can be folded several times so that the polishing surface does not become clogged. A final light buffing with a power-tool mop gives an extra lustre to the paint (Fig. 11.3).

After a time it may be found that the paintwork remains dull despite thorough washing. This is because an oxidized film has gradually formed over the surface. The film can be removed by means of one of the liquid body cleaners or haze removers which have a slightly abrasive action and expose a fresh paint surface. The cleaner itself produces a high gloss, but its use should be followed by wax polishing to protect the newly-exposed paint.

Bright Metal. The bumpers, hub plates, radiator grille and similar parts must not be neglected. Several kinds of metal are in use for bright parts, requiring different treatments.

Chromium-plated steel is much used on older cars, but to a lesser extent on recent ones. The quality of the plating varies, and the cheaper kind is easily attacked by acids present in polluted city atmospheres and should be washed frequently. A better quality is used on most recent cars, while small parts are often plated zinc castings or brass. When the plating becomes tarnished, judicious use of a chrome cleaner will restore the shine, but never use ordinary metal polish. Wax polish is good for plating, providing a protective film, and there are also transparent sprays for this purpose.

Little can be done if chromium plating eventually begins to peel, blister or show pitting by rust, though polishing the

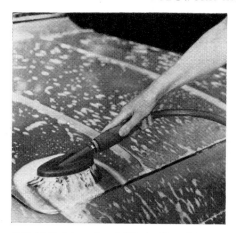

FIG. 11.2. A hose brush fitted with a shampoo dispenser in the handle is useful for a quick but thorough wash-down (Flexy). (*Right*) FIG. 11.3. A power drill fitted with a lambswool mop on a flexible backing pad gives a brilliant polish (Stanley-Bridges).

parts affected with penetrating oil may help to ward off further deterioration.

Anodized aluminium is widely used for radiator grilles and some other parts. This is immune to rust and corrosion due to dampness or atmospheric pollution, and requires only washing with soapy water. Do not clean this metal with dry rag, as it tends to scratch easily, and wax-polishing is unnecessary.

Stainless steel is much used for window and radiator surrounds, hub plates, strips and mouldings. The best grades (chrome nickel), used on luxury cars, have a brilliant gloss, are fully corrosion-resistant and require only washing. Cheaper grades known as chromium iron or chromium steel are used on many popular cars. These also need only washing in normal service, but sometimes show slight traces of corrosion. Chrome alloys can be successfully treated with ordinary metal polish.

CLEANING THE INTERIOR

Where carpets are fitted, it is important to brush out or vacuum-clean the car interior regularly, as sharp road grit, sand

and dirt will soon damage the fabric. Dirty carpets need a carpet shampoo, and their edges and fastenings should be inspected occasionally. Rubber mats can be cleaned with a household detergent or an upholstery cleaner.

Most popular cars are upholstered in some kind of p.v.c. plastics material, either plain or grained like leather. Rexine is also to be found, and some cars have seating of either a woven nylon cloth or p.v.c.-coated fabric, allowing air permeability. In the luxury class, real leather remains a favourite, though this is sometimes used only for the wearing surfaces on seats.

Vinyl and nylon materials are best cleaned with a damp cloth and a little toilet soap—not detergents. Imitation leather, with its grained surface, is better treated with a soft brush and a proprietary upholstery cleaner (this applies also to the grained plastics hoods used for some convertibles). Stubborn marks on plastics can usually be shifted if a little ammonia is added to the water.

Natural leather rarely requires attention, but dirt can be removed with a damp cloth or ordinary soapsuds. The recommended treatment for preserving leather, however, is occasional cleaning with saddle soap, which is sold by shoe shops and leather shops.

There are many older cars with cloth headlinings, which always become stained and dirty due to traffic haze, exhaust fumes, tobacco smoke, hair oil and so on. They are difficult to clean and the best that can be done as a rule is to brush well with a soapy solution or a carpet shampoo. Avoid getting the headlining really wet, or it may come away from the roof and cause rust marks to show through the material.

Stain Removal. Chemical stains need to be approached with particular care. A golden rule is always to remove them as quickly as possible; old stains are sometimes impossible to remove without harming the material. Leather and plastics materials are generally easy to clean, using soap, methylated spirits or white spirit.

On fabrics such as cloth seats, seat covers and carpets, more care is needed. Fruit stains can be washed off with warm water; if they are stubborn, try ammonia or carbon tetrachloride (obtainable from chemists). Grease marks, chocolate, ice cream stains and lipstick stains also respond to carbon tetrachloride. Spilt tea and coffee should be washed off while fresh; ammonia may be used on an old stain.

Blood should be washed off while fresh with cold water—hot water will set the stain. Tar spots are best treated with a proprietary tar solvent. Ink spots can be removed by an ink eradicator (sold by stationers) or with ammonia if fresh. Paint spots must be dissolved with an appropriate paint thinner.

BODY REFINISHING

Body repainting is very much a job for the professional, and though many service stations offer respraying among their services it is better to go to a specialist firm where proper spraying facilities and trained operators are available. The amateur's efforts are best restricted to touching up scrapes and scratches, and painting over minor repair work.

Most modern cars are sprayed in the factory with a chemical rust inhibitor and then given several coats of paint. The professional refinisher will use the appropriate process—cellulose, air-drying synthetic enamel, stoving (heat-baked) enamel, or acrylic-resin paint—to obtain results approaching the original finish. The amateur must make do with paints as closely approximating the original as possible.

For touching in scratches and blemishes, some car manufacturers supply small paint kits or paint pencils in correct matching shades, and there are also aerosols of spray paints on the market. Where the finish has been marked by a paint or chemical stain but is not damaged, it is often possible to clean it by treatment with rubbing-down compound (see below) or a body cleaner.

Brush Painting. For more ambitious work, tins of brushing cellulose and synthetic enamel are available. It is essential that the paints used are compatible both with each other and with the original finish. Thus, for cellulosing, a primer, primer-surfacer, undercoat and finish coat may all be required, and the paint manufacturer's recommendations should be followed in selecting them.

Cellulose will cause bubbling or lifting if applied over certain types of synthetics, while acrylics may not be suitable for application over cellulose. Paint suppliers are always ready to advise on such matters, and they can also assist with the important question of colour matching. New paint often fades or darkens as it weathers, and what may appear an exact match when new can be two different shades after a period of exposure to the weather.

Good results cannot be obtained unless careful attention is given to preparation of the surface. If only the finishing coat has been scratched, clean off all dirt, grease and loose paint with white spirit, then touch in with a paint pencil or small, soft brush. If bare metal has been exposed, a suitable primer must first be applied to provide a paint key and inhibit rust formation.

Where the exposed metal is rusty, corroded or roughened, more preparation is needed. Light rust is best removed by rubbing down with a medium grade of wet-or-dry abrasive paper, until the metal is bright and free from pitting. More severe rusting may be wire-brushed and then removed with a liquid rust remover or treated with a zinc-rich cold-galvanizing preparation. The latter "kills" the rust and prevents further rust formation, fills in the depression and provides a suitable key for any kind of paint.

For a perfect surface, rub down after cleaning with a fine grade of wet-or-dry abrasive used with plenty of water. Rubbing-down compound, a very finely abrasive cutting paste, is useful for preparing an existing paint surface and will not scratch the surrounding finish.

To ensure that the new paint surface is level with the old, a paste-type "stopping" compound should be used. The surface, cleaned and dried, is first given a coat of primer. When this is dry, the stopping is

applied. Build it up in layers, allowing each to dry before appyling the next, until the surface is slightly above the surrounding finish; after hardening, rub down level with wet-or-dry abrasive (Fig. 11.4).

For cellulosing, at least two coats of undercoat or primer-surfacer are desirable, each being smoothed after drying hard with wet-or-dry paper, used wet. The finish coat is best applied with a very soft camelhair brush, sold for the purpose. Spread a fairly full coat quickly, without attempting to "brush out". If required, this too can be rubbed down and a second coat applied to obtain a better result.

For synthetic enamels, use an ordinary soft-bristle paintbrush, and apply rather less paint. It can be brushed out to give an even finish, but the enamel quickly starts to dry. Again, two finish coats may be required.

When hard-dry, the new finish may be carefully polished with rubbing-down compound or ordinary metal polish, to cut back brush marks and merge the new paint into the old. Finally, the area should be wax-polished.

Spray Painting. Effective results can be obtained with a small spray gun, but its use needs some degree of skill, and spraying is more suitable for large areas such as complete panels than touch-in jobs. After cleaning up the affected area and dealing with rust, apply a primer and cellulose stopping as already described. The next step is to mask all the surrounding areas, including glasswork, with sheets of newspaper and masking tape.

The professional sprayer pays careful attention to mixing and thinning of the paint to obtain the correct viscosity, to adjustment of the air pressure, and to adjustment of the atomizing jet. The amateur has more limited control over the job, but reasonable results will be obtained if a spraying grade of paint is obtained, a little thinners used, and the spray-gun manufacturer's instructions obeyed.

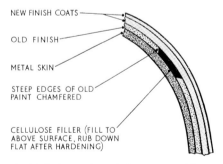

NEW FINISH COATS

OLD FINISH

METAL SKIN

STEEP EDGES OF OLD PAINT CHAMFERED

CELLULOSE FILLER (FILL TO ABOVE SURFACE, RUB DOWN FLAT AFTER HARDENING)

FIG. 11.4. Stages in painting over a chip on bodywork finish to give an imperceptible repair. Sharp edges around the chip are cut back with abrasive paper before filling.

The atmosphere should be dust-free, and it helps to dampen the workshop floor. Carry out practice spraying on an odd piece of material before starting the actual work, the idea being to use the spray-gun in controlled, even sweeps across the work surface. Two or three undercoats will be required, each being rubbed down with fine-grade abrasive when dry, and then three finishing coats. When hard-dry, the final coat can be polished with a little rubbing-down compound on a piece of cloth, washed and dried, then wax-polished.

Wood Refinishing. Wood is used internally for facias and door cappings, and externally as battening on some estate cars. The finish is usually thin, to give full effect to the grain, and it may wear off in time. It is difficult for the amateur to restore a perfect finish to internal wood trim, and probably the best method is to strip the remains of the old finish with fine glasspaper, smooth the bare wood with a fine grade of cabinet-maker's glasspaper, then apply a thin coat of cellulose-based wood finish or varnish.

For exterior trim, a good marine varnish or clear polyurethane wood finish is best, again after glasspapering. Several thin coats, carefully "flowed" on with a varnish brush, give a high-gloss, durable finish.

BODY REPAIRS

Major external repairs are generally beyond the scope of the amateur, but it is often possible to make good minor damage without specialized equipment. There are two main types of damage: that caused by impact and that caused by corrosion.

Impact Damage. Minor damage is often confined to dents, to which thin-sheet panelling is especially prone. Unless the denting is simple and easy to get at, it is unlikely that knocking it out will prove very satisfactory; panel-beating calls for specialized skill and equipment. If such work is tackled, use a rubber or rawhide mallet in preference to a hammer, with perhaps a shaped hardwood block as a dolly to fit the curvature required. The panel should be backed with something resilient while being hammered, such as a sandbag or a hot-water bottle filled with earth.

While reasonably satisfactory work may be done in this way, the average motorist will find it easier to deal with a small dent by filling it and painting over. One suitable filler is plastic metal, also known as metallized putty filler. This is applied like putty, but sets hard and can be sanded down and painted with any kind of paint. A thin piece of shaped wood can be used to mould the profile required, and the putty trued up when hard by rubbing with emery paper wrapped over the same mould (Fig. 11.5).

An alternative material that is easy to use is cold-setting resin filler of the kind supplied with glass-fibre repair kits (described below). Equal quantities of the resin paste and the hardener are mixed thoroughly and applied in the same way as metal putty. This filler has excellent adhesion and can be applied over a rusty area. When set hard, it may be sanded down and painted to give a perfect finish.

Corrosion Damage. If rust on bodywork is neglected, it can soon corrode large areas of panelling and other parts. The lower parts of doors, wings and the rear apron are particularly vulnerable, but rust can also eat through the metal at joints, under door-frame bottoms, under plated strips and beadings, and under valances. Professional repairers normally deal with such damage by welding, but this is outside the scope of most amateurs. If the damage is in an inconspicuous position, one repair method is to fix a metal patch over the hole or split, securing it with rivets, bolts or self-tapping screws.

A far neater job, and one that is just as effective, is obtained by using a glass-fibre repair kit. These kits usually contain a polyester resin paste, a powder filler, a liquid catalyst which causes the resin to set hard, and a quantity of glass-fibre mat or scrim material. The resin alone, or mixed with filler, can be used to fill dents and splits. It does not shrink or crack, even when applied thickly.

The glass-fibre mat or scrim is intended for the repair of larger holes and rusted-out areas, providing a reinforcement which virtually restores the original strength of the panel. The hole may first have to be blanked off with a piece of waxed card, and then the mat and resin are used according to the instructions supplied with the kit (Fig. 11.6). The job should be left for about 24 hours to harden before being sanded down and painted.

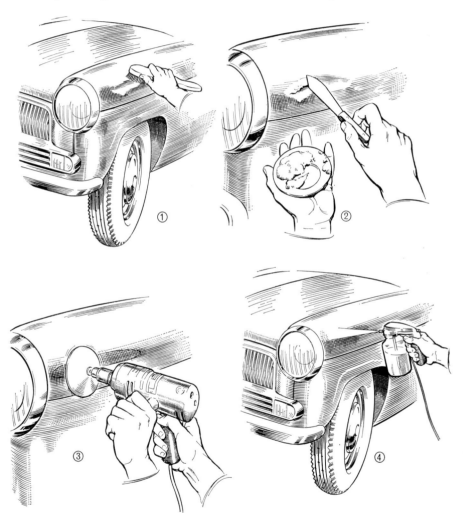

FIG. 11.5. Filling in a dent with cellulose filler or plastic metal. (1) The dent is wire-brushed to remove loose paint and rust. (2) Filler is applied with a putty knife and built up to stand proud of the surface. (3) After drying hard, the patch is sanded down level. (4) Undercoat and finishing coats are applied by brush or sprayer.

Professional Repairs. While minor impact damage can be corrected by the methods already mentioned, it is always best to have a car checked over by engineers in the event of its being involved in a collision, even though external damage may appear slight. This is because there is always a risk of distortion with bodies of monocoque construction, which may seriously affect steering, suspension and road-holding, the alignment of mechanical components, braking effectiveness, or the closure of doors.

A well-equipped repair shop has sets of pulling, pushing, and stretching or re-forming equipment, operated either manually or by hydraulic or pneumatic power. With these and special gauges it is possible to force a distorted structure back into correct alignment in all planes, checking against jigs to ensure that it is dimensionally correct. Faulty structural members and skin panels can generally be replaced by manufacturers' spare parts, though this may not be possible where the car is old or of foreign make. Such repair work is, of course, expensive and usually an "insurance job."

Skilled panel beaters can work wonders with coachwork repairs, using special tools

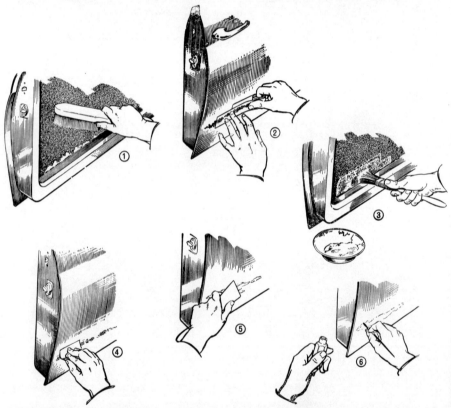

FIG. 11.6. Using glass fibre to repair a rusted door panel. (1) All rust, grease, dirt and loose paint is cleaned off. (2) Rusted holes are sealed over with strips of cellulose tape. (3) The glass fibre is applied to the back of the door in accordance with instructions in the kit. (4) After setting, the cellulose tape is removed and filler used to fill external blemishes. (5) The patch is then scraped and sanded down to give a smooth finish. (6) Finally, the patch is painted by brush or sprayed as in Fig 11.5, to blend with the surrounding finish.

FIG. 11.7. Methods of fixing interior door handles. (1) A spring clip behind the escutcheon engages in a groove in the handle shank. It can be pressed out of position with a flat piece of metal. (2) Fixing by a steel pin passing through the handle shank. Press the escutcheon inwards to expose and withdraw the pin. (3) The handle is secured by a sunken retaining screw.

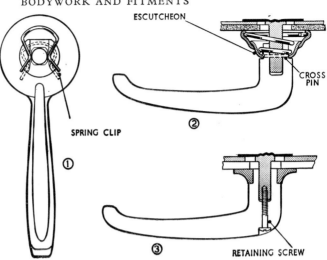

and techniques. Dents, for instance, may be hammered out with special hammers and dollies, the "flow" of the metal being precisely controlled. It is possible to shrink a stretched portion by thickening the metal with carefully graduated and direct hammer blows. Less expert operators obtain similar results by heating the affected area with an oxyacetylene flame, and then quenching it suddenly with damp asbestos pulp.

Mechanical Repairs. Apart from replacing damaged accessories such as fog lamps, these are mainly a matter of dealing with door and window gear. Door handles and locks, hinges, bonnet locks, window raising gear and similar parts are best left alone if they are working properly, apart from a little regular lubrication.

Some door locks and hinges are provided with a small lubrication hole into which light oil should be injected. An effective way to lubricate a lock is to spread graphited penetrating oil on the key and use this to turn the lock several times. The door striker plates need a trace of light grease (candlegrease is better as it does not soil passengers' clothes), unless nylon jaws are fitted when no lubrication is required.

The details of door mechanisms vary and it is advisable to consult the manufacturer's workshop manual before attempting to dismantle or adjust such items. They can usefully be inspected, cleaned and lubricated at intervals, however. To gain access to these parts it is normally necessary to remove the inside handles and trim panels.

The method of removing a door or window handle may not be apparent until the collar or escutcheon plate surrounding the shaft is prised away from the handle (Fig. 11.7). On some cars the collar is spring-loaded and on being pushed inwards will reveal a pin that passes through the shaft. This can be tapped out with a nail. In some cases the trim material may have to be pressed inwards to expose the fastening, while in others the collar has a hole and can be rotated to expose the pin through this. Another fastening device is a spring circlip which fits in a groove behind the collar and can be sprung out of position with a piece of thin metal or plastic.

The trim panel on the door may be secured by plated screws, but a more common method is to use concealed spring clips mounted around the back edge of the panel which fit into holes in the door. The

263

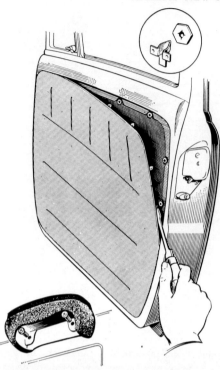

FIG. 11.8. Most door trim panels are secured by concealed spring clips which fit into holes around the door frame, and can be prised out with a screwdriver. Armrests may be fixed to the trim itself or secured by concealed screws.

tapping screws, may have to be removed first. The window should be lowered as far as possible, and the rubber window stop removed, to allow the glass to be lifted out. The guide channels can then be cleaned and new felt or sealing material glued into place. Sprinkle the new felt with french chalk or talcum powder to act as a lubricant.

Windscreens and other fixed lights are held in channelling of special self-sealing type. This is obtainable from factors and is applied with the aid of a sealing compound. Water leakage into a car sometimes occurs through a window surround, and repairs can be made with flexible sealing compound or an adhesive to re-seal unstuck rubber.

Door locks give little trouble, but a door may develop rattles or fail to close properly because of wear on the lock and striker, wear on the hinges, or slight distortion of the door frame. Most striker plates on modern cars can be adjusted to take up such wear. The screws securing the striker should be loosened and the striker tapped gently to move it slightly inwards. Then tighten the screws and check the closure of the door. The adjustment must be made precisely, and it is important to retighten the screws very securely (Fig. 11.10).

Interior Repairs. Renovation of upholstery is best entrusted to skilled trimmers, but tears in seats, squabs and headlinings can be repaired by the careful owner, such work being made easier if a trimmer's semi-circular needle is available. Seats which have sagged can often be improved by stuffing with fresh kapok or fitting a foamed rubber insert of suitable thickness. Spring cases are rarely used in modern cars, and the foamed cushioning and rubber webs now in use are not difficult to repair or replace (Fig. 11.11).

Headlinings present more of a problem. Cloth linings are usually stuck on or sewn in, and may tear if any attempt is made to remove them. The safest way to deal with

panel can be removed by prising it free a little at a time with a screwdriver (Fig. 11.8). On an older car the spring clips may be rusted and difficult to move, in which case the panel should be prised away enough to apply penetrating oil to the clips. After a short while it should be possible to pull off the panel without breaking the clips.

An amateur can do little to repair faulty window gear, the assembly usually being replaced as a complete unit (Fig. 11.9). (A likely cause of trouble on an old car is worn teeth on the quadrant that is operated by the winding handle.)

A loose or rattling window is usually due to worn felt in the guide channels. The window surround, which is held by self-

these is to sew or stick on patches and use adhesive to refit material that has become torn or detached. Plastic headlinings are often clipped to rods in the roof and are easier to remove, but replacement may need more than one pair of hands.

The usual cause of trouble with fabric carpets is that holes are worn where the driver's heels dig in. The simplest and most satisfactory repair is to attach a square of rubber to the worn area with a suitable adhesive.

FITMENTS

All cars are supplied with fitments such as driving mirrors and sun visors, while interior heaters, radios, seat belts and so on are often available as extras. In addition, there is a vast range of proprietary accessories which can be bought and fitted by the motorist. Some of these, including electrical accessories, instruments and performance equipment, are discussed in other chapters, but certain fitments call for consideration here.

Safety Belts. Cars must now be supplied with built-in anchorage points for seat belts, and there is no difficulty in fitting belts of the type preferred by the owner. Where such mountings are not provided, some care is needed in fitting these, since the strength of the belts will be no more than that of their anchorages. The fitting instructions supplied by the belt manufacturer must be correctly carried out. They usually entail some dismantling of the trim and drilling of the structure. High-tensile steel bolts and nuts must be used. If the floor is thin due to corrosion, an extra-large anchor plate should be fitted.

Heaters. Some cars have a heater fitted as standard equipment, while in others provision is made for fitting one as an

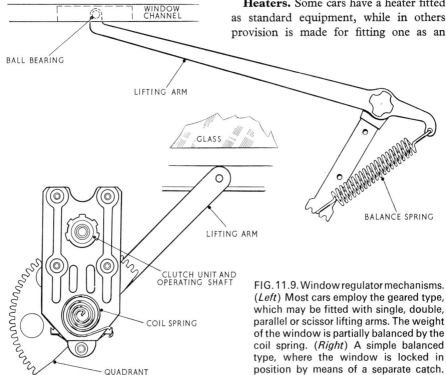

FIG. 11.9. Window regulator mechanisms. (*Left*) Most cars employ the geared type, which may be fitted with single, double, parallel or scissor lifting arms. The weight of the window is partially balanced by the coil spring. (*Right*) A simple balanced type, where the window is locked in position by means of a separate catch.

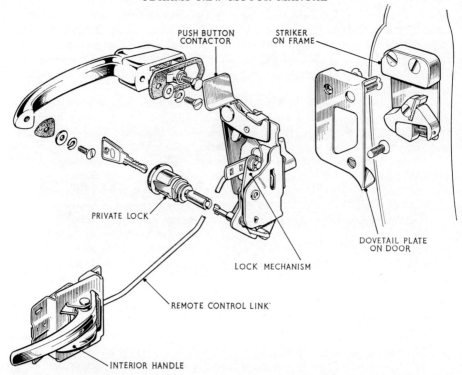

PUSH BUTTON
CONTACTOR

STRIKER
ON FRAME

PRIVATE LOCK

DOVETAIL PLATE
ON DOOR

LOCK MECHANISM

REMOTE CONTROL LINK

INTERIOR HANDLE

FIG. 11.10. Construction of a door lock, with push-button operation and a private lock. Lock parts should be kept greased and the lock oiled. The striker can be adjusted to compensate for looseness due to wear, after loosening the three fixing screws.

optional extra. There are also heaters on the market which can fairly easily be fitted to almost any modern car (Fig. 11.12). Generally it is best to have this item fitted by a service station, but the owner can do a successful job if the fitting instructions are followed carefully.

There are two types: the recirculating heater, which warms and circulates air already in the car, and the fresh-air heater, which draws in a constant flow of fresh air through a bonnet grille, warms it and passes it into the interior. The usual principle is to pass hot water from the engine cooling system through a small radiator, over which the incoming air flows. For increasing the air flow when the car is stationary or moving slowly, a booster fan driven by an electric motor is

provided, and to allow the system to function as a cold-air ventilator during the summer a tap is often fitted in the heater hose connection which shuts off the hot water supply.

Special tappings may be provided in the cylinder block to which the heater connections may be made, otherwise connections must be made into the radiator hoses. The hot water is extracted from a point between the water pump and the thermostat, so that the heater will work even when the thermostat is closed, and is returned to the cooling system by a connection at the bottom of the cylinder block or in the lower hose. Trouble sometimes occurs through an air lock forming in the system after the radiator has been drained and refilled. In this case the upper heater

FIG. 11.11. Details of a modern front seat. This type gives long service, but it is not difficult to replace the foam rubber cushion or the rubber webbing straps which support it.

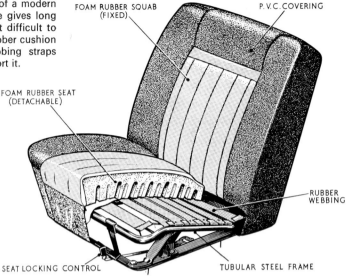

FOAM RUBBER SQUAB (FIXED)

P.V.C. COVERING

FOAM RUBBER SEAT (DETACHABLE)

RUBBER WEBBING

SEAT LOCKING CONTROL

TUBULAR STEEL FRAME

hose must be disconnected and the engine run for a time, until all air in the heater system has been bled off by the flow of water from the open hose.

Electrically, it is only necessary to connect the fan motor to the ignition switch, or to an accessory terminal that is controlled by the ignition switch.

As the addition of a heater increases the capacity of the cooling system, it is often desirable to fit a different thermostat which operates at a higher temperature; the car manufacturer will advise on this point. Once fitted, however, a heater normally needs no maintenance except occasional attention to the tightness of hose joints and the condition of the hoses. If the heater's output falls below normal, a likely cause is a faulty thermostat, unless the water tap has not been fully opened.

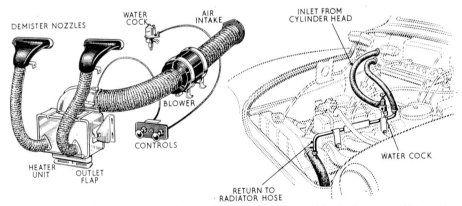

DEMISTER NOZZLES

WATER COCK

AIR INTAKE

INLET FROM CYLINDER HEAD

BLOWER

CONTROLS

WATER COCK

HEATER UNIT

OUTLET FLAP

RETURN TO RADIATOR HOSE

FIG. 11.12. Installing an accessory heater. (*Left*) A popular type of fresh-air heater which can be installed in various positions under the instrument facia or parcel shelf. Closing the water cock enables the heater to distribute unheated air during the summer months. (*Right*) Water pipe connections for a recirculating-type heater. The heater is fed from the cylinder block and the return pipe is connected into the radiator lower hose.

Windscreen Wipers and Washers.
Wipers are, of course, fitted on all cars, while the screen washer has become accepted as a standard item of equipment and is fitted to most current models. Electrical wiper operation is considered in Chapter 10 (see page 244).

Vacuum-operated wipers are still found on a number of older cars. These work from the suction (vacuum) present in an engine's induction system when it is running, and in some cases are supplied from a vacuum pump incorporated with the fuel pump. Some cars are also fitted with a vacuum reservoir tank to supplement operation when the engine is running under heavy load and the normal vacuum is much reduced.

Failure or slow operation of a vacuum wiper is nearly always due to loss of vacuum from the system; in other words, air is getting into the system through leakage between the wiper unit and the engine manifold. It may be possible to find and correct the leakage; otherwise the best remedy is to replace the tubing, which can prove difficult if it passes up to the top of the screen behind the headlining. If the wiper works in one direction only, the trouble is likely to be caused by wear on its valve mechanism or paddle.

With all types of windscreen wipers, it is desirable to replace the wiper blades annually, as worn blades tend to smear the screen. On most cars the arm makes a push fit on a splined spindle-drum.

Screen washers may be manually operated by a plunger pump, electrically operated, or vacuum operated by engine suction (Fig. 11.13). The manual type is efficient and easiest to install, fitting instructions being provided with the kit. The washer control should be mounted close to the wiper switch, and the water container can be fitted in the engine compartment or above the parcel shelf, keeping the run of tubing as short as possible.

Clean water should always be used for refilling the container, as the fine-bore jets are easily clogged, and for the same reason care should be taken not to smear wax polish over the jets. If a jet becomes

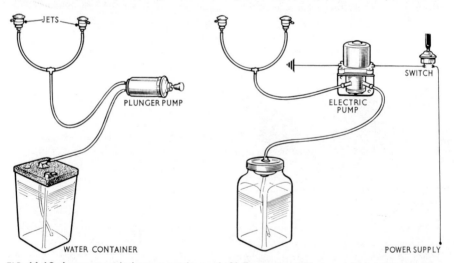

FIG. 11.13. Accessory windscreen washers. (*Left*) Easy to install in any vehicle, this type has a plastics water container, a manual pump mounted on the dashboard, and two jets connected with plastics tubing. (*Right*) Kits are on the market for converting a manual screen washer to electric operation. The pump is located in any convenient position on the engine bulkhead and the switch replaces the manual pump control.

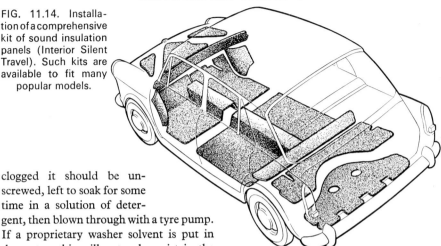

clogged it should be un-screwed, left to soak for some time in a solution of deter-gent, then blown through with a tyre pump. If a proprietary washer solvent is put in the water, this will not only assist in the removal of oily film on the screen but will act as an anti-freeze agent in cold weather. Do not put engine anti-freeze in the washer —it is likely to attack the paint finish around the screen surround.

Undersealing. Many cars today are sprayed with bituminized paint on the underbody at the factory, which acts as an effective underseal and prevents corrosion. Other cars can be similarly protected by spraying or brushing on a thick layer of rubberized paint, which also provides useful sound insulation. This material is available for do-it-yourself application, but it is a messy job.

Undersealing should be carried out as soon as possible while the car is brand new, as the surfaces treated must be perfectly clean and the work must be done before any rusting has started. A service station will steam-clean the underside if it is dirty, and dry it thoroughly before spraying on the underseal.

Sound Insulation. In many cars of integral chassis-body construction, in which stressed metal floor and roof panels form the main structural elements, road noise is sometimes audible as a persistent drumming. Engine noise, too, can be a nuisance in a small car. Road noise may be amplified by such things as the suspension

coil springs, or by an empty area inside the car such as the boot acting as a sound box.

With recent models, manufacturers have begun to pay more attention to this prob-lem, covering the dash and front floor panels with layers of felt and plastic foam. Other parts of the body may still transmit a good deal of noise, however, and a remarkable improvement in running quiet-ness can often be obtained by fitting addi-tional sound insulating pads.

A cheap way to achieve this is to buy some rubberized felt or vinyl-coated foam plastic, cut this to size with the aid of paper templates, and glue it on with a suitable "power" adhesive. Each area must be thoroughly cleaned and dried before the material is stuck into place, and care must be taken not to obstruct air intakes, drain pipes, wires and moving parts. The main areas to cover are the bonnet lid and engine bulkhead (use non-inflammable material here), the boot lid and the floor. For a more effective job the roof, side panels and doors should also be dealt with, though this work may prove more difficult.

There are also kits of ready-cut insula-ting panels on the market designed for easy fitting, practically all popular models of recent years being catered for. A typical installation is shown in Fig. 11.14.

CHAPTER 12

BUYING AND RUNNING A CAR

CHOOSING one's car is essentially a personal matter, and most motorists have definite ideas on what type of vehicle they prefer. Some general notes on buying a new or used model may prove useful, however, particularly where economic aspects are concerned.

Of the various types of car available today, the great majority are saloons. These can be classified into (a) small cars up to 1,000 c.c. engine capacity; (b) light cars of 1,000-1,500 c.c.; (c) medium cars of 1,500-2,000 c.c.; (d) large cars over 2,000 c.c. The size, equipment and carrying capacity of cars in the same class are often similar, but performance, quality of construction and running costs vary more widely.

Manufacturers frequently offer several versions of each basic model. The cheapest will be the standard model. The de luxe model is usually identical mechanically but has refinements of trim and extra fitments such as a heater and clock. While such items can be bought separately and fitted to a standard model, this often proves more expensive in the end than buying the fully equipped de luxe type. In some cases an alternative model with a more powerful engine is offered, often designated Super. A recent trend is to offer a still more expensive version called a *grand touring* or G.T. This is fitted with an engine modified to give improved performance, usually accompanied by superior braking and suspension, and is designed for the motorist who seeks the characteristics of a sports car allied with saloon comfort.

From the buyer's point of view, the principal differences between the four classes of saloon are as follows. The small saloons in class (a) are generally low-priced, cheap to run, maintain good resale value and have adequate performance, but are limited as to their equipment and accommodation. The light cars in class (b) are more expensive, but have better carrying capacity as well as the other advantages of class (a). They are especially suitable for family use, and this also applies to the medium cars of class (c).

The latter are heavier, larger and more durable; they cost more to buy and operate, while repairs and overhauls are likely to be more expensive, but they offer advantage in comfort, quietness and refinement. The large cars of class (d) are in the luxury category and tend to be popular mainly among businessmen. Cars of over 1,500 c.c. capacity mostly depreciate in resale value to a much more marked extent than the smaller models.

Purchasing a New Car. The large motor manufacturers appoint *distributors* to act as primary selling agents for their products and *main dealers* to serve specified areas. Normally, both these agents handle that manufacturer's vehicles exclusively, backed by works-trained staff and extensive service and repair facilities. In addition, the manufacturer appoints a large number of local agents, who often handle a variety of makes. One can order a new car from any of these types of trader with confidence, knowing that they will give full service both during and after the sale.

While one may have a clear idea of the type of car that suits one's requirements, it is often difficult to decide which of several similar models is preferable. A recommended aid to selecting a new car is to study the road test reports published by the motoring magazines. The best of these give an impartial assessment of the car's behaviour under exacting conditions, with useful information about dimensions, capacities, maintenance requirements and so forth.

Performance Figures. The technical data included in most road test reports can prove useful when models in the same price range are being compared. Fuel and oil consumption and maximum speed figures are of obvious significance. However, high cruising speed is more important than maximum attainable speed to the motorist who needs to make long, fast journeys. For commuters and city motorists the question of acceleration is perhaps more important. The road tests usually give figures for (a) acceleration through the gears, that is the time taken for the car to reach, say, 20, 40 and 60 m.p.h. from rest, and (b) top-gear acceleration, the time taken for the car to reach its cruising speed from a low speed in top gear.

Where these figures show that a car has good acceleration through the gears but relatively poor top-gear acceleration, the inference is that it has a fairly small engine in relation to its total weight. Driving it will entail frequent gear-changing, and it will be more suitable for congested roads than long-distance operation. Conversely, where there is fairly sluggish acceleration through the gears coupled with good top-gear performance, the car is probably heavy but has a flexible engine—a characteristic of six-cylinder family cars. Good figures in both categories indicate a powerful engine in relation to the total weight (but fuel consumption may be high). Poor acceleration in both respects suggests that the car is "overbodied": the engine power is barely adequate for the total weight. A high figure for B.H.P. per ton laden is

indicative of lively performance, while a high top-gear speed per 1,000 engine r.p.m. suggests that the engine will be running well inside the limits of its capacity at normal cruising speeds and should therefore have a long life. Another significant figure is the area swept by drum brake linings. The larger this area, the more effective will be heat dissipation from the linings and the longer their life.

While all these points help in making a final choice, it is essential also to make a check list of one's personal requirements and see whether the car under consideration matches up to these. Do not forget to include the width and length of your garage; there must at the least be room enough to enable you to enter and leave the car when it is standing inside.

CHECKING THE COST

Motorists quite often know exactly what they require in the matter of a car's technical specification, yet can be remarkably ill-informed about the expenditure it will involve. After collecting certain essential figures, a few calculations should give a reasonable approximation of the cost of running any particular model.

Fixed Costs. Begin by writing down the cash price of the car you have in mind or else the maximum price envisaged, and estimate the annual mileage you will drive. Then make a list of the annual fixed charges that will be incurred whether the car is actually on the road or not. These are as follows:

1. Motor vehicle licence.
2. Driving licence.
3. Rent of garage or rates payable on your private garage.
4. Insurance premium (get a comprehensive policy for a new car).
5. Depreciation. You can assume that the market value of the average new car will diminish by 30 per cent in its first year, then 15 per cent in its second year, then 10 per cent each year afterwards.

271

(Regarding depreciation, the rates quoted are only approximate and vary according to the type of car, the mileage it covers, the condition in which it is maintained, etc. One can often obtain a better idea of how a particular model depreciates by checking the prices asked for second-hand specimens of varying age.)

Running Costs. Next, make a list of the running charges that will be incurred in a full year's operation. These are:

1. Petrol. The amount used annually will depend upon the car's consumption as well as the mileage run. Average consumption for a light car is 30 m.p.g., for a small car nearer 40 m.p.g.

2. Oil. Consumption of engine oil varies with different cars, but 800 miles per pint is a fair average.

3. Servicing and maintenance. If this is to be undertaken by a service station you can obtain their rates for servicing at different mileage intervals, the cost of materials used being extra. The cost of a monthly car wash might be added.

4. Repairs and replacements. These are naturally more difficult to forecast, but with a new car you can reckon on replacing the battery after two years and the sparking plugs after 10,000 miles, relining the brakes at 20,000 miles, fitting a new set of tyres at 25,000 miles and a new clutch a.d track-rod joints at 30,000 miles. The cost of these replacements is obtainable from a dealer, and can be averaged over three or four years.

5. Miscellaneous. Allow a few pounds to cover such items as anti-freeze, cleaning materials, lamp bulbs, wiper blades and small accessories.

If you now add the total of running costs to the total of fixed charges and then divide by the annual mileage, this will give the *cost per mile* for running your car. At low annual mileages (up to about 8,000) there is a considerable saving in using a small car with an economical engine. At high mileages (over 12,000) the small car's economy

in cost per mile is far less marked, and this is where the superior comfort and durability of a large car may make it a better buy.

BUYING A USED CAR

Many novices find it difficult to decide whether to buy a new or second-hand car when first taking to the road. Obviously, the price of a used car can represent a considerable saving on that of a new one, but this could well be cancelled out by expensive repairs and shorter life, to say nothing of the inconvenience of possible breakdowns.

If one plans to cover a mileage of say 12,000 miles a year or over, it will nearly always prove more economical to buy a new car, provided this is properly run-in and treated with care. For the many pleasure motorists who drive only a few thousand miles a year, however, a sound second-hand model can be economically attractive.

The best buy, if it can be afforded, is a one-owner car up to about two years old, which has run a modest mileage for its age, carries a guarantee and is offered by a reputable dealer. It is always safer to buy from a well-established firm with workshops where vehicles are overhauled before being put up for sale, than from dealers without service facilities. It is risky to buy from the shadier type of small dealer who may not be above disguising serious faults in a car, or from a private seller who may be honestly unaware that his car is in poor condition.

The advice already given on choosing a new car can be applied very largely when buying second-hand. It is often tempting to snap up a smart-looking car on offer at an attractive price. But has it the accommodation you need? And adequate performance? Are spare parts going to be available? Will it fit your garage? And above all, is it in sound condition, both structurally and mechanically?

It is this last question that needs your most careful attention. *Never be stampeded into buying a used car before it has been carefully checked.* If you are sufficiently knowledgeable, you can make a reasonably thorough examination yourself—and if the seller raises any objections, then look elsewhere for your car. Otherwise, you can get an expert friend to check it with you; or a garage may let you have the services of their mechanic for a small fee. An excellent alternative is to ask for an engineer's report from either the A.A. or the R.A.C. (you must, of course, be a member of the association concerned!).

Checking a Used Car. Assuming you make your own inspection, here is a list of the more important points to watch for (Fig. 12.1).

1. Start by examining the bodywork. If this seems neglected, the mechanism too may be in poor condition. If the bodywork is poor though the car runs well, remember that body repairs can often be far more expensive than replacing mechanical parts. And if the car has been repaired after serious crash damage, think hard before you buy. Previous damage may be revealed by looking carefully along the top, sides and ends of the body for signs of distortion or badly fitting doors, bonnet and boot cover, and at the panelling and underframe for signs of welding.

Check along the lower part and round doors and windows for signs of rusting— particularly the bottom edges of the doors. Rock the doors to see whether the hinges are worn and note whether they will close easily without heavy slamming. Check whether the window glass is discoloured, whether the windows wind up and down properly, and whether there are any traces of leakage through the window seals. Then look inside at the condition of the upholstery, floor covering, headlining and trim, and see whether the seats slide and lock properly on their runners.

2. Get underneath the car as far as you can. Look for signs of damage or corrosion on the underbody, oil leakage from the engine, gearbox and rear axle, water leaks from the radiator and lower hose, lack of lubrication in steering joints, universal joints and spring shackles, and rusting or burn-out of the exhaust pipe and silencer.

3. Examine the tyres, including the spare (this is often the worst). Considerable tyre wear is only to be expected on a used car, but it is as well to know whether replacements will soon be needed. If the tyres are cracked in the side walls and show heavy wear on the outer sides of the treads, this suggests that the previous owner has neglected the tyre pressures—and perhaps other servicing as well. Very uneven wear on the two halves of each front tread is a bad sign; either the wheels are out of alignment or else the body has been buckled slightly in a collision.

4. Check what tools are supplied. Probably some of the original kit will be missing, but you are entitled to expect a jack, a wheel nut wrench, and in appropriate cases a starter handle. Check that all lamps work with normal brilliance, not forgetting the brake lights. Switch on the ignition and see whether the warning lamps and instruments register.

5. Open the bonnet and look inside. If the engine is dirty and oily, the battery dirty or corroded, ignition cables greasy, loose or frayed, the fan belt worn or slack, or any other parts loose or damaged, you may take it that the previous owner has given little attention to the car. Rust marks around he engine joints betoken water leakage, oil streaks indicate a faulty sump joint or oil seals, and wet petrol on the carburettor bowl and petrol pump reveal fuel leakage. Look at the oil level on the engine dipstick. Black oil does not necessarily show anything amiss, but if the oil feels slightly gritty it is long past its time for renewal.

Next, if the car has a starter handle, use this to crank the engine with ignition off.

273

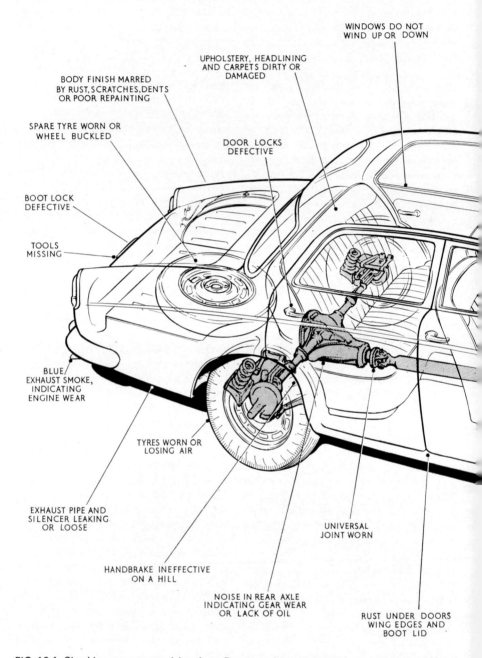

WINDOWS DO NOT
WIND UP OR DOWN

UPHOLSTERY, HEADLINING
AND CARPETS DIRTY OR
DAMAGED

BODY FINISH MARRED
BY RUST, SCRATCHES, DENTS
OR POOR REPAINTING

SPARE TYRE WORN OR
WHEEL BUCKLED

DOOR LOCKS
DEFECTIVE

BOOT LOCK
DEFECTIVE

TOOLS
MISSING

BLUE
EXHAUST SMOKE,
INDICATING
ENGINE WEAR

TYRES WORN OR
LOSING AIR

EXHAUST PIPE AND
SILENCER LEAKING
OR LOOSE

UNIVERSAL
JOINT WORN

HANDBRAKE INEFFECTIVE
ON A HILL

NOISE IN REAR AXLE
INDICATING GEAR WEAR
OR LACK OF OIL

RUST UNDER DOORS
WING EDGES AND
BOOT LID

FIG. 12.1. Checking over a second-hand car. Because of the doubtful history of many used cars, it is advisable to have a thorough check made before purchase. This is best carried out by an experienced mechanic, but if one is not available this illustration should be helpful as it indicates

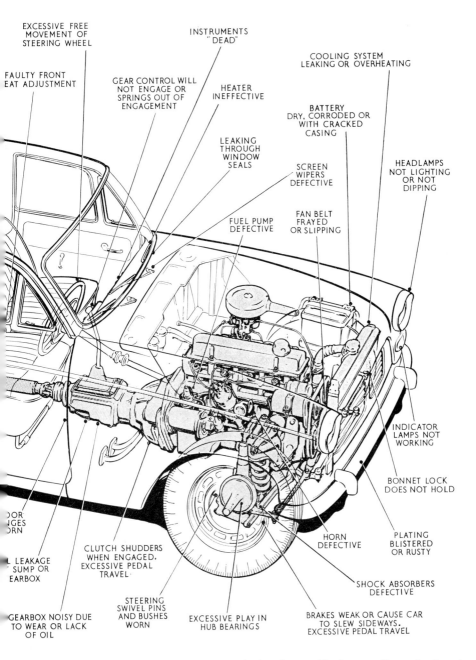

EXCESSIVE FREE
MOVEMENT OF
STEERING WHEEL

INSTRUMENTS
"DEAD"

COOLING SYSTEM
LEAKING OR OVERHEATING

FAULTY FRONT
EAT ADJUSTMENT

GEAR CONTROL WILL
NOT ENGAGE OR
SPRINGS OUT OF
ENGAGEMENT

HEATER
INEFFECTIVE

BATTERY
DRY, CORRODED OR
WITH CRACKED
CASING

LEAKING
THROUGH
WINDOW
SEALS

SCREEN
WIPERS
DEFECTIVE

HEADLAMPS
NOT LIGHTING
OR NOT
DIPPING

FUEL PUMP
DEFECTIVE

FAN BELT
FRAYED
OR SLIPPING

INDICATOR
LAMPS NOT
WORKING

BONNET LOCK
DOES NOT HOLD

)OR
JGES
)RN

L LEAKAGE
SUMP OR
EARBOX

CLUTCH SHUDDERS
WHEN ENGAGED.
EXCESSIVE PEDAL
TRAVEL

HORN
DEFECTIVE

PLATING
BLISTERED
OR RUSTY

SHOCK ABSORBERS
DEFECTIVE

GEARBOX NOISY DUE
TO WEAR OR LACK
OF OIL

STEERING
SWIVEL PINS
AND BUSHES
WORN

EXCESSIVE PLAY IN
HUB BEARINGS

BRAKES WEAK OR CAUSE CAR
TO SLEW SIDEWAYS.
EXCESSIVE PEDAL TRAVEL

the points that need attention. These points are further discussed in the text. If examination of the car suggests that it is in generally satisfactory condition, it should then be road-tested to check for mechanical and body noises at different speeds and under varying road conditions.

As each piston rises on its compression stroke, you should be able to detect a definite resistance, and this should be about the same for all cylinders. If the crankshaft rotates easily, with little resistance on compression strokes, the engine may be generally worn or its valves may be in poor condition. A noticeable lack of compression on one cylinder only usually indicates a sticking valve (or perhaps a broken spring).

6. At this point you should ask for the engine to be started, after first feeling the radiator tank to ensure that it is cold. Note whether the engine starts readily and whether much smoke is emitted from the exhaust pipe while it is idling. Clouds of blue smoke are nearly always a sign of oil being burned. If the smoke is more of a dirty black it indicates that the fuel mixture is over-rich and the carburettor controls need adjusting.

Unusual noises emanating from the engine as it warms up should be regarded with suspicion. It requires an expert to diagnose faults in this way, but it is not too difficult to detect the continuous rattle of a worn timing chain at the front of the engine, the noticeable clicking (varying with engine speed) from inside the rocker cover that tells of maladjusted valve rockers, or the rapid tapping sound of a worn piston slapping against its cylinder wall at the start of each power stroke. Beware of regular thudding or knocking sounds that appear to come from within the crankcase; they may be due to worn bearings and expensive to cure.

7. When the engine is warm you should request a trial run of at least ten miles, taking the wheel yourself. First, check the instruments. If fitted, the temperature gauge should be rising steadily towards normal heat, the oil pressure gauge registering full pressure, and the ammeter indicating a small "charge" current while the engine is idling. Where gauges are absent, at least check that the ignition and oil warning lights go out as soon as the engine speed is raised above idling. Before moving off, declutch and see whether the lower gears can each be engaged quietly and easily.

8. While driving, listen for signs of rough running from the engine at different speeds and when pulling under load (try to include one or two ascents and descents of steep hills in the route). Listen also for whine or noisy operation of the gearbox and final drive, and squeaks and rattles generally. Note whether the engine accelerates well, without flat spots, in each gear, and whether the instruments continue to register normally.

9. By driving deliberately over sunken manhole covers and bumpy patches you can get some idea of how the shock absorbers are coping and note whether shocks are transmitted back through the steering gear. There should be no feeling of excessive play in the steering, and if the wheel is held very lightly on a level road the car should tend to maintain its straight course. After making this test, and still holding the wheel lightly, apply the brakes hard and note whether the car tries to slew to one side as it is halted (indicating faulty brake adjustment). Listen for squealing or rubbing sounds when the brakes are applied (signs of worn shoe linings), and try at least one emergency stop. See whether the hand brake will hold the car on a steep incline.

10. Some other points to check on the test run: the clutch should engage smoothly and quietly; neither heavy pressure nor undue travel should be needed on clutch and brake pedals before they operate; the horn, indicators, wipers and headlamp dipswitch should work properly; the temperature gauge should not rise above normal and oil pressure should not fall too low; the engine should restart immediately after it has been switched off for a few minutes.

Before finally deciding to accept the car be sure to ask for the registration book and check all entries. Do not forget that a current vehicle test certificate should be handed over with the car if it is eligible for the M.O.T. test.

RUNNING IN A NEW CAR

Most motorists are aware that the engine in a new car needs to be carefully run in during the initial stage of its life. Many, however, do not realize that all the other moving parts on the car likewise require running in, or that this applies equally to a reconditioned engine or transmission component. So important is this matter that the makers of some expensive cars ensure that their vehicles are fully run in before being handed over to customers. As this service adds considerably to costs, mass-produced cars are given only preliminary running in and the completion of the process becomes the owner's responsibility.

Running in an engine is necessary because, however carefully the bearing surfaces may be finished, they are still very slightly rough. Viewed under a microscope, the surfaces of the cylinder walls, crankshaft journals and similar wearing parts appear to be made up of a series of hills and valleys, the largest variation being perhaps no more than one ten-thousandth of an inch. To sight and touch, these surfaces appear mirror-smooth, but when working rapidly together the roughness is sufficient to generate appreciable friction. During the car's running-in period, the projections on these working surfaces are gradually worn down until a perfectly smooth surface is obtained. If the bearings are heavily loaded during this process, excessive friction and heat will be produced, when there is some risk of the bearing metal melting and parts seizing up.

Some working parts may also change very slightly in shape as they heat up and expand. This may result in tight spots, and a certain amount of distortion can occur as the stresses induced in various parts during manufacture are gradually released due to

this repeated heating and cooling. Because of such distortion occurring during the early life of the engine, it is not uncommon for tight spots to develop after the first couple of hundred miles or so, in an engine which may have worked fairly freely when new.

A further consideration is that as the roughness of new parts reduces the tolerances between them, their lubrication is less effective which again tends towards overheating. If the lubricant in use is too thick or contaminated, this trouble will be worsened.

Apart from the engine, such components as gears, axles and hub bearings present a similar problem, but to a lesser extent because their loading is lighter and they run under far cooler conditions.

How to Run In. During this critical period, while the engine is operating it is making the rough working surfaces rub together—a form of lapping or polishing action. It used to be commonly recommended that a new car should be driven slowly (up to about 30 m.p.h. in top gear) during the first 200-300 miles, the speed being gradually raised over the next few hundred miles. Today, most manufacturers lay less emphasis on maintaining low speed than on the avoidance of heavy loading. This is because it has become appreciated that the successful lapping of metal surfaces depends upon a combination of high speed and light pressure.

The modern idea is to drive at moderate speeds while running in, but always with the throttle partly closed and with liberal use made of the gears. It is vital never to allow the engine to slog hard—up hills, accelerating from rest, or when moving slowly in heavy traffic. The handbook supplied with a new car invariably gives recommended speeds in each gear while running in, and these should not be exceeded.

If no handbook is available, as may be the case when a reconditioned engine is installed, the following running-in speeds are recommended:

First 200 *miles:* Maximum in top gear, 35 m.p.h. Maximum in third, 25 m.p.h.

From 200-500 *miles:* Maximum in top gear, 40 m.p.h. Maximum in third, 30 m.p.h.

From 500-1,000 *miles:* Maximum in top gear, 50 m.p.h. Maximum in third, 35 m.p.h.

In each case, the maximum speed quoted should not be held for more than a mile or so at a time, and should at first be permitted on downhill stretches only, when a small throttle opening can be used. If a starting handle is provided, the engine should occasionally be turned over manually, when the general stiffness or feeling of tight spots will indicate how running in is progressing. Watch the temperature gauge frequently while running in. If this rises above normal it indicates that the engine is tending to overheat, perhaps because of bursts of speed being held too long.

Lubrication. It has been pointed out that clean engine oil of the correct grade is essential for successful running in, and the sump dipstick must be checked regularly to ensure that the supply is kept up to the maximum mark. (Remember that oil assists in cooling as well as lubricating.) After about 500 miles of running, the oil must be drained, the sump flushed out, and fresh oil put in. Most manufacturers provide a free service at this mileage.

While carrying out this first service, the dealer should also check the tightness of the cylinder head and manifold nuts, which often loosen slightly during the early period of running, look for water leakage from the hoses and oil leakage from the sump, check the valve rockers for correct clearances, and check the distributor timing and contact breaker setting. Similarly, these items should be attended to when a reconditioned engine is being run in.

An aid to effective lubrication during running in is the use of an upper cylinder lubricant. This is a light oil which is added to the petrol in the tank and carried into the engine with the fuel mixture. It ensures that the pistons, rings and upper parts of the cylinders are lubricated during the first few minutes of warming up, when restricted bearing clearances may make it difficult for the engine oil to reach these parts. As engine lubrication is likely to be inefficient at low idling speeds during the running-in period, it is desirable to set the carburettor controls on a new car to give a fairly fast idle (600-800 r.p.m.), resetting for normal idling after running in has been completed.

Running in is a gradual process, and cars vary widely in the time they take to become fully run in. Indications that running in is nearing completion are when no tight spots can be detected by turning the starting handle, and smooth performance is obtained at all speeds without signs of overheating. This should occur by about 1,000 miles of running, but as much as 3,000-4,000 miles may be covered before an engine is free enough to deliver full power.

SERVICING AND MAINTENANCE

For any car, whether new or second-hand, to give economical, trouble-free running under all conditions, an essential requirement is thorough and *regular* attention to its needs. This is equally important from the aspect of roadworthiness—in modern traffic conditions a badly maintained vehicle is a danger to all. These periodic attentions can be grouped under (*a*) *servicing*—keeping the car in running order by replenishing its fuel, oil, water, tyre pressures etc., also lubrication and cleaning; and (*b*) *maintenance*—dealing with the progressive effects of wear and tear and taking steps to prevent further troubles developing.

Manufacturers constantly seek to make motoring easier, and such developments as long-lasting lubricants, improved oil filtration, sealed-in joints, self-lubricating bearings, sealed cooling systems and self-adjusting brakes and clutches have drastically reduced the average car's maintenance requirements. Even on the latest models, however, there is much that the conscientious owner can do to guard against trouble and ensure maximum performance year after year.

Part Exchanges. A matter that should be mentioned here is the steady trend towards fitting replacement parts in exchange for faulty ones, in preference to making repairs. This has partly come about because the enormous increase in motor traffic has left the repair trade with a dearth of skilled mechanics, while rising labour costs make repairs ever more expensive. There is also the fact that some parts of a car's mechanism are now made to standards of precision that make repair work often impracticable.

It is, of course, possible to fit a new unit in place of a damaged one, at least if the car is a recent model. The advantage of fitting an exchange unit, by which is meant a "used" part that has been restored to factory standards, is that for practical purposes it will give as good service as a new unit and the cost will be considerably less. All major manufacturers offer factory-reconditioned engines and transmission units, while proprietary components such as carburettors, starter motors, generators, relined brake shoes and steering parts are also available in this way. Provided the correct type of replacement is ordered and installation is competently carried out, reputable part-exchange units can be relied on for satisfactory service.

Manufacturers' Maintenance Schemes. Most manufacturers have also introduced special servicing arrangements for their cars, in collaboration with their appointed dealers. Some supply service vouchers for use at fixed mileages. These are handed to the dealer carrying out the

work, who is required to attend to all jobs itemised on the voucher and charge on the basis of standard fees laid down by the manufacturer. Others provide vouchers which are paid for by the owner, again covering specific attentions at fixed mileage intervals. The prepaid voucher is handed to the dealer, who will make no charge except for materials used.

The merit of these schemes is that they make it a simple matter for the owner to see that all service attentions are undertaken at the prescribed intervals. For the owner who prefers to do his own servicing, the car instruction book always includes full details of what must be done.

Maintenance Preparations. There is little advantage in tackling one's own maintenance unless properly equipped for the work. The first essential is some kind of service logbook in which details of all operations can be recorded (incidentally, the existence of a well-kept servicing record can be an asset when it comes to selling a car). The logbook should show the date and total mileage each time servicing is undertaken, with details of items dealt

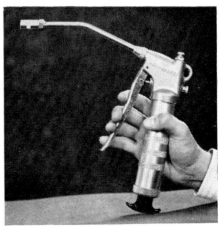

FIG. 12.2. General-purpose high-pressure grease gun, suitable for routine maintenance work (Wanner). The cheaper pom-pom type of grease gun is also very effective, but develops much less pressure than the lever-operated gun illustrated.

DRIP TRAY   FUNNEL   PRESSURE OIL CAN   POURER   TOPPING-UP PUMP

FIG. 12.3. Useful lubrication equipment. The pressure oil can should have a nylon or flexible metal spout for reaching awkward points. The topping-up pump is particularly handy for reaching inaccessible oil fillers on transmission units.

with and brands of oil, etc., used. If the total mileage at which the next service falls due is also recorded, this will act as a useful reminder.

For lubrication, a pressure-type grease gun (Fig. 12.2) and a long-spouted oil can (Fig. 12.3) are required; some owners like to have two or three guns for use with different types of oil or grease. An oil pourer and a flat container large enough to receive all oil drained from the engine sump will also be wanted (an old washing-up bowl or a petrol can cut in half may serve for the latter).

Special keys or spanners are often needed for the drain plugs on the sump, gearbox and final drive unit, and these may be included in the tool kit or can be bought from garages. A list of other useful tools for maintenance will be found in Chapter 15.

MAINTENANCE CHART

The chart on page 281 gives a schedule of routine maintenance attentions, typical of modern popular cars. It must be understood that there may be deviations from this in individual cases. For example, certain manufacturers no longer recommend changing the oil in transmission units at any time during the life of the car; they are satisfied with topping up the oil at intervals of 6,000 or even 12,000 miles. In a number of instances, chassis lubrication (greasing of steering joints, suspension, brake cables, etc.) is now dispensed with

almost entirely. The chart is designed to cover the requirements of most cars built within the last few years.

Some further notes on these maintenance items will be useful. Care of the battery, for instance, is vital to the performance of this component, and if the car is out of use for long periods one should make a practice of checking the electrolyte level at least once a month rather than every 1,000 miles.

The careful owner will make a general inspection of his car occasionally—say after carrying out the 6,000-mile maintenance check. Bolts and nuts should be tested for tightness and the engine and under-chassis parts cleaned. An oily engine can be wiped over with a cloth wetted in paraffin oil, then dried with a clean cloth, and particular care should be taken to see that the sparking plugs, ignition leads, distributor and coil are clean and dry.

This inspection and cleaning may bring to light evidence of leakages which should be remedied without delay. The radiator hoses are vulnerable to water leaks. Persistent leakage at their joints can often be cured by fitting new worm-drive hose clips, which give a better grip than the plain type, but if a hose itself is faulty the only cure is to replace it. Water leakage at the cylinder head joint will often be accompanied by oil leaks, and usually indicates a faulty gasket, though it is possible that a holding bolt has worked

TYPICAL MAINTENANCE CHART

EVERY 1,000 MILES
1. Check the level in each battery cell and top up with distilled water. Clean the battery top and connections.
2. Lubricate greasing points on the steering, front and rear suspension, brake cables etc. (mainly older models).

EVERY 3,000 MILES
Carry out the 1,000-mile items, and in addition:
3. Drain the engine sump and refill with fresh engine oil.
4. Check the fluid levels in the brake and clutch hydraulic reservoirs.
5. Check the oil levels in the gearbox and final drive unit and top up as required.
6. Lubricate the steering box on worm-gear systems.
7. Top up the dashpot oil on S.U. carburettors.
8. Check the fan belt tension. A maximum play of $\frac{1}{2}$ in. at the middle of the longest run is usually recommended.
9. With adjustable clutches, check the clutch release adjustment.
10. Check all wheel nuts for tightness, or else change wheels around if it is desired to equalize wear on tyre treads.

EVERY 6,000 MILES
Carry out the 3,000-mile items, and in addition:
11. Change the engine oil filter element.
12. Clean the element in gauze-type carburettor air cleaners. Change the oil in oil-bath air cleaners.
13. Clean the oil filler breather cap or crankcase ventilator.
14. Check the valve rocker clearances and adjust if necessary. A common clearance, with engine cold, is 0·012 in., but it is best to obtain manufacturers' own figures.
15. Clean the petrol pump filter.
16. Clean the float chamber and jets on Zenith and Solex carburettors.
17. Lubricate the distributor and check the contact breaker gap, which should be 0·014–0·016 in. on most popular cars.
18. Check the ignition timing and adjust if necessary.
19. Clean the sparking plugs, and check the points. The gap should be 0·025 in. for most modern cars.
20. Lubricate the water pump, where this attention is needed.
21. Drain the gearbox and refill with fresh transmission oil.
22. Drain the final drive unit and refill with hypoid oil.
23. Top up shock absorbers with the correct fluid, except in the case of sealed units.
24. Clean out the front hubs, repack with grease and adjust the bearings. On some models, grease the rear hubs.
25. Inspect the pads on disc brakes for wear.
26. Lubricate the throttle linkage, pedal bearings, door hinges, locks, bonnet catch, boot hinges and similar parts.
27. Have the front wheel alignment checked on a garage's precision track gauge.

EVERY 12,000 MILES
Carry out the 6,000-mile items, and in addition:
28. Lubricate the generator shaft bearing.
29. Lubricate the steering unit on rack-and-pinion systems.
30. Replace the filter element in paper-type air cleaners.
31. Clean the suction chamber, piston and float chamber on S.U. carburettors.
32. Flush out the radiator and cooling system.
33. Check the alignment of the headlamp main beams.
34. Fit a replacement set of sparking plugs.
35. Remove the engine sump and clean the oil pump strainer.
36. Check the rear spring U-bolts for security.

loose. The places to watch for oil leakage are mainly the engine sump joint, the rocker cover joint, and the front crankshaft seal. Again, judicious tightening of bolts may effect a cure, otherwise the answer is to fit a new gasket or seal.

Petrol leakage can occur only in the supply system, and a weak point here is the cover over the petrol pump filter. Regular removal of this cover for the purpose of cleaning the filter may presently result in damage to the cork washer, which should then be replaced.

Lubrication is a straightforward job, yet there are right and wrong methods of going about it. Always clean round a filler hole or greasing point before lubrication, and never use dirty oil or grease. It is a mistake to over-lubricate, and manufacturers often specify the number of strokes of the oil gun to be applied to an oiling point. Otherwise, one should stop as soon as the oil or grease begins to exude from the joint.

Grease nipples contain a one-way valve in the form of a spring-loaded ball. If this becomes choked with dirt, the gun will have no effect. Gently probing inside the nipple with a piece of wire usually clears this trouble, but if not a piece of cloth can be stretched over the nipple before the gun is applied. Enough pressure should then be produced to force the grease into the joint. If the body of a nipple breaks off, the stub can be removed by using the tang end of a file to unscrew it, and a replacement nipple screwed in.

If a used car is bought on which maintenance has been neglected, such items as locks, hinges and control linkages may be very stiff or even seized-up. The remedy is to inject penetrating oil, leave this to soak until the stiffness has been overcome, and then lubricate the part with the appropriate oil or grease.

Engine Tune-up. A certain amount of wear and tear develops in the car's moving parts after a period of running, while dirt and deposits of various kinds build up, and in consequence the normal standard of performance begins to suffer. Acceleration and pulling power drop off, fuel consumption increases, and such troubles as starting difficulty, overheating and rough running may appear. The work required to restore the normal performance is known as a "tune-up" and in the Maintenance Chart is covered by items 11-19.

It will be seen that tuning amounts to cleaning and adjusting certain parts on the engine and in the ignition and fuel systems. A regular tune-up, carefully carried out, will ensure that the car's original performance is maintained for many thousands of miles' running. Chapter 4 gives practical information on carrying out the work.

General Overhaul. Every 24,000 miles it is desirable for a general inspection and overhaul to be made. The work includes checking for wear in the steering, suspension, transmission and brakes, reverse-flushing the cooling system, overhauling the electrical components and if necessary stripping the engine. This overhaul is best entrusted to a competent service station, but much information on such matters will be found in other chapters.

CAR CARE IN WINTER

Every experienced motorist knows that a car is likely to deteriorate far more rapidly during the winter months than in summer, even though it may run a smaller mileage. Rain, snow and smog soon set up rusting on bodywork and corrosion on bright metal. Fog, mist and the pervasive dampness of winter days are more insidious, entering the interior to harm upholstery and bright parts, and causing condensation everywhere under the bonnet. The grit that is spread on icy roads "sandblasts" a car's underbody very effectively when it is travelling fast, and the salt and chemicals used for de-icing are equally effective agents of corrosion. An engine

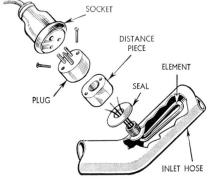

SOCKET

DISTANCE PIECE

ELEMENT

SEAL

PLUG

INLET HOSE

FIG. 12.4. Engine heaters for winter use. The paraffin-type sump heater is placed on the garage floor and the hanging heater can be hung inside the bonnet (Raydyot). An electric mains heater fitted into the lower water hose (*left*) keeps the coolant warm in readiness for an instant start; a socket on a flexible mains lead connects to a plug on the heater or remotely fitted on the dashboard.

can suffer heavy wear if its cooling system is inefficient or its lubrication is affected by low temperatures, while starting can be troublesome and cause a heavy strain on the battery.

Lubrication and Cooling. The one-time problem of engine oil turning thick and gummy in cold weather, thereby preventing proper lubrication of working parts, has been largely solved with the introduction of multigrade oils. These are recommended by most car manufacturers nowadays, being thin enough at low temperatures to offer full protection in all but arctic conditions. However, multi-grades are not considered suitable for worn engines, and some owners prefer to keep to monogrades for reasons of economy.

If separate "summer" and "winter"

grades are in use, it will be necessary at the outset of winter to drain off the summer-grade oil and refill with a suitable winter grade. Being thinner (of higher viscosity), the winter-grade oil both reduces drag on the starter motor and ensures more rapid lubrication of cylinder bores and other parts when the engine starts from cold. It is generally considered good practice to clean out the engine with flushing oil after draining the summer grade, though some manufacturers (notably Volkswagen) are definitely opposed to this.

At the same time as changing the oil, the cooling system should be filled with a good anti-freeze agent, as described in Chapter 4 (page 113).

Difficult Starting. Getting the engine to start on a very cold morning is now a less prevalent problem than formerly, but most motorists encounter it at some time or other, particularly if their car is an older model. If the car is housed in a warm, dry garage and meticulously maintained this trouble may never arise, but if it stands all night in the open or in a damp, unheated garage even a new car can prove difficult to start on a freezing morning.

As implied, good maintenance is the first essential. The battery especially is liable to deterioration in winter; it must be kept dry, clean and fully charged, with good electrical connections. There is a heavy drain on the battery in winter when headlamps, fog lamps, wipers and other accessories are in frequent use, apart from which its power output is greatly reduced as the temperature falls to freezing point. Unless normal operation of the car is sufficient to maintain the battery in peak condition, it is wise to provide a freshening charge from a suitable charger unit at intervals throughout the winter.

The generator and starter motor, both vital components, must obviously be in good working order although they require little routine maintenance. The ignition system, however, needs regular checking. The coil, distributor and leads must be kept clean and dry, while dirty or worn-out sparking plugs are a common source of winter starting and running troubles. The petrol supply system should not be neglected, and a useful tip is to check that the choke control linkage works freely, giving full operation of the carburettor choke valve.

A starting handle is an asset in getting a stiff engine to start on a cold morning, but many modern cars have no provision for one. In the latter case, easy starting becomes wholly dependent upon keeping the battery fully charged. If a starting handle is available and the battery is thought to be low, a recommended routine is to switch on the ignition and leave it on until the electric petrol pump stops beating; then switch off and pull out the choke control. Give the engine a few turns with the starting handle, switch on the ignition again and start in the normal way.

Quite often, after trying for some time to start a reluctant engine, it will fire after being left untouched for five or ten minutes. This may be partly because the engine's stiffness has been reduced by cranking and the battery has recuperated sufficiently during the interval to give just enough current for starting, but the main reason is probably that petrol that had condensed on the inner surfaces of the inlet manifold and cylinder head has now evaporated. Evaporation of the wet fuel can be speeded up by wringing out a cloth in boiling water and laying it along the inlet manifold for a minute or so before operating the starter. Only a little heat may be enough to dry off the petrol and give a start.

Again, if a number of attempts at starting have been made with the choke control pulled out, firing may be prevented because of globules of moisture condensing on the points of the sparking plugs. This may be condensed petrol or water, the latter being the more likely if the engine has actually fired once or twice but failed to run. The remedy is to take out plugs and heat them in a flame, or pour a little petrol into the body of each and ignite it, then replace the plugs quickly and try starting again while they are still hot.

Rapid Warming Up. Once a start has been obtained, the car should be driven away with the least delay. The practice of allowing the engine to run at idling speed until it warms up leads to corrosion developing rapidly in the cylinder bores, which are not yet receiving their normal lubrication. Until it has heated to full running temperature, the engine should not be heavily loaded and it is advisable to drive in third or second gear for a short distance. The temperature gauge should soon show that water in the cylinder head is reaching operating temperature, but it must be remembered that the sump oil (even multigrade) takes longer to warm up and provide a full flow to all moving parts. Do not allow the engine to run under load, therefore, the moment the temperature gauge reaches "normal."

Heaters, Blinds and Muffs. Portable garage heaters for keeping an engine and particularly the sump oil warm overnight are less popular than they used to be, since multigrade oils do not need to be cosseted. However, a small paraffin sump heater or safety lamp is still useful in a damp garage, keeping the engine and battery warm and preventing under-bonnet condensation (Fig. 12.4). Most types will burn for about 250 hours on one filling, and they can make all the difference to starting on a winter's morning. A properly designed paraffin heater for garage use is constructed on the principle of a miner's safety lamp, so that there is no fire risk even when the heater is used in a petrol-laden atmosphere. There are also electric all-enclosed heaters of the greenhouse type which can be plugged into the

mains supply and placed under the sump at night.

Another useful type of heater is the electric immersion heater for permanent installation within the car's cooling system (Fig. 12.4). It may be designed to fit inside the lower hose or in place of an engine-casting core plug. Current is supplied from a socket on a flexible mains lead which can be connected to a plug mounted on the heater unit or on the bulkhead or facia. These pre-heaters consume little current and are most effective in warming both the coolant and the engine itself, ready for an instant start.

A simple and popular method of improving cold-weather starting and running is to fit a radiator blind, radiator muff, or some form of blanking material such as a sheet of hardboard behind the radiator grille. These are undoubtedly useful on the majority of cars, even those with a small grille, since only a limited flow of air through the radiator is required for

FIG. 12.5. Another aid to rapid warm-up in cold weather is a radiator blind. The type shown is easily installed, and its dashboard control is a self-locking chain attachment that allows various positions of the blind (Mory).

285

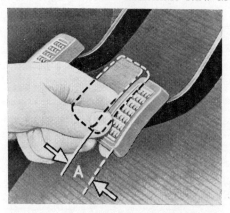

FIG. 12.6. Braking check. Distance A, the amount of free movement of the brake pedal before braking begins to take effect, should generally be no more than $\frac{1}{4}$ in. There should be a good reserve of travel beyond this point.

cooling purposes in cold weather. Total blanking-off, however, can lead to boiling of the coolant. There are several types of roller blind with a pull-cord designed to be operated from the facia, making it easy to control the blind as required (Fig. 12.5). The use of heaters, blinds and muffs can all help to provide reliable starting and rapid warm-up in the coldest conditions, and in a season or two can save their cost in the reduction of wear on cylinders and pistons alone.

THE M.O.T. VEHICLE TEST

Every car over three years old is subject to the annual Ministry of Transport test, undertaken by garages which have been designated authorized testing stations. Since the refusal of a test certificate means that the car is not permitted to be used on the public highway until repairs have been made and a further test taken, it is very much in the owner's interest to ensure that his car is in a roadworthy condition before it is presented for testing.

The three main items that must be checked by the examiner are the braking system, steering gear and lighting equipment. In addition, the examiner may refuse to make the necessary road test if the car appears to be unsafe in other respects. Worn tyres, a loose driving seat or faulty seat adjustment, heavy corrosion of the underbody or a damaged wing are examples of faults which may cause a car to be rejected for testing, and the test may also be refused if the underbody is very dirty or the steering linkage, suspension and brake parts are heavily caked with mud. It is therefore advisable to clean all parts affected and put right any obvious mechanical or body defects before making a systematic check as follows.

Braking System. Braking efficiency is required to be tested by means of a stationary brake tester or a meter carried in the car during the road test, and on four-wheeled vehicles the foot brake system must return an efficiency of at least 50 per cent and the hand brake system at least 25 per cent. An owner can easily decide whether his brakes are in fact efficient by making his own test on the road.

The brake action should be smooth and powerful, without any tendency to make the car slew to one side or the other when applied at speed, and the brake pedal should have a good reserve of travel as the brakes begin to bite, while the hand brake should be capable of holding the car when parked on a steep incline. If these conditions are not fulfilled, the shoes may need adjusting or their linings replaced. Do not omit a close inspection of the hydraulic system, examining the level of fluid in the reservoir and the pipe unions and flexible hoses for signs of leakage.

Finally, the rods and cables of the hand brake system should be checked over for signs of slackness, rubbing and chafing, or fraying of cables, while clevis pins, nuts, split pins, etc. must be secure.

Steering Gear. Here the first step is to see whether there is excessive free play or lost movement in turning the steering wheel from lock to lock, or any trace of binding towards the extremes of the wheel's travel (Fig. 12.7). As a general guide, lost motion on the wheel should not be more than about $1\frac{1}{2}$ in. The steering wheel should also be pulled and pushed bodily in line with the steering column. Any detectable movement in this direction is a sign of wear in the steering unit, usually on the bottom of the steering shaft, and provision is made for taking up such wear in most systems.

Excessive free movement in turning the wheel may be a sign of wear on the steering cam or worm, but is more often due to general wear in the ball joints of the linkage to the wheels. Wear in rack-and-pinion systems is likely to be confined to the exterior joints rather than the gearing. The linkage joints, idler and steering pivots should all be well lubricated (except where sealed joints are used) and again all nuts, split pins, etc. should be examined, while the mounting of the steering unit should be checked for security.

Next, jack up the front end of the car and try to rock each front wheel on its hub, also pushing and pulling along the axle to find out whether play is present. These tests may reveal wear on the steering pivots or slackness of the wheel hub bearings, both of which can lead to refusal of a test certificate.

Lighting Equipment. In this test the examiner must satisfy himself that the lamps meet the requirements of the Road Vehicles Lighting Regulations. The driving lamps (head, side and rear) and reflectors must be in efficient working order, and the headlamp beams must be correctly aligned to prevent dazzle when dipped. Officially, the non-obligatory lamps—fog lamps, direction indicators, reversing lamps, etc.—do not come within the scope of the test, but it is as well to check that they are in working order and do not contravene the regulations regarding height or bulb wattages.

If a thorough check is carried out along

FIG. 12.7. Steering check. The amount of free movement at the steering wheel rim (A) should be approximately $1\frac{1}{2}$ in. There should be no perceptible movement when the wheel is pulled bodily (B). Excessive play in either case indicates wear in the steering gear.

these lines and any necessary repairs or adjustments made in advance, the car can be submitted for testing with reasonable confidence. Even so, it is possible that the examiner may find some fairly obscure but potentially dangerous defect, in which case he must give details on the rejection form. It is then quite legal for the owner to drive the car home, put matters right, and drive back to the testing station for a further test. Only if the car is in a definitely dangerous condition—such as having completely non-effective brakes—must it be left at the garage for repairs or towed away for this purpose.

Should an owner feel that the car has been unfairly rejected he may appeal, within 14 days, to the Ministry of Transport. The vehicle will then be examined by technical officers of the Ministry, usually at the testing station concerned, and they may grant a test certificate. Full details of the appeal procedure can be obtained from any authorized testing station.

CHAPTER 13

FUELS AND LUBRICANTS

BOTH fuels and lubricants for automobile use are obtained from crude petroleum. Crude oils vary according to their source but in general are complex mixtures of hydrocarbons, that is, chemical compounds of hydrogen and carbon. By a process of distillation these crude oils are split into a number of less complex groups of hydrocarbons. These are known as "cuts" or fractions, each having a range of boiling points. The fraction with the lowest range of boiling points gives us petrol, the next gives white spirits, then come the lighter gas oils (used as diesel fuel), and so through the range of heavier diesel and boiler fuels to lubricating oils.

PETROL ENGINE FUELS

The production and marketing of motor fuels is a world-wide industry, and enormous sums are expended annually in promoting individual brands. Faced by so many competitive claims, the motorist may well wonder how petrols differ from each other and how he can choose one that will best meet his needs. It will be helpful to understand, firstly, that the most important basic properties of a petrol are its volatility and its resistance to detonation.

Volatility. Because of its low boiling point range most of the constituents of petrol readily evaporate at room temperature. This ability to vaporize readily enables petrol to be admitted to an engine cylinder in vapour form mixed with air, to be ignited by a spark.

If the petrol's volatility is too low it will not be adequately vaporized and may tend to be deposited in the induction pipe, so that the cylinders farthest from the

carburettor receive a weaker mixture than those nearest. Thus there will be poor distribution of the charge with consequent variation in the power developed per cylinder. Also, on cold mornings insufficient petrol will be vaporized to provide a combustible mixture and starting may be difficult.

If the volatility is too high there will be an excessive loss by evaporation in the petrol tank. This may also occur on the suction side of the fuel pump or at sharp bends in the supply pipeline, giving rise to the condition called vapour lock. Volatility is affected by atmospheric conditions, and much research has been devoted to making modern petrols sufficiently volatile in all weathers.

Detonation. Volatility is not, however, the most important property of a petrol nowadays. The thermal efficiency of an internal combustion engine increases as the compression ratio is raised, but the limit to increasing the compression ratio depends on the fuel used. If the compression ratio is increased too far a metallic hammering noise known as "pinking" or "detonation" will result, and when this is severe the engine's power output falls and overheating results. Excessive detonation can cause serious damage to an engine.

Detonation arises from the fuel burning with explosive violence instead of smoothly and evenly. When ignition takes place in a gaseous mixture there is a momentary "ignition lag" before any perceptible rise in pressure occurs. The length of this delay period depends upon the molecular structure of the fuel, and it greatly influences the nature of subsequent combustion in an

288

enclosed space. In normal burning the spark initiates a flame which proceeds steadily through the mixture, causing a progressive increase in temperature and pressure well ahead of it. Behind the flame is burnt gas, in front of it is unburnt gas approaching conditions for spontaneous combustion.

If the time taken for the flame to pass across the combustion chamber is longer than the ignition lag of the unburnt gas, then spontaneous combustion with consequent rise in pressure may occur at a number of points in advance of the flame front. The mixture detonates, and shock waves strike the cylinder wall and travel back and forth in the unburnt gas (Fig. 13.1).

Tendency to detonate can be caused by poor engine design and by adverse running conditions, but the primary factor is the delay period of the fuel in use.

Octane Numbers. The system of octane numbering is used to measure the resistance of a fuel to detonation. This system is based on a comparison of the fuel with a mixture of heptane (designated octane No. 0), which has the least resistance to detonation, and iso-octane (designated octane No. 100), which has the highest resistance. Thus, if a given fuel has the same resistance to detonation as a mixture of 90 per cent iso-octane and 10 per cent heptane, it is said to have an octane number of 90. Synthetic fuels have now been developed with an even higher resistance to detonation than iso-octane—resulting in the appearance of octane numbers above 100.

For any particular fuel, the tendency to detonate can be reduced by keeping the length of flame travel as short as possible. Using a flat-topped piston, the ideal combustion chamber would be a hemisphere with the sparking plug at the topmost point. The nearest approach to this is obtained by using overhead valves, and engines of this design have largely superseded the side-valve type because they permit much higher compression ratios, and therefore higher thermal efficiency.

It may be noted that while this desired hemispherical combustion space is usually provided by machining a chamber in the cylinder head, on some modern engines the cylinder head is flat and a combustion chamber of suitable shape is machined in each piston crown (Fig. 13.2).

The octane number of the fuel to be used in any given case depends on both the compression ratio and the design of the cylinder head, but all engines will show much the same response to *change* in the octane number of the fuel used. Consequently, while it is not possible to equate compression ratios with octane numbers for all cases, the proportionate increase in the permissible compression ratio for a given increase in fuel octane number will be much the same in most engines.

NORMAL FUEL COMBUSTION

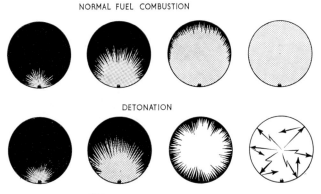

FIG. 13.1. How detonation occurs. The upper sequence shows the progressive spread of flame during normal fuel combustion. The lower sequence shows detonation occurring as part of the fuel charge burns spontaneously; the resulting shock waves in the cylinder cause the characteristic "pinking" sound.

DETONATION

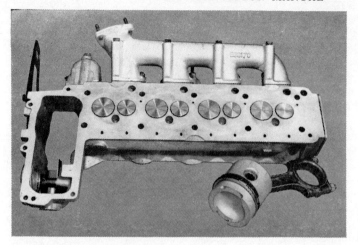

FIG. 13.2. In this engine the combustion chamber is formed in the crown of the piston, giving an unrestricted hemispherical shape, and the chamber is closed by a flat cylinder head (Rover).

The following is an approximate guide to the fuel octane number to be used in overhead valve engines having compact combustion chambers of good design:

Compression Ratio	Minimum Octane Number
6	70
7	81
8	90
9	96
10	100

If detonation should be met with in a given case the obvious answer is to try using a petrol having a higher octane number. In some circumstances, as when travelling in remote areas abroad, it may not be possible to obtain petrol of adequately high octane number. In this event a temporary expedient is to retard the ignition slightly while running on the unsuitable fuel.

The energy content of a fuel is expressed as the calorific value per pound, and is very much the same in all petrols. The efficiency with which a petrol is burned in a mechanically sound engine depends on the compression ratio, and there is no benefit in the form of increased power output or fuel economy to be obtained by using petrol having a higher octane number than is necessary to avoid detonation. The motor-

ist is therefore advised to use a petrol of the minimum octane number suitable for his engine, change to a higher grade if signs of detonation or rough running appear, then experiment with different brands *of that grade* until he finds which one appears to give best results (in terms of smoothness, performance and m.p.g.) in his particular engine.

Although in Britain most petrols are classified for sales purposes into grades under such names as "regular", "premium" and "super", these have no definite significance in regard to octane numbers. Indeed, there has been a tendency for octane numbers of branded petrols to rise almost year by year, so that what is "regular" grade today was "premium" grade only a few years ago.

In order to simplify matters from the motorist's viewpoint, the British Standards Institution has introduced a system of grading petrols which uses stars to indicate the octane ratings. The B.S.I. gradings are: 5 stars, 100 octane or above; 4 stars, 97-99 octane; 3 stars, 94-96 octane; and 2 stars, 90-93 octane and special economy grades.

Additives. The octane number of a petrol may be raised by blending the base spirit with higher octane fuels or by the use of an additive or "dope". The additive in most common use is tetra-ethyl lead—an extremely poisonous substance which imparts its insidious toxicity to the fuel to which it is added.

Petrol companies use many other additives in different brands, including solvent oils to maintain cleanliness in the induction system, chemicals to prevent icing-up of the carburettor, chemicals to prevent the fouling of sparking plugs, neutralizers to suppress chemical reactions between petrol and engine metal, and anti-oxidants to prevent gummy deposits forming in fuel pipes. It is mainly the presence of these additives which gives different qualities to petrols of the same octane number.

LUBRICATION

The function of a lubricant is to reduce the amount of friction resulting from the relative motion of mating parts. Suppose we have a block sliding over a horizontal surface (Fig. 13.3). If the two mating surfaces are clean and dry considerable force will be necessary to move the weight of the block, the ratio of this force to the weight being known as the coefficient of friction. If a layer of lubricant is now placed on the surface the force required to drag the block along will be greatly reduced.

What happens is that a thin film of oil first adheres to the dry surface of the block and also to the other surface. An oil wedge builds up between these two oil films, and motion will take place by each successive thin layer of oil sliding over its adjacent layer. The layer on the underside of the block will be moving with the speed of the block, the adjacent layer will move a little slower and so on, until we reach the layer on the horizontal surface which will be at rest.

The resistance to the sliding of successive layers over each other is a measure of the viscosity of the oil. If the force pressing the two surfaces together is small,

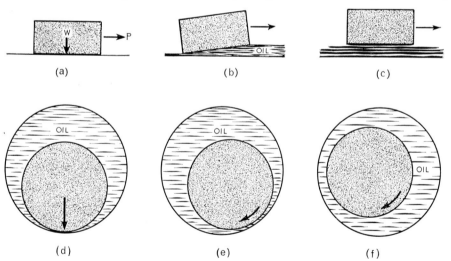

FIG. 13.3. Fluid film lubrication. (*a*) A block of weight W when dragged along a dry surface requires considerable force (P) to overcome friction. (*b*) When the two mating surfaces are lubricated an oil wedge builds up between them. (*c*) The fluid oil films slide over each other, reducing friction. The same state of affairs applies in the case of a shaft running in a bearing. At (*d*) the shaft is stationary and resting on the bottom of the bearing. (*e*) As rotation begins, an oil wedge develops causing the shaft to ride up. (*f*) The shaft rotates supported by successive films of oil sliding over each other.

291

then a "thin" lubricant (one of low viscosity) will be sufficient to allow an oil wedge to develop, but if the force is large then a thick, treacly lubricant (one of high viscosity) will be required. Such lubrication is known as "fluid film" lubrication, and is very desirable in machines since it gives minimum wear and minimum resistance to relative movement of the mating parts.

It will be seen that the degree of viscosity is an important factor in determining the efficiency of a lubricant. A further point is that viscosity decreases with increase in temperature; in other words, oils flow more freely when heated. Two methods of measuring viscosity at different temperatures are the Redwood and Saybolt systems. To simplify matters so far as motor oils are concerned, however, the Society of Automotive Engineers in America has devised a classification in which an oil which comes within a specified range of viscosities at one particular temperature is given an "S.A.E." number.

S.A.E. Grades. Based on the Saybolt system, there are four S.A.E. grades of engine oils for summer use (viscosity measured at 210 deg. F.) and three grades for winter use (viscosity measured at 0 deg. F.). These are shown below.

S.A.E. Summer
Grades: 20 (lowest viscosity)
30
40
50 (highest viscosity)

S.A.E. Winter
Grades: 5W (lowest viscosity)
10W
20W (highest viscosity)

It is possible for an oil to meet the requirements of more than one grade, in which case it is designated "multigrade". For example, a multigrade oil of S.A.E. 10W/30 possesses a viscosity within the S.A.E. 10W range at 0 deg. F. and within the S.A.E. 30 range at 210 deg. F. These multigrades have largely displaced the "monogrades" for use in engines today, though the latter

are considered preferable when an engine is in poor condition.

We have seen how the viscosity required of an oil is dependent upon the force pressing the mating surfaces together. If the viscosity is too high (lubricant too thick), much greater force will be necessary to make the successive layers of oil slide over each other, the result being loss of power due to the increased friction. If viscosity is too low (lubricant too thin), the intervening layer of oil may be squeezed out from the mating surfaces and contact occurs between the oil films adhering to those surfaces. This is known as "boundary lubrication". Friction is now greatly increased, but it varies considerably for different oils of the same viscosity.

Boundary lubrication conditions can occur in any machine, particularly when starting up or running slow, if the oil layers have not yet formed or parts are not receiving their full supply of lubricant. The conditions prevailing between an engine piston and cylinder at the end of each stroke are especially severe; the adherent oil film may be removed, resulting in metal-to-metal contact and consequent scuffing of the piston.

It was this problem of "thin film" or boundary lubrication which led to the development of additives for oils. These are especially important in the case of engine oils, as we shall see.

ENGINE LUBRICATION

Motor engineers have an old saying about using the cheapest fuel the car will run on and the best oil one can afford, and there is a good deal of wisdom in this. Modern engines are absolutely dependent on the efficiency of their lubricant; and most of the advances of recent years— higher power, higher road speeds, better fuel consumption, less maintenance and less frequent need for overhauls—have been made possible by improvements in engine oils.

Engine Oil Requirements. It is instructive to consider what is demanded of the oil in an engine today. In the first place, engines produce far more power than did engines of the same size only a few years ago. They do this partly by being made to work harder: they run under increased stresses, at higher speeds and higher temperatures. At the same time, their oil capacity has tended to become smaller as engines have become more compact, and the oil change period has been greatly extended—often to 6,000 miles. So a smaller quantity of oil must now last far longer and operate under far more severe conditions than a few years ago. Only modern high-quality oils can meet these requirements.

As already explained, it is essential for the oil to have a suitable viscosity *at the working temperature* of the engine in order to build up the fluid films between working surfaces. Since too high a viscosity causes loss of power through increased friction, it follows that the oil should have the lowest viscosity compatible with avoiding the danger of boundary lubrication conditions. The introduction of additives known as "viscosity index improvers" has made possible the multigrade oils which have a suitable viscosity over a wide range of running temperatures.

In an internal combustion engine the lubricating oil may not only act as a lubricant but also to some extent as a coolant. During its passage through the engine, and especially in the crankcase, the hot oil is being whirled around in intimate contact with air. These conditions are ideal for promoting oxidation of the oil, aided by products of fuel combustion which escape from the cylinders into the sump (including a good deal of water under cold-running conditions).

A black, pasty product of oxidation and contamination is known as sludge. It may be deposited on moving parts, in oil channels, in the crankcase, or may be held in suspension in the oil. In a bad case, it may block up vital small oilways and cause ruination of a bearing through oil starvation.

Oil passing up past the pistons may be decomposed into carbon, resinous and asphaltic substances that are deposited in the piston ring grooves, leading ultimately to sticking of the rings so that they can no longer perform their function of securing full compression. An oil therefore needs to have detergent qualities, so that these decomposition products will be washed off the metal surfaces and held in suspension in the oil until trapped by the oil filters.

An oil may be naturally detergent or its detergency can be improved by the use of additives. The process of oxidation can be resisted by the use of anti-oxidant additives, and it is the use of these which has allowed the introduction of extended oil-change periods. They are the essential factor in the so-called "long-life" oils which are now marketed.

A naturally detergent oil may have the ability to wash away deterioration products but it will not necessarily have the ability to maintain these in suspension. Thus another kind of "dispersant" additive called a peptizing agent is used which has the ability to break up large sludge particles and facilitate their removal. In addition, an anti-corrosive additive is required because a detergent oil may attack certain types of bearings such as copper-lead and cadmium-nickel.

Although a straight mineral oil provides fluid films that will resist wear on the working surfaces of an engine, there are certain combinations of moving parts where the pressure is great enough to rupture the films and allow rapid wear to occur. A particular example is the valve-gear cams and tappets, where heavy loads are imposed on quite small areas. An anti-wear additive is therefore used in modern oils to provide local protection of such parts.

One type of anti-wear additive consists of oil-soluble compounds, while solids such as graphite have been used in the past. Molybdenum disulphide has attracted attention for its anti-wear properties, though there are differences of opinion as to whether this substance adheres satisfactorily to previously lubricated surfaces. Recently, one famous oil manufacturer has introduced an anti-wear additive termed "liquid tungsten" for engine oils. This is actually an oil-soluble tungsten compound which is claimed to provide excellent wear protection by combining with constituents of other additives in the oil at heavily stressed parts of the engine.

The use of such anti-wear additives has greatly reduced the need for frequent adjustment of valve gear.

Engine Lubrication System. The majority of engines employ similar arrangements for allowing the oil to do its work, though there are variations in design. The wet sump—a pan at the bottom of the engine which contains the oil supply—is in almost universal use, and from this the oil is circulated under pressure to all working parts.

The oil is circulated by means of a submerged pump, driven by the engine (often from a skew gear on the camshaft). Some kind of wire gauze suction strainer is invariably fitted over the pump inlet to ensure that any solids present in the sump are kept out of the lubrication system (Fig. 13.4). The pump incorporates a pressure relief valve which maintains the designed pressure in the system under all conditions —it is mainly required to prevent excessive pressure developing under cold-starting conditions, when the oil may be less fluid than normal.

Leaving the pump, the oil passes through another filter, normally located in a container attached to the crankcase. Since it is operating under pressure, this filter can provide a much finer degree of filtration than the gauze strainer, and it plays a vital

FIG. 13.4. Primary filtration of the engine oil is obtained by fitting a gauze strainer over the pump intake. In this engine the intake is a floating type so that the gauze is always held just below the surface of the oil, where it is unlikely to become clogged.

part in ensuring good lubrication. It must clean the oil, protect the engine against wear by removing tiny abrasive metallic and sludge-type particles that have passed the pump strainer, and must remain effective over a long period so that "long-life" oils can be used to full advantage.

In most engines the filter is of the full-flow type, in which the whole of the oil passes through the filter element (Fig. 13.5). A simple relief valve is incorporated to allow circulation of the oil if the element becomes completely choked, though in this event the oil will not be filtered. Older cars are sometimes fitted with a by-pass type of oil filter, in which a proportion of the oil is passed through the filter element and cleaned while the remainder passes direct into the engine. Over a period of running the whole of the oil is thus filtered, and lubrication will be maintained even if the filter becomes choked.

From the filter, oil passes along a main gallery to reach various parts of the mechanism. In a typical engine there may be channels to each of the main bearings, drillings in the crankshaft that conduct oil to the big-end bearings, drillings in the connecting rods that lubricate the cylinder bores, and drillings in the cylinder block that supply the camshaft bearings and timing gear. Oil is also fed at reduced pressure to the valve gear.

Hints on Engine Lubrication. Many cars are fitted with a warning lamp which lights up when oil pressure falls to a few pounds per square inch. This is a danger signal that should not be ignored—the engine should be stopped immediately and not restarted until the cause of the trouble has been found.

Other cars have an oil-pressure gauge instead of the warning lamp, and this can be more useful to the knowledgeable driver. The normal pressure varies considerably with different engines, though a common figure is between 35 and 45 lb per sq in.

If all is well, there will be a higher than normal reading when the engine starts running from cold, because the cold oil is too thick to be released fully by the relief valve; the resulting higher pressure helps in circulating the cold oil. When the engine is running hot, pressure should be low at idling speed, but should rise as the engine is accelerated. Once normal pressure has been reached, however, accelerating the engine further should make little or no difference to the gauge reading because the relief valve will be in full operation.

When an engine has run a high mileage and clearance at the bearings has increased because of wear, the oil pressure may remain consistently below normal. If general wear in the engine is not too severe, normal pressure may be restored by using a heavier grade of oil (such as a multigrade 20W/50 instead of a multigrade 10W/30). It must be borne in mind, however, that the volume of oil flowing through the worn bearings will be reduced when thicker oil is used. On the other hand, less oil will flow past the pistons to be burned in the combustion chambers, so oil consumption will be reduced. In the light of these facts, the use of a heavier engine oil is best regarded as a temporary palliative for a worn engine.

The careful owner will check the oil level on the sump dipstick regularly and keep the oil topped up to its maximum level. This is important with regard to the oil's function as a coolant—lack of oil in the sump leads to its overheating. Apart from this, it is essential to change the oil completely at the specified intervals. Although the suction strainer and pressure filter trap any solids suspended in the oil, they cannot filter out liquid contaminants. These include unevaporated fuel that passes into the sump via the pistons, water resulting as a by-product of fuel

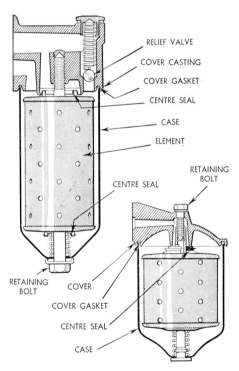

RELIEF VALVE
COVER CASTING
COVER GASKET
CENTRE SEAL
CASE
ELEMENT
RETAINING BOLT
CENTRE SEAL
RETAINING BOLT
COVER
COVER GASKET
CENTRE SEAL
CASE

FIG. 13.5. A full-flow oil filter (*upper*) is fitted with a relief valve which operates if the element becomes choked. The by-pass type (*lower*) permits only a partial flow through the element and no valve is required.

combustion, and acids resulting from the solution of burnt gases.

When a car is used mainly for "stop/start" motoring—short journeys in cold weather or use in heavy town traffic with prolonged periods of idling—the engine may never attain its normal running temperature for any length of time, and proper combustion cannot be obtained. The result is an increase in dilution of the oil by water and acids, while more carbon is formed. The additives in the oil that combat these contaminants are more rapidly exhausted and the protection given by the oil is reduced. If the car is used later for longer journeys at higher speeds (e.g., holiday touring), a lacquer may quickly form on the piston ring grooves and cause ring-sticking. In these conditions, therefore, it pays to change the oil more frequently than normal.

TRANSMISSION LUBRICANTS

Transmission oils in general are subject to considerable churning action and function as coolants, carrying away the heat generated by friction. In epicyclic gearboxes in particular the churning of the oil resulting in entrained air may lead to the oil foaming, while water may be present from humid air drawn in when the gearbox cools down. Gearbox oils may therefore contain a foam suppressant and both corrosion and oxidation inhibitors. Special additives are similarly used for other transmission applications, and the S.A.E. grading system distinguishes between these different types of lubricants.

The spiral bevel rear-axle gearing found in some older cars requires only a straight mineral oil unless tooth loading is heavy, when an extreme-pressure (E.P.) additive may be called for. Most cars today employ hypoid bevel rear-axle gears, in which conditions are very severe. The heavy loading and sliding action imposed by such gears on the oil film has led to the development of special extreme-pressure lubri-

cants designated hypoid (HYP.) oils.

Special oils have also been developed for automatic transmission units where they may have to provide both the hydraulic medium in the torque converter and the lubricant in the gearbox. With these it is especially important to use only the lubricants specified by the manufacturer.

Greases. Motorists are sometimes in doubt as to whether an oil or a grease should be used for lubricating chassis components. From a lubrication point of view greases in general are inferior to oil. They are less stable, particularly at high temperatures, and because of their greater consistency they offer greater frictional resistance than oils and are therefore less suitable for use at high speeds. Their advantages are that they are not so easily removed as oil, they seal bearing ends, they provide some measure of lubrication over a long period, they are more convenient to use at inaccessible points, and they do not drip.

A modern grease consists of a metallic soap which acts as a carrier, mixed with a mineral oil, and the nature of the grease depends primarily on the soap used. Many special types have been developed for automobile applications.

Lithium soap is the basis of most multipurpose greases, suitable for both chassis points and wheel bearings. Some manufacturers specify a high-melting-point (H.M.P.) wheel bearing grease, while there are also waterproof semifluid chassis greases. Certain water pumps require a special packing grease, and zinc oxide "white" grease has been specially formulated for brake parts. Sometimes graphite is incorporated in a grease, being particularly useful for road springs and for brake cables in metal conduits.

It will be realized from the foregoing that there is a great deal more to lubrication of the various parts of a car than giving an occasional dose of any oil or grease that happens to be handy.

CHAPTER 14

INCREASING THE PERFORMANCE

MOST motorists nowadays are aware that any modern engine is capable of giving greatly increased power without detracting significantly from other desirable qualities, and the question may be asked why the major manufacturers do not include in their car specifications the various modifications that result in higher performance.

The answer is that for many years it has been quite easy for the motorist to obtain additional power and speed, *provided he was prepared to pay for it.* Extra performance costs more, and this is why the manufacturer, working to keep prices down, does not as a rule provide for it. He knows, too, that the number of drivers seeking higher performance from their cars is small compared with those who are content to accept the maker's specification.

There are other reasons why family cars are not designed to give the best possible performance. The reputation of many such cars depends to a considerable extent on their reliability, and the less highly stressed are a car's components, the less likely are they to fail, or wear rapidly. Parts are therefore specified to allow a generous factor of safety. Furthermore, production costs must be considered, and machine-shop operations facilitated, particularly in these days of computer-controlled automatic machine lines.

It will be appreciated that the built-in safety factor resulting from the maker's specifications tends to be reduced as performance capabilities are increased. Nevertheless, many cars do have their engine power increased from time to time (normally when a new model is introduced), in order to gain better acceleration

or higher top speed. The growing congestion of our urban roads makes rapid acceleration attractive to most drivers, while the development of motorways and other modern trunk roads outside the towns has made possible the maintenance of high cruising speeds for long periods.

MANUFACTURER'S PERFORMANCE MODIFICATIONS

It is worth considering briefly the ways in which a car maker thus steps up the performance of his production engines, before going on to describe what the owner can do to boost his own engine.

One common method of obtaining more power from an existing engine design is by increasing the compression ratio. That this is possible without prejudicing the essential requirements of flexibility and smooth running is due to steady improvements in engine fuels (described in Chapter 13). Another basic modification is to enlarge the cubic capacity of the cylinders, usually by increasing the cylinder bore diameter. This almost invariably involves modifying the internal dimensions of the cylinder block casting in order to retain sufficient metal in the cylinder walls, but the alteration is not usually difficult.

Other methods of increasing an engine's power output might be the adoption of "sports" engine features, such as a special camshaft, larger valves, and special manifolds. Unless its cubic capacity has been increased, the higher-powered engine is usually unchanged both in overall size and as regards dimensions of the main bearings, crankpin diameters, valve-gear components, and so on. However, it must be remembered that in some cases there may be invisible but important changes in the material or metallurgical treatment of two apparently identical parts, producing very different behaviour in service.

It must be added that the modern car has many standard parts that will successfully absorb heavier duty without alteration or modification of any kind. This permits the "conversion" of the car to give extra performance, within limits of safety, which we shall now consider.

"HOTTING-UP" AN ENGINE

Engines of popular cars follow a fairly standard basic design, and the requirements for obtaining increased power from any particular engine can be covered comparatively simply. This is demonstrated by the flourishing "performance conversion" industry consisting of firms who market replacement equipment, the items of which differ only in detail, and undertake basically similar "hotting-up" operations on such engine parts as combustion chambers and porting. Typical of the services offered by these firms is raising the compression ratio, hand-finishing the cylinder head to allow easier gas flow, fitting multiple carburettors, and fitting easy-flow exhaust systems.

When the amateur considers "hotting-up" an engine, it is essential to start with a firm grasp of the fundamental principles of the subject. It is also important to decide just what degree of extra performance is desired, bearing in mind the safety margins already mentioned, driving facilities required, and the inescapable fact that extra power costs money.

INCREASING THE COMPRESSION RATIO

The object of this modification is to obtain an increase in final gas pressure at the end of the compression stroke in order to make the following explosion more

powerful (due to its correspondingly higher pressure); greater torque is thereby exerted on the crankshaft. But obviously the compression pressure depends on how much gas is drawn into the cylinder on the preceding induction stroke. Thus, a low-compression engine that inhales a weighty charge of mixture will produce a higher final pressure than will be obtained from a so-called high-compression engine if its manifolds and port areas are so poorly designed that it cannot draw in a full charge.

Even in the best designs, the amount of mixture inhaled per stroke varies considerably with engine revolutions, falling off at high speeds because of the decreased time available for the cycle to be performed.

The effect of raising the compression ratio can thus be unpredictable unless the general design of the engine is studied carefully. This applies not only to the carburettor arrangement, manifold and port layout, for example, but also to the valve timing. The designer's intentions can be gauged from quoted figures for maximum horsepower and torque, indicating whether he designed a unit with the accent on high engine revolutions to produce power and thus demanding much use of the gearbox, or one which emphasized pulling power and "slogging" capabilities at lower crankshaft speeds.

The latter type has, in fact, almost completely disappeared. Today's high-revving engines in standard form develop up to 20 per cent more power than their prewar counterparts, although the basic layout is unchanged. This increase cannot be ascribed merely to a higher compression ratio and higher maximum revolutions, because there is also a large torque increase throughout the speed range. Since adequate flexibility is still maintained, valve timing has not been aimed to produce high maximum power at the expense of adequate low-speed pulling, which would be quite unsuitable in modern conditions. Thus the

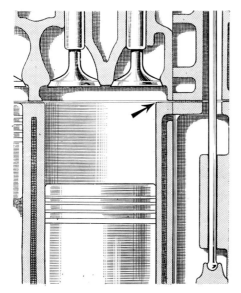

FIG. 14.1. When machining the cylinder head to obtain a higher compression ratio, all working clearances (such as that shown arrowed) must be maintained to allow for valve float.

modern engine evidently inhales a greater volume of mixture, and burns it more efficiently than did its predecessor. All this is obtained from improved combustion chamber design, better port and valve shapes, more efficient action in opening and closing the valves, and better manifold shapes.

The standard method of raising the compression ratio is by machining metal from the gasket-face of the cylinder head. There is usually sufficient metal thickness to enable this to be done with safety, but it is important for internal clearances between valves and piston crowns to be maintained, and the effect on the shape of the combustion space must be taken into account (Fig. 14.1). A very small increase can sometimes be obtained in an engine with a fairly thick copper-asbestos gasket by substituting a gasket of thin sheet copper, but for this to succeed it is essential that the mating faces of the head

and block are perfectly mated; otherwise the gasket will almost certainly "blow".

Some engine makers vary the size of the piston to alter the compression ratio. This is done by designing the pistons with a crown completely flat for maximum ratio, but with varying degrees of concavity for lower ratios. This practice is sometimes combined with a variation in the depth of the combustion chambers.

IMPROVING CARBURATION

Apart from altering the compression ratio, one popular method of increasing power that rarely fails to have worthwhile results is to replace the complete induction system on a single-carburettor (or choke) engine with a multiple carburettor installation (or, alternatively, the equivalent double-choke type). The main advantage gained is derived from bringing the carburettor chokes closer to the corresponding inlet ports, thus minimising the length of manifold and reducing "flow confusion".

Although the theory that an interposed length of manifold may function as a ram charger is sometimes advanced, this holds good only at certain combinations of engine revolutions and throttle openings, and may well be disadvantageous at other times by causing a reduction of torque when it is needed. In any case, the full advantages of ramming can only be obtained with virtually straight-through passageways from air intake to valve, as in some racing engine designs, which

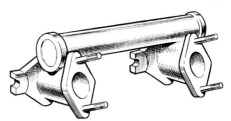

FIG. 14.2. A popular standard design of induction manifold for twin-carburettor engines which has proved very satisfactory in use under all conditions.

299

obviously calls for a separate inlet port for each valve and one choke or carburettor feeding each port. On four-cylinder units, this arrangement usually comprises two double-choke carburettors, making for a neat and compact installation.

In siamesed inlet port arrangements, the filling between the paired cylinders is inherently unequal, but single chokes to the ports help to reduce this inequality. It is necessary to couple the port flanges by a cross-balance tube or duct (Fig. 14.2), which evens out the impulses to some extent and also tends to eliminate dashpot-flutter on an S.U. carburettor. The bore of the balance duct is arrived at by experiment to obtain the best size for giving smooth acceleration on a wide throttle without irregularity. Manifolds that are marketed by specialist tuning firms are designed with all these factors built in, some typical examples being illustrated in Fig. 14.3.

It is sometimes possible to improve performance by substituting a modified inlet manifold for the standard, while retaining the single carburettor already fitted. Any advantage gained will be due to greater dimensional accuracy, improved surface finish making for better gas flow, and probably some compromise to the standard hot-spot. A "colder" manifold provides greater volumetric efficiency, but more time is taken to reach operating efficiency in warming up from cold, and the carburettor choke control must be used intelligently with these designs to avoid wasting petrol and perhaps also endangering proper engine lubrication.

In reducing manifold flow resistance and improving distribution to the cylinders, multiple carburettors allow the engine to produce appreciably more power. However, some engine designs have valves and ports of only moderate size, in order to provide a high speed of flow and good turbulence at moderate throttle openings. If some sacrifice of these features is acceptable, more power at high revolutions can usually be obtained by increasing the

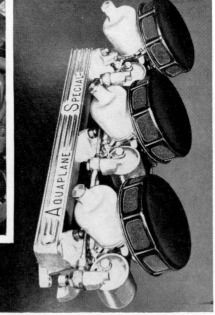

FIG. 14.3. Multi-carburettor conversions. (*Left*) Twin Stromberg CD carburettors with a special manifold as a bolt-on unit for a B.M.C. Mini (Alexander). (*Right*) Triple S.U. carburettors on an aluminium manifold for a Ford (Aquaplane).

port and valve-throat area, and the size of the inlet valves.

EXHAUST IMPROVEMENTS

Altering the exhaust system to gain more power is a practice of long standing, though the result is often confined merely to making more noise. Nowadays the arrangements for either replacement or modification of the exhaust system are so numerous that it is necessary to be very clear about what is required before making a choice.

The idea of a well-designed system is to scavenge waste products from the cylinder head efficiently so that the charge that follows is uncontaminated by exhaust gas. This requirement, involving high-speed gas flow, depends for its ultimate effect on the high-frequency wave-motion set up in the gas column. In designing for this, the first rule to follow is that, taking the system as a whole, the requirement becomes of less importance as the gas proceeds downstream. For example, at the cylinder end, the manifold has considerable influence on power, but modifications at the tail end of the exhaust pipe are of negligible significance.

Replacement Exhaust Systems. Any replacement system must be capable of being fitted without undue disturbance of other components on the car, and many special systems can only do this by departing from what would have been the best design for maximum power. The best of those available do improve scavenging of the engine in this way.

If a four-cylinder engine firing 1-3-4-2 is considered, there are two cylinders successively exhausting, at each end of the manifold. This means that with normal valve overlap, pressurizing of one cylinder by exhaust "residuals" is all too easy. The direction arrows in the upper section of Fig. 14.4 show the kind of balance which determines whether the cylinder preceding in its exhaust sequence will be scavenged, or will have some exhaust added to its

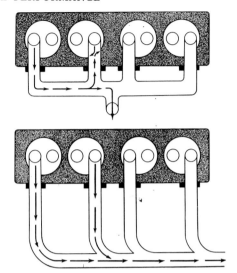

FIG. 14.4. Improving exhaust gas flow. (*Upper*) Flow confusion can be caused in a standard manifold due to overlapping exhaust strokes of adjacent cylinders. (*Lower*) A multi-branch manifold induces a much superior gas flow pattern.

contents. Some exhaust gas from the left-hand cylinder has entered the manifold of the second cylinder, to be drawn in on the overlap of the induction stroke.

In the lower illustration, it will be seen that while the same firing sequence applies, the gas flow from the left-hand cylinder now traverses a longer branch which maintains the gas speed some way from the port, so that it flows into the main downpipe at high velocity. The adjacent exhaust branch has an identical pipe attached, and the same effect is obtained but to a lesser extent because in this case only a residual exhaust stream is left. Reverse flow from the left-hand cylinder into the other is thus eliminated. Because of its increased capacity, this system also tends to give an overall reduction in average manifold pressure.

For an even more efficient system it is necessary to sub-divide the branches as shown in Fig. 14.5, thus ensuring that there are discharges from two cylinders, at

301

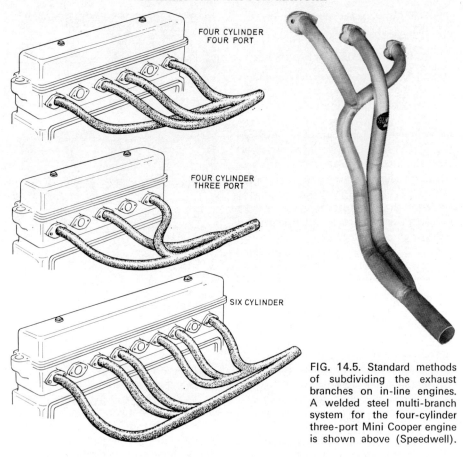

FOUR CYLINDER
FOUR PORT

FOUR CYLINDER
THREE PORT

SIX CYLINDER

FIG. 14.5. Standard methods of subdividing the exhaust branches on in-line engines. A welded steel multi-branch system for the four-cylinder three-port Mini Cooper engine is shown above (Speedwell).

regular intervals, into one of the duplicated downpipes. These are either united further down the pipeline or led into a double-entry silencer. A similar principle applies to six-cylinder engines, bearing in mind the usual firing order of 1-5-3-6-2-4.

Silencers. All silencers operate by converting gas friction into heat, which is dissipated. This principle applies both to baffle types and to the straight-through absorption type, with its apparently clear passage. The working principle of the straight-through type, which is highly regarded because of its pleasant exhaust note and robust construction, is that in passing down the central perforated tube, the sound waves penetrate into the sur-

rounding pack of close-woven absorbent material of steel wool, glass wool, or wire mesh. By setting up vibrating movement in the pack, the wave amplitude and the noise are reduced (Fig. 14.6).

Assuming that the silencer is of adequate size, its effect depends on the size of outlet pipe in relation to the inlet. With an unaltered bore size throughout, there is some internal bore friction, but little silencing effect. With a reduced outlet bore, the increased resistance thus induced forces the waves to enter the jacket. This effect, along with the smaller outlet bore, appreciably reduces the noise.

Tailpipe Attachments. There are a number of tailpipe attachments on the

FIG. 14.6. Most cars are fitted with a baffle-type silencer (*left*), containing plates which tend to restrict exhaust flow. The straight-through type (*right*) is more expensive but offers less resistance to gas flow.

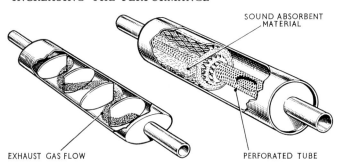

SOUND ABSORBENT MATERIAL

EXHAUST GAS FLOW

PERFORATED TUBE

market, sometimes sold as "exhaust boosters". Many of these do no more than alter the exhaust note and enhance the appearance of the tailpipe, advantages that some owners consider to be worth while. Other fittings are claimed to possess some form of wave-damping or ejector principle, obtained by means not always comprehensible. The main difficulty about devices that depend on car speed for an advantageous extractor action is the unpredictability of the air flow at the rear of the vehicle caused by various obstructions, and the virtual impossibility of obtaining an adequate air-collection area in the confined space available beneath.

Special Camshafts. Manufacturers often vary the camshaft characteristics between basically similar engines, to suit a particular vehicle. On the same principle, special camshafts are marketed for popular engines to provide a choice of valve timings and lifts. In considering the various opening periods and overlap that are specified by these manufacturers, it should be remembered that no indication is usually given of the *rate* of lift of the valve.

A long period during which the valve is open, for example, might imply that the acceleration rate (or rate of lift to the fully-open position) is moderate, so that high loads are avoided. But a shorter open period might give the same result in terms of total flow through the valve if a quick-lift cam contour is fitted. This needs very robust valve gear, and modern engines running at high speeds do not usually employ cams having short periods and small overlap. In these, a

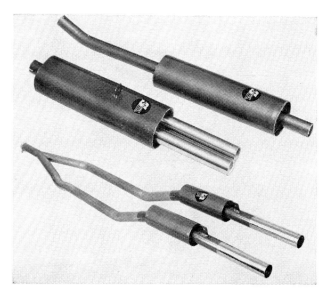

FIG. 14.7. (*Upper*) An exhaust system conversion kit which comprises a noise-reducing expansion chamber and a silencer with twin tailpipes. (*Lower*) A divided system for a sports car with eparate silencers and tail-pipes (Speedwell).

FIG. 14.8. The Shorrock supercharger is of the vane type and has a rotor running on ball bearings. Kits are available for several popular cars and can easily be fitted by the owner.

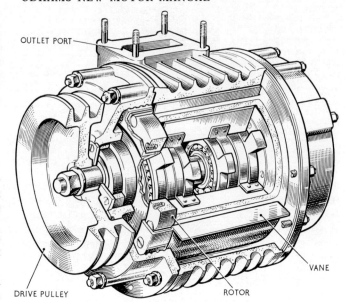

OUTLET PORT

VANE

DRIVE PULLEY

ROTOR

large amount of overlap can be used at quite moderate engine revolutions. This timing also gives effective breathing at peak revolutions.

If the induction system imposes limitations on peak revolutions, increasing the overlap timing will not overcome this, though possibly more mixture will be inhaled simply because of the longer opening period. Even so, benefit at high engine speeds will be felt only over a very limited range, while at lower speeds the excessive overlap is likely to reduce torque by allowing mixing of the backflow and charge as already described. The extra loading on the camshaft drive and valve gear must also be taken into account.

Thus, a special camshaft is necessary for competitive events where extensive modifications on the lines already described have been made, because the standard shaft, though excellent for all-round motoring, may be the final bar to maximum power at peak engine revolutions. But a special camshaft must never be regarded as a single easy-to-fit substitute for other components or assemblies.

SUPERCHARGERS

Many years ago, the low-pressure supercharger was an established and almost essential aid to success with small cars in reliability trials. Today, it is again coming to the fore as a simple method of obtaining a very considerable increase in power. Its attractions as a power booster lie mainly in the torque characteristics it gives to the engine over a wide speed range, and its simplicity of fitting, which leaves the engine virtually as standard. Disadvantages are the extra weight, reduced accessibility in the engine compartment, the additional drive required from the engine, and cost. These disadvantages are of greater or lesser importance depending on the type of car and its purpose, but there is little doubt that the "feel" of a supercharged car in its power delivery cannot be got by any other means.

On the debit side, there is the obvious fact that the blower takes power from the engine to drive it. The frictional losses in a well-designed blower and its drive are very small, but they do represent an addition. Under certain operating conditions, the pistons actually receive a low-pressure thrust on the induction stroke which may be considered as offsetting these losses to some extent.

With atmospheric induction, the mixture

intake varies over the engine speed range, due to the various causes already explained. But with the inlet charge under positive pressure, the cylinders can be filled to atmospheric pressure, or to any desired pressure within reason above this, so overcoming the inherent pumping limitations of the engine. In addition, a supercharged mixture is thoroughly atomized by its passage through the blower.

Superchargers of both the Rootes and vane types are available with all accessories for various popular engines (Fig. 14.8). In making a choice, the important matter is that the pressure must be kept within the engine's capabilities; there is no question of using the high pressures commonplace in racing engines.

The power gain through the normal range of the engine can be roughly assessed as being proportional to the weight of mixture burnt in a given time. Thus, assuming the ideal of an engine receiving its mixture at 15 lb per sq in. (atmospheric pressure), and having its cylinders completely filled thereby: the addition of a blower supplying mixture at 5 lb per sq in. will pump in an extra volume equal to one-third of the original. The power from each explosion will thus be 33 per cent more than when unblown.

As this power is obtained within the normal speed range of the engine, there is no extra mechanical stressing as a result of inertia build-up—the increase in stress that occurs with increasing speed. But there is an additional power loading on bearings that can be high in certain circumstances and may result in more rapid wear, comparable with that on an "unblown" engine of similar power obtained by running at higher speed.

As there will be on occasion 30-40 per cent more mixture passing through the engine, a good deal of extra heat is generated. Most engines are able to accept this without modification if the lubrication and cooling systems are in first-class order. A well-designed extractor-type exhaust system will disperse this extra heat, but the blower itself also helps by distributing heat more evenly between cylinders because of its more uniform mixture.

Petrol consumption will obviously be affected by a blower. It is difficult to make a comparison with a modified atmospheric engine, since no amount of tuning can really compare with the sheer "punch" over the range of engine speed given by the blower, and this must obviously be paid for in petrol.

As a blower in effect supplies the mixture equivalent of a larger engine, it may be asked how the characteristics of a blown engine compare with an unblown bigger-capacity engine of similar power. As an example, the comparison might well be stated as 1,000 c.c. blown being

FIG. 14.9. Typical Shorrock supercharger installation on a Triumph. The kit includes a special manifold, a crankshaft pulley with twin driving belts, and a larger capacity carburettor to handle the additional volume of mixture.

equivalent to 1,500 c.c. unblown. Much depends on the driver's likes and dislikes, but in general, the smaller engine has many advantages apart from its size and probably lower weight. Its lively feel is a consequence of the smaller reciprocating parts producing lower inertia stresses, and a smooth power delivery obtained by the equal filling of cylinders.

VEHICLE MODIFICATIONS

A car that has had its engine power increased must maintain a very high standard of road safety, with brakes, suspension, and road-holding beyond reproach. There are many accessories available that enable the standard components to be improved to cope with extra performance.

A notable aid to braking power can be obtained with a vacuum-operated hydraulic brake booster, applying pressure through the normal brake pipelines. These units are described more fully in Chapter 9 (page 217). When fitting such an accessory it is necessary to ensure that the rest of the braking system is fully up to the extra loading and braking reactions, and this applies also to axle attachments and suspension units. Special competition brake linings are often useful, though possibly requiring more finesse and heavier pedal pressure in operation than standard; the improvement in braking is usually quite apparent.

Higher speeds and faster cornering may also show the need for improved springing and road-holding. The usual effect of increasing the speed of a typical saloon car is to produce excessive roll and see-sawing. Stronger springs that help to overcome these defects are sometimes available, particularly from those manufacturers who support rallies. Improved shock absorbers that can be substituted for the standard ones should also be considered.

In addition, there are anti-roll torsion bars, tie-links to prevent rear axle wind-up

on acceleration, and other aids designed to improve the suspension at high speed. These are available from motor accessory firms, and most of them have been proved in use over the years. As with engine tuning, the extent of such modifications must depend on the role intended for the car, as there are inherent speed limits to cornering on public roads that do not apply in racing.

Transmission. It is frequently possible for a tuned engine to drive through a higher gear ratio (using the term in its popular sense), and if only a small increase in power has been added, oversize tyres may provide the answer. It is important not to overgear, particularly in Britain, where fast acceleration and maintaining a good speed on undulating roads are major driving considerations.

An overdrive unit is the best answer to the problem of excessive engine speeds on a motorway, for example, and the drastic alteration of the rear axle ratio sometimes proposed as an inexpensive alternative to overdrive is seldom satisfactory. Most drivers soon tire of the incessant gear-changing that is necessary with such an alteration and other difficulties arise. Intermediate gears with this arrangement are frequently not in correct relationship, while some gearboxes do not take kindly to the indirect third gear being used as top for miles on end.

Clutch. The modern clutch has a good margin of capacity to cope with the abuse it may have to withstand in service. It can generally accommodate some increased torque, but if this is excessive, modification might be advisable. One common improvement is a pressure unit with stronger springs to provide greater frictional contact, combined with special competition linings on the driven plate able to withstand heat to a greater degree without slipping. Disadvantages of this modification are an increased pedal pressure and a slightly less smooth take-up.

CHAPTER 15

THE WORKSHOP AND TOOL KIT

REPAIR and overhaul work requires the facilities of a reasonably well equipped workshop if it is to be done efficiently, and the car owner who intends to do such work should give some thought to this matter. In most cases, of course, the home garage will also serve as a workshop, and this arrangement does have the advantage that the car itself and all tools and equipment are at hand under one roof (Fig. 15.1).

The garage-workshop needs to be weatherproof, clean, and have at least enough space for a small bench and tool storage. The ideal would have ample working space all around the car, an easily cleaned floor, an inspection pit about four feet deep with a strong cover for safety, a convenient water supply, several electrical outlets, good lighting and heating, and a comprehensive array of mechanic's tools. The motorist who can claim all these is fortunate indeed! However, anything that can be done on the lines indicated will help to promote good working conditions, and a few tips on fitting up the garage may be useful.

Lighting, heating and ventilation are all important in the workshop. The workbench should be positioned so as to receive the maximum natural light, supplemented by electric lighting. A fluorescent tube is recommended, or else a lamp on an adjustable bracket mounted above the bench. A safety-type inspection lamp on a flexible cable is almost essential when working in the engine compartment or underneath the car.

Heating is desirable both for keeping the car and tools dry and for comfortable working, and an all-enclosed electric radiator will serve very well in the average small garage. If it is mounted on the wall under the workbench it will warm the mechanic and be out of harm's way. In some cases it is possible to install a radiator fed by the domestic central heating system, but any form of heater having an exposed flame is not permitted in a garage.

All switches and electrical outlets should be installed at least four feet above floor level; any electrical fittings below this height must be either flameproof or totally enclosed. A 13-ampere twin switched socket-outlet fitted above the bench is the best means of supplying current for a battery charger, power drill, inspection lamp, soldering iron, etc. The usefulness of an inspection pit will be doubled if it has a lamp inside, but this should be of the armoured bulkhead type for safety. All electrical equipment must, of course, be properly installed, earthed and tested.

Ventilation is important because of the presence of petrol fumes and it is sensible to have a ventilator grille fitted in one wall. Furthermore, the exhaust gases of an engine are lethal, and if the car engine is run in a badly ventilated garage carbon monoxide emitted from the exhaust system can quickly become concentrated enough to cause death without warning. It is therefore a wise precaution when running an engine on test to ensure that the exhaust pipe discharges into the atmosphere through open garage doors.

Fire precautions, too, must be taken seriously and the garage-workshop should be provided with a foam-type fire extinguisher or at least a bucket of sand (water is useless against a petrol fire).

WORKING IN THE GARAGE

Maintenance and repair is an absorbing interest for the enthusiast, and quite ambitious work can be carried out in a modest workshop. At the same time, there are hazards in some garage operations that should never be ignored.

The risks of petrol fumes and exhaust gases have been mentioned, but it cannot be over-emphasized that petrol is a dangerous substance and must always be treated as such. Do not leave open containers of petrol for cleaning purposes about the garage, nor petrol-soaked rags, and do not permit smoking in the vicinity of fuel. Allow a hot engine to cool to a safe degree before disconnecting any part of the fuel system that might result in petrol wetting the power unit or exhaust system. Remember, too, that if the building is situated within 20 ft. of another building you are not permitted to store more than two 2-gallon cans of petrol in the garage, apart from what may be in the car's tank.

Lifting a car is an operation that always requires special care. The light jack supplied with the car is intended to facilitate

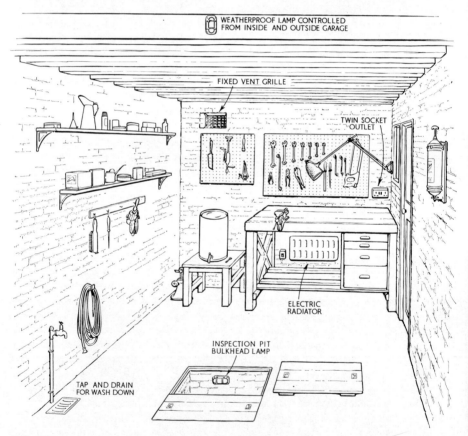

FIG. 15.1. Layout of a well-equipped garage-workshop with provision for lighting, heating, ventilation and water supply. Each tool on the hardboard panel above the bench has its outline painted behind, so that missing tools can easily be identified. The switch unit for the electric heater should be fitted with a warning light.

308

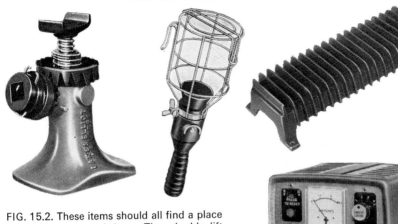

FIG. 15.2. These items should all find a place in the garage-workshop. The double-lift screw jack shown has a capacity of 15 cwt. (Lake & Elliot). The battery charger, for 6 V or 12 V batteries, has variable current control up to 3 amperes maximum (Davenset). The all-enclosed portable air warmer can be used for sump heating or general warmth (Belling). The inspection lamp has an earthing terminal and a push switch in a shockproof handle (Stadium).

changing a wheel, not to support the car while you are working underneath, and it is advisable to buy a heavy screw jack or hydraulic jack for workshop use (Fig. 15.2). If the car has to be lifted bodily, the safest procedure is to jack up one corner, insert some solid baulks of timber to take the weight at this point, then withdraw the jack and repeat the operation at each of the other corners.

If only one pair of wheels is to be lifted, chock the other pair securely to prevent the car moving—many fatal accidents have occurred through a car slipping while on the jack. Take care in choosing the part of the car that is to bear on the jack or timber blocks. Never place the jack under the engine sump, clutch housing, gearbox, petrol tank or floor panels; instead, use a strong cross-member, side member, the rear axle casing, or some other part of the main chassis structure.

A useful alternative to a garage jack is a pair of wheel ramps, up which the front or rear wheels can be driven (Fig. 15.3). Non-slip ramps of welded steel are on the market, or one could construct strong timber ramps. These should be about 12 in. high, 12 in. wide, and two or three feet long for safety.

A greasy floor in the garage is a danger, and any oil or grease should at once be wiped off. If a greasy patch develops, the easiest way to remove it is to buy a can of degreasing fluid. When well worked in, this emulsifies the oil and grease, which can then be hosed away with plenty of water. Degreasing fluid is also invaluable for cleaning mechanical parts from the car, as it will shift the thickest grease or oily dirt without damage. A well-maintained vehicle should not leak oil, although a small amount often dribbles from breathers and odd corners, but leakage can occur due to a loose drain plug or defective seal. The appearance of oil on a floor that is normally kept clean will immediately draw attention to such trouble. If leakage is suspected,

FIG. 15.3. Welded steel wheel ramps make it possible to work underneath a car in comfort and safety (Bowmonk). Some designs permit one ramp to stack on top of the other, saving storage space.

spread a sheet of newspaper under the car and leave it overnight. If the paper is found to be stained next day it is easy to check where the oil is coming from.

Scrupulous cleanliness in the workshop is the mark of the good mechanic, since dirt and dust are the enemy of all mechanical and electrical parts. Keep muddy gardening tools and the like well away from the workbench, see that the car tools are clean and dry before use, and make a habit of cleaning every component removed from the car before it is refitted.

WORKSHOP EQUIPMENT

The one really essential fixture in any workshop is a suitable bench, and although an old table or box sometimes serves well enough, it is always better to have a purpose-made workbench. These can be bought fairly cheaply (many greenhouse and shed manufacturers offer a range of portable benches), or a handyman can construct one to suit the space available. Obviously, the bench must be strong and rigid and for this reason it is a good idea to screw it firmly to the wall.

The bench illustrated in Fig. 15.4 was designed by *Homemaker* magazine for amateur construction. It costs only a few pounds to make and uses simple but strong joints. The bench top is made from four

pieces of 6 × ¾ in. tongued-and-grooved boarding, of which the piece that butts up to the backboard needs to have its tongue planed off. The four pieces should first be slotted tightly together and the overall width measured. This gives the dimension shown in the detail drawing A. The leg sections are glued and screwed together, and it is best to secure each joint with one screw only during construction, inserting additional screws after the various members have been adjusted for squareness. All essential dimensions are given on the drawing, but these can be varied to suit individual requirements. For a bench longer than about 6 ft. an extra leg section should be added to the middle.

The next essential is a good mechanic's vice with four-inch jaws. It pays to buy a good-quality vice which can be used for many household jobs as well as work on the car. The vice shown in Fig. 15.5 is a well-known type that is particularly suitable for garage use, as it is provided with several useful features. The vice should be mounted close to one of the bench legs so that downward thrust will be taken without bending the bench top.

Accommodation for tools is important, and much damage can result from heaping them into a box or leaving them lying about the bench. Tools can be kept in an

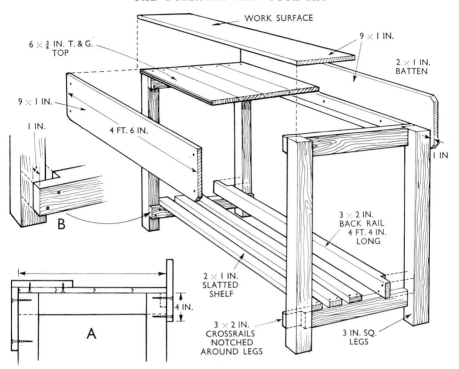

WORK SURFACE

6 × ¾ IN. T. & G.
TOP

9 × I IN.

2 × I IN.
BATTEN

9 × I IN.

I IN.

4 FT. 6 IN.

I IN.

B

3 × 2 IN.
BACK RAIL
4 FT. 4 IN.
LONG

2 × I IN.
SLATTED
SHELF

4 IN.

A

3 × 2 IN.
CROSSRAILS
NOTCHED
AROUND LEGS

3 IN. SQ.
LEGS

FIG. 15.4. An easily made workbench. It is 4 ft. 6 in. long by 2 ft. wide, and the legs are 2 ft. 6 in. by 3 in. square. A separate board screwed to the bench top provides a replaceable work surface. Large mirror plates at the ends of the back board enable the bench to be screwed firmly to a wall. Construction of the bench is described in the text.

engineer's steel toolbox, with trays and compartments, or in cupboards fitted with suitable racks, shelves and hooks. If the garage is dry enough, another method is to arrange the tools in regular use on a sheet of perforated hardboard fixed to the wall and fitted with hooks and brackets. Some mechanics like to paint an outline of each tool in the appropriate position on the board so that each can be returned to its proper place and any missing ones identified at a glance from the "shadow" outline.

A separate set of shelves should be provided for items such as lubricating and washing equipment, cans of oil and spare parts, the tool accommodation being reserved exclusively for tools. Screws, nuts, washers and similar small parts are best

FIG. 15.5. Engineer's vice with 4 in. jaws and swivel base (Record). Features include a hardened steel anvil, pipe grips, pipe and rod bender, screwed plug for holding a cylinder head, and detachable fibre jaw grips for protecting soft or plated surfaces.

housed in a plastics cabinet with many small drawers.

TOOLS

Nowadays, the average popular car tends to be supplied with only the bare minimum of tools, although more expensive models often have an extensive kit. There are certain tools which every motorist is advised to carry, if only for emergency use, whereas the workshop kit will depend on how much maintenance work it is proposed to do. Two items of advice may be offered regarding tools. First, always buy the best that can be afforded—tools may look alike, but the quality in a good tool is to be found in its material, accuracy, balance and other factors that may not be visible. Secondly, it is better to build up a kit from a few essentials as experience suggests, rather than start with a large and expensive collection that may prove of limited use in practice.

Car Tool Kit. Assuming that at least a jack and wheel brace have been provided by the manufacturer, the following tools and spare parts are suggested for carrying on the car. They take up little space in a tool roll, bag or box, and enable many routine service checks to be carried out as well as minor breakdown repairs.

Tools: Tyre pump; tyre pressure gauge; pair of tyre levers; puncture repair kit; set of feeler gauges (for valves, sparking plugs and contact breaker points); three screwdrivers (6 in. plain and crosshead, and small electrical type); 14 mm box-type plug spanner with handle or tommy bar; three set (open-ended) Unified spanners from $\frac{7}{16}$ in. to $\frac{7}{8}$ in.; small adjustable spanner; 6 in. side-cutting pliers; small oil can.

Spares: Fan belt; sparking plug; condenser; one headlamp bulb; one side/rear lamp bulb; roll of electrical insulating tape; roll of copper wire for lashing-up broken parts; set of tyre valve inserts.

Workshop Tool Kit. The tools listed

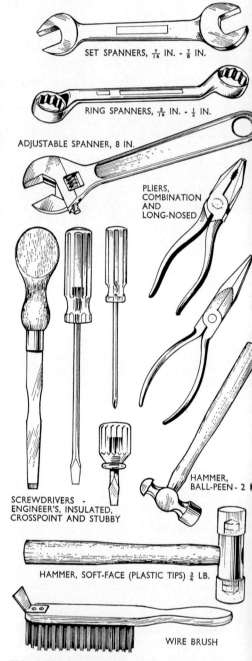

SET SPANNERS, $\frac{7}{16}$ IN. - $\frac{7}{8}$ IN.

RING SPANNERS, $\frac{3}{16}$ IN. - $\frac{1}{2}$ IN.

ADJUSTABLE SPANNER, 8 IN.

PLIERS, COMBINATION AND LONG-NOSED

SCREWDRIVERS - ENGINEER'S, INSULATED, CROSSPOINT AND STUBBY

HAMMER, BALL-PEEN - 2

HAMMER, SOFT-FACE (PLASTIC TIPS) $\frac{3}{4}$ LB.

WIRE BRUSH

FIG. 15.6. Garage tool kit. The hand tools illustrated are a selection of those most useful to the motor mechanic, and form a

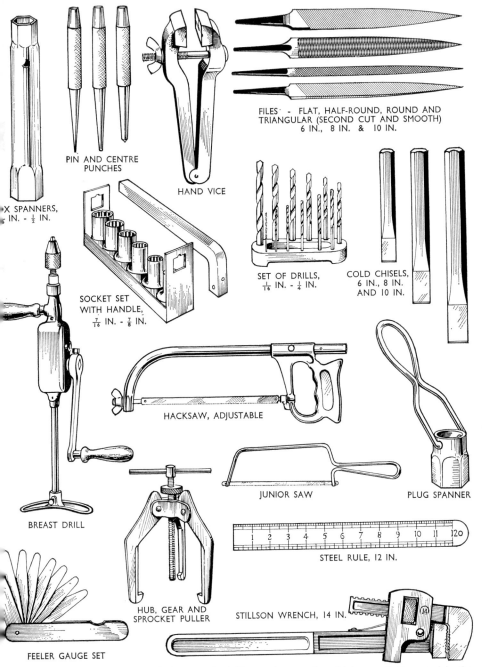

PIN AND CENTRE
PUNCHES

FILES - FLAT, HALF-ROUND, ROUND AND
TRIANGULAR (SECOND CUT AND SMOOTH)
6 IN., 8 IN. & 10 IN.

HAND VICE

X SPANNERS,
IN. - ½ IN.

SET OF DRILLS,
$\frac{1}{16}$ IN. - $\frac{1}{4}$ IN.

COLD CHISELS,
6 IN., 8 IN.
AND 10 IN.

SOCKET SET
WITH HANDLE,
$\frac{7}{16}$ IN. - $\frac{7}{8}$ IN.

HACKSAW, ADJUSTABLE

JUNIOR SAW

PLUG SPANNER

BREAST DRILL

STEEL RULE, 12 IN.

HUB, GEAR AND
SPROCKET PULLER

STILLSON WRENCH, 14 IN.

FEELER GAUGE SET

basic kit that can be extended as required. The various tools, which are all discussed in the text, can be obtained individually, or a comprehensive kit housed in a fitted tool box could be purchased. Mechanics' kits are available from leading tool suppliers.

below form the basis of a useful mechanic's kit with which many repair and overhaul jobs can be undertaken (Fig. 15.6). First, however, it seems desirable to mention the various types of screw threads used on car components, as these affect the choice of some tools.

Almost all British cars of recent years employ Unified threads throughout, either coarse (U.N.C.) or fine (U.N.F.), and for practical purposes these are interchangeable with the S.A.E. threads used on American cars. Continental cars mostly use metric threads, which the British car industry is likely to adopt in the future. Whitworth and B.S.F. threads are now to be found only on early post-war models. For screws on electrical components and instruments, the B.A. thread in numbered sizes is commonly used.

Unified threads can generally be identified by a pair of linked circles marked on one of the flats of the hexagon, or by a shallow circular depression on the bolt head. Nuts, bolts, etc., fitted with these differing types of threads cannot be interchanged.

Spanners. Various types are available, and in each case it is essential to select spanners to suit the threads in use. The professional mechanic's first choice is usually a ring spanner, and although a good set of these in chrome vanadium or other special alloy is rather expensive, it will last a lifetime. For more awkward locations a set of box or tube spanners, operated by a tommy bar, is most useful to the motorist, although mechanics may prefer to invest in a set of socket spanners complete with special handles and extensions.

Only if none of these types is available should one use an open-jaw spanner, which is more liable to slip and damage the nut, while an adjustable spanner can be regarded as the last resort but worth having in the kit. A really comprehensive spanner kit for a British car might therefore be made up of these:

Set of Unified ring spanners, $\frac{3}{16}$ to $\frac{1}{2}$ in.
Set of Unified box spanners, $\frac{3}{16}$ to $\frac{1}{2}$ in.
Set of Unified set (open-jaw) spanners, $\frac{7}{16}$ to $\frac{7}{8}$ in.
Set of B.A. spanners, Nos. 0-6.
One adjustable spanner, 8 in.

Wrenches. A 14 in. Stillson wrench and a pair of 9 in. Footprint grips are useful heavier tools for the busy mechanic, but less essential to the motorist unless he intends to do major overhaul work. A torsion wrench is invaluable, however, even if somewhat expensive. This is a tool which is designed to break when tightened to a preset degree of tension, and its use in conjunction with a socket wrench is always preferable where definite tension figures are stipulated for nuts and bolts such as those retaining the cylinder head, rocker gear, valve cover, bearing caps, manifolds, leaf springs, road wheels and so on. For the odd overhaul job it is sometimes possible to borrow a torsion wrench from a garage.

Hammers. A ball-peen hammer of about 1 lb. weight is essential, and a heavier size also desirable. A hide or plastic faced hammer is most useful for soft metals, knocking out dents and freeing a tyre from a wheel rim.

Screwdrivers. Apart from those in the car kit, it would be worth while having a large screwdriver (about 12 in.), a stubby-handled type for awkward locations, and one or two insulated screwdrivers. A good ratchet type can be a timesaver.

Files. Many types of file are made, with different kinds of teeth. To start with, one should obtain a 10 in. flat rough file and a similar size "second cut" file (useful on cast iron and alloys), an 8 in. flat smooth file, and a few 8 in. second cut and smooth files in half-round, round ("rat-tail") and square profiles. Other types, such as a heavy dreadnought file, warding files and needle files can be added as the need arises. Keep each file permanently fitted with its own handle—loose handles are dangerous.

Pliers. Again, several types are available, but for a basic kit the best are a pair of 8 in. side-cut or combination pliers and a smaller pair of long-nosed pliers, those with insulated handles being handy for electrical work.

Hacksaws. The adjustable type with a pistol-grip handle is recommended for accurate cutting, together with a selection of coarse, medium and fine blades. Apart from this, a junior saw, which has a narrow blade sprung into position, is inexpensive and suitable for many jobs on the car.

Drill. Drilling equipment is among the basic tools of the mechanic and it is wise to obtain the best quality one can afford. There are three types of drill that can be recommended. An electric pillar drill for bench mounting is the best for heavy work, accuracy and ease of operation. For most amateurs, however, one of the popular portable drills with a range of accessory equipment is probably more attractive, as apart from its mobility it can be used for wire-brushing, grinding, decarbonising, cleaning up a cylinder head and manifolds, surface finishing and many other jobs (Fig. 15.7). The cheaper models have ¼ in. chucks, but one with a larger capacity is a better investment.

FIG. 15.7. The most useful power tool for the home mechanic is a portable electric drill (Black & Decker). For safety's sake, the ordinary "three-wire" type must be properly earthed, but double-insulated "two-wire" types should *not* be connected to an earth.

When lack of a mains supply rules out an electric drill, a good-sized two-speed breast drill will be found better for drilling metal than a small hand drill. Sets of high-speed steel twist drills, from $\frac{1}{16}$ to $\frac{1}{4}$ in., can be bought complete with a drill holder. An adjustable hole cutter is useful to the motor mechanic for making holes in panels, etc.

FIG. 15.8. The wide range of accessories available for electric drills makes many workshop operations quick and easy. Shown in use are a grinding wheel (Stanley-Bridges) and a wire brush attachment (Black & Decker).

Bench Grinder. A hand-operated emery wheel, bench mounted, will keep metal-cutting tools sharp, whereas wood-cutting tools are sharpened on an oilstone.

Special Tools. Special drifts, extractors, gauges and other tools are required for overhaul work on many cars and are supplied to the trade by the manufacturers. In some cases it is possible for the motorist to order such tools from the manufacturer or a specialist tool firm. Essential tools required for top overhaul are mentioned on page 136. A universal type of gear or sprocket puller is useful to the more advanced motorist for extracting hubs, races, sprockets and other parts.

Miscellaneous. Other small tools to complete the basic workshop kit include a 12 in. engineer's steel rule, two cold chisels ($\frac{1}{2}$ and 1 in.), a centre punch and a pin punch, a wire brush, a hand vice, a caliper gauge, a pair of shears or tin snips, and a wire file card for cleaning file teeth.

Screwing Tackle. This is not likely to be required by the average home mechanic, but where thread cutting is contemplated it will be necessary to obtain a suitable set of stocks and dies for cutting external threads, and taps and tap wrenches for cutting internal threads. These must, of course, be selected to suit the type and sizes of thread required.

ACKNOWLEDGEMENTS

Thanks are due to the following for their kind co-operation and permission to reproduce illustrations:

AC-Delco Division of General Motors Ltd.
Alexander Engineering Co. Ltd.
Aquaplane Co. Ltd.
Armstrong Patents Co. Ltd
Avo Ltd.
Belling & Co. Ltd.
Black & Decker Ltd.
Borg & Beck Co. Ltd.
Borg-Warner Ltd.
Bowser, Monks & Whitehouse Ltd.
Britax (London) Ltd.
The British Motor Corporation
Castrol Ltd.
The Dunlop Company Ltd.
Evershed & Vignoles Ltd.
Fiat (England) Ltd.
Flexy Brushes Ltd.
Ford Motor Company Ltd.
Girling Ltd.
C. & J. Hampton Ltd.
Hardy Spicer Ltd.
Hill Equipment Ltd.
Homemaker (Odhams Press)
Interior Silent Travel Ltd.
Jaguar Cars Ltd.
Lake & Elliot Ltd.
Lockheed Hydraulic Brake Co. Ltd.
Joseph Lucas Ltd.

Mory & Co. Ltd.
NSU (Great Britain) Ltd.
Partridge, Wilson & Co. Ltd.
Radiomobile Ltd.
Raydyot Ltd.
The Rootes Group
The Rover Company Ltd.
Salisbury Transmissions Ltd.
A. Schrader's Son
Servais Silencers Ltd.
Shorrock Superchargers Ltd.
Smiths Industries Ltd. (Motor Accessory Division)
Speedwell Performance Conversions Ltd.
Stadium Ltd.
Standard-Triumph Motor Co. Ltd.
Stanley-Bridges Ltd.
Step Industrial Ltd.
S.U. Carburetter Co. Ltd.
Suntester Ltd.
Tecalemit (Engineering) Ltd.
Trico-Folberth Ltd.
Triplex Safety Glass Co. Ltd.
Vauxhall Motors Ltd.
Volkswagenwerk AG
Western-Thomson Controls Ltd.
Wilmot Breeden Ltd.
Zenith Carburetter Co. Ltd.

INDEX